WORKBOOK

Student Notes and Problems

CHEMISTRY 30
Alberta

CASTLE ROCK
RESEARCH CORP

Rao, Gautam, 1961 –

STUDENT NOTES AND PROBLEMS – Chemistry 30 Workbook

ISBN: 978-1-77044-242-9

1. Science – Juvenile Literature. I. Title

Published by

Castle Rock Research Corp.

2000 First & Jasper

10065 Jasper Avenue

Edmonton, AB T5J 3B1

20 19 18 17 16 15 14

Publisher
Gautam Rao

Contributors
Debra Hay
Jennifer McMaster
Dr. Ian Phillips

Reviewers
Dr. David Vuletich
Darrol Colgur
David Watson

Dedicated to the memory of Dr. V. S. Rao

STUDENT NOTES AND PROBLEMS WORKBOOKS

Student Notes and Problems (SNAP) workbooks are a series of support resources in mathematics for students in grades 3 to 12 and in science for students in grades 9 to 12. SNAP workbooks are 100% aligned with curriculum. The resources are designed to support classroom instructions and provide students with additional examples, practice exercises, and tests. SNAP workbooks are ideal for use all year long at school and at home.

The following is a summary of the key features of all SNAP workbooks.

UNIT OPENER PAGE

- Summarizes the curriculum outcomes addressed in the unit in age-appropriate language
- Identifies the lessons by title
- Lists the prerequisite knowledge and skills the student should know prior to beginning the unit

LESSONS

- Provide essential teaching pieces and explanations of the concepts
- Include example problems and questions with complete, detailed solutions that demonstrate the problem-solving process

NOTES BARS

- Contain key definitions, formulas, reminders, and important steps or procedures
- Provide space for students to add their own notes and helpful reminders

PRACTICE EXERCISES

- Include questions that relate to each of the curriculum outcomes for the unit
- Provide practice in applying the lesson concepts

REVIEW SUMMARY

- Provides a succinct review of the key concepts in the unit

PRACTICE TEST

- Assesses student learning of the unit concepts

ANSWERS AND SOLUTIONS

- Demonstrate the step-by-step process or problem-solving method used to arrive at the correct answer

Answers and solutions for the odd-numbered questions are provided in each student workbook. A *SNAP Solutions Manual* that contains answers and complete solutions for all questions is also available.

CONTENTS

Organic Chemistry

Equilibriums of Acid-Base Systems

Answers and Solutions

Appendix

THERMOCHEMICAL CHANGES

When you are finished this unit, you will be able to…

- Apply the equation $Q = mc\Delta T$ to the analysis of heat transfer

- Explain how stored energy in the chemical bonds of hydrocarbons originated from the sun

- Define enthalpy and molar enthalpy for chemical reactions

- Write balanced equations for chemical reactions that include energy changes

- Use and interpret ΔH to communicate and calculate energy changes in chemical reactions

- Predict the enthalpy change for chemical equations using standard enthalpies of formation

- Explain and use Hess's law to calculate energy changes for a net reaction from a series of reactions

- Use calorimetry data to determine enthalpy changes in chemical reactions

- Identify that liquid water and carbon dioxide gas are reactants in photosynthesis and products of cellular respiration and that gaseous water and carbon dioxide gas are the products of hydrocarbon combustion in an open system

- Classify chemical reactions as endothermic or exothermic, including those for the processes of photosynthesis, cellular respiration and hydrocarbon combustion

- Define activation energy as the energy barrier that must be overcome for a chemical reaction to occur

- Explain the energy changes that occur during chemical reactions, referring to bonds breaking and forming and changes in potential and kinetic energy

- Analyze and label energy diagrams of a chemical reaction, including reactants, products, enthalpy change and activation energy

- Draw and interpret enthalpy diagrams for chemical reactions

- Explain that catalysts increase reaction rates by providing alternate pathways for changes, without affecting the net amount of energy involved

- Explain the discrepancy between the theoretical and actual efficiency of a thermal energy conversion system

PREREQUISITE SKILLS AND KNOWLEDGE

Prior to starting this unit, you should be able to
- Find and verify the solutions of rational equations
- Rewrite linear expressions in terms of the dependent variable
- Solve problems involving length, volume, area, time, mass, and rates derived from these
- Solve problems involving percentage errors
- Design an appropriate measuring process or device to solve a problem
- Understand the concepts of thermal energy, temperature, change of state, heat transfer, thermal expansion, and energy conservation
- Describe and understand the particle model of matter
- Use ratios and proportions in a problem-solving context
- Use interpolation and extrapolation to make predictions
- Solve one- and two-step linear equations
- Apply $Q = mc\Delta T$ to the analysis of heat transfer and simple calorimeter data

Lesson 1 *ANALYZING HEAT TRANSFER*

The atoms and molecules in any sample of matter are in constant random motion. Depending on the phase or state of a sample of matter, the atoms and molecules are capable of vibrating, rotating, and translating (actually changing location) to varying extents. The energy of molecular movement is kinetic energy. The temperature of a sample of matter is a measure of the kinetic energy of its molecules and atoms. Heat is the name given to the energy transferred between two substances that have different temperatures.

When a substance changes temperature, its molecules undergo a change in kinetic energy. An increase in temperature signifies an increase in kinetic energy. A decrease in temperature signifies a decrease in kinetic energy.

The quantity of kinetic energy, *Q*, lost or gained when a sample of matter with mass *m* undergoes a change in temperature, ΔT , is given by the following equation: $Q = mc\Delta T$

where Q = kinetic energy lost or gained in units of joules (J)
    or kilojoules (kJ)
  m = sample's mass in grams (g) or kilograms (kg)
  ΔT = sample's change in temperature (°C)
    c = specific heat capacity of the substance (J/g · °C or kJ/kg · °C)

The specific heat capacity of a substance is the amount of heat needed to raise the temperature of 1 g of that substance by 1°C. Substances with large heat capacities can absorb large quantities of heat energy with only small increases in temperature. Substances with small heat capacities can absorb small quantities of heat energy with significant increases in temperature.

The heat capacity of water is higher than that of most other substances. Larger amounts of heat must be transferred to either warm or cool a given mass of water than for most other substances. This explains why large bodies of water tend to moderate the air temperature of their surroundings. The human body, which is over 60% water by weight, is able to maintain a fairly constant temperature despite changing external temperatures.

A Selection of Heat Capacities:

Substance	Specific Heat Capacity (J/g · °C)
$H_2O_{(l)}$	4.19
Polystyrene foam(s)	1.01
Dry air	1.01
Most metals	0.1–1.0

[Handwritten notes in margin:]

NOTES

↓temperature = ↓kinetic energy
↑temperature = ↑kinetic energy

kinetic energy = Q
mass = m
temperature = ΔT
} $Q = mc\Delta T$

Example

How much heat energy is absorbed when 10.0 kg of aluminum, initially at a temperature of 20°C, warms up to its melting point, 660°C, but does not melt?

Solution

$c_{Al} = 0.897 \text{ J/g} \cdot °C$

$Q = mc\Delta T = (10.0 \text{ kg})(0.897 \text{ kJ/kg°C})(660°C - 20°C)$

$Q = 5.74 \times 10^3 \text{ kJ} = 5.74 \text{ MJ}$

Example

A 2.50 kg sample of water has a temperature of 85.0°C. What is the final temperature of the water if it loses 220 kJ of heat energy?

Solution

$$Q = mc\Delta T \Rightarrow \Delta T = \frac{Q}{mc}$$

$$\Delta T = \frac{220 \text{ kJ}}{(2.50 \text{ kg})(4.19 \text{ kJ/kg} \cdot °C)} = 21.0°C$$

This represents a temperature drop in the sample.

$T_f = T_i - \Delta T = 85.0°C - 21.0°C = 64.0°C$

The final temperature is 64.0°C.

Example

What mass of water, at 25.0°C, requires 2.25 MJ of heat energy to warm up to 100°C? (Note: Assume the water being heated is below sea level in order to allow for heating to 100°C without changing states.)

Solution

$$Q = mc\Delta T \Rightarrow m = \frac{Q}{c\Delta T}$$

where $\Delta T = 100°C - 25.0°C = 75.0°C$

$$m = \frac{(2.25 \times 10^3 \text{ kJ})}{(4.19 \text{ kJ/kg} \cdot °C)(75.0°C)} = 7.16 \text{ kg}$$

This mass of water is 7.16 kg.

Example

Metal blocks A and B have the same mass, but block A has a lower heat capacity than block B. Both blocks are placed on a hot plate such that each block receives the same amount of heat energy. When the hot plate is turned off, which block is at a lower temperature?

Solution

First, let $Q_A = m_A c_A \Delta T_A$ and $Q_B = m_B c_B \Delta T_B$.

Assume that $Q_A = Q_B$ (as stated in the question).

Therefore, $m_A c_A \Delta T_A = m_B c_B \Delta T_B$.

Since $m_A = m_B$, the following equation results once like terms are collected:

$$c_A \Delta T_A = c_B \Delta T_B$$
$$\frac{c_A}{c_B} = \frac{\Delta T_B}{\Delta T_A}$$

Since $c_A < c_B$, then $\Delta T_B < \Delta T_A$.

Because $\Delta T_A < \Delta T_B$, the temperature of Block B has increased less than that of Block A; hence, the temperature of Block B is lower.

This is consistent with the idea that a substance with a high heat capacity experiences a small increase in temperature after absorbing a given quantity of heat.

PRACTICE EXERCISES

Formula: $Q = mc\Delta T$

1. Determine the amount of heat energy lost when a 300 g sample of copper $(c_{Cu} = 0.385 \text{ J/g°C})$ cools from 300°C to 20°C.

2. A 100 g piece of iron $(c_{Fe} = 0.449 \text{ J/g} \cdot \text{°C})$ and a 100 g piece of aluminum $(c_{Al} = 0.897 \text{ J/g} \cdot \text{°C})$, both initially at 25°C, are heated in a flame until they reach a temperature of 500°C. Determine the amount of energy each metal absorbs. How much more energy does the aluminum absorb than the iron?

3. Liquid sodium metal $(c_{Na_{(l)}} = 1.23 \text{ J/g°C})$ is used as a coolant in several French nuclear reactors. Determine the amount of heat energy that is absorbed by 1.00 Mg of liquid sodium metal warming from 200°C to 700°C.

4. If 1100 kJ of heat energy is transferred to 5.00 kg of water at 20.5°C, what will be the final temperature of the water?

5. Samples of platinum $(c_{Pt} = 0.133 \text{ J/g} \cdot \text{°C})$, , copper $(c_{Cu} = 0.385 \text{ J/g°C})$, and aluminum $(c_{Al} = 0.897 \text{ J/g} \cdot \text{°C})$ each have an initial temperature of 20.0°C. If each metal sample is supplied with the same amount of heat energy at the same rate, which metal sample would reach 300°C first and why?

Lesson 2   PHOTOSYNTHESIS, CELLULAR RESPIRATION, AND HYDROCARBON COMBUSTION

The energy needed for powering most activity in the biosphere comes from the sun as solar radiation. Solar radiation is absorbed by Earth's surface, heats the atmosphere, and causes the movement of water, the most abundant greenhouse gas, into the atmosphere by evaporation.

Phytoplankton at the ocean's surface and green plants on land absorb solar radiation by photosynthesis, a complex process represented by the following net equation:

$$6CO_{2(g)} + 6H_2O_{(l)} \rightarrow C_6H_{12}O_{6(s)} + 6O_{2(g)}$$
$$\Delta_r H° = +2\ 802.5 \text{ kJ}$$

$\Delta_r H°$ can also be represented as $\Delta H°$. The subscript r stands for reaction.

Solar energy is stored as chemical potential energy in the form of carbohydrates such as glucose and cellulose. Because plants absorb solar energy, this reaction is endothermic.

Aerobic organisms, including plants, oxidize glucose in their mitochondria to release energy for metabolic processes. Cellular respiration, an exothermic reaction, can be represented by the following net reaction equation:

$$C_6H_{12}O_{6(s)} + 6O_{2(g)} \rightarrow 6CO_{2(g)} + 6H_2O_{(l)}$$
$$\Delta_r H° = -2\ 802.5 \text{ kJ}$$

$H_2O_{(l)}$ (not $H_2O_{(g)}$) is a reactant in photosynthesis and a product in cellular respiration.

Over millions of years, buried dead plant material from bogs and swamps, kept at high temperatures and under immense pressure, transformed and produced the extensive coal deposits found underground in some areas of the world, such as Alberta. Plant material, itself the product of solar radiation and photosynthesis, was transformed into coal, a more energy-dense fossil fuel.

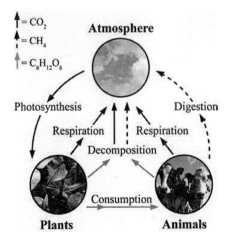

NOTES

A simple diagram of the carbon cycle illustrates the interconnection of photosynthesis, cellular respiration, and the combustion of fossil fuels. Plants convert $CO_{2(g)}$ into starches, sugars, and oxygen. Animals consume these starches and sugars to make the energy they need for metabolic processes. The geological transformation of both plant and animal material produce fossil fuels that are burned as fuel sources. The use of fossil fuels has lead to a large increase in atmospheric $CO_{2(g)}$ and other greenhouse gases over the last 200 years.

The highest grade of coal, called anthracite, is almost entirely carbon, $C_{(s)}$. The Industrial Revolution, a period in the late eighteenth and early nineteenth centuries, was fuelled almost exclusively by coal, which was burned to boil water for the steam engines that were needed for most industrial activities. The world still relies extensively on coal for producing electricity.

In the formula $C_xH_{y(g,\,l,\,s)}$, the x-variable represents the number of carbon atoms, and the y-variable represents the number of hydrogen atoms in the hydrocarbon. Hydrocarbons can be found as gases, liquids, or solids in their natural state

Fossil fuels can be thought of as a chemical store of ancient solar energy because all the energy stored in the chemical bonds of hydrocarbons originated from the sun. The burning of hydrocarbons by combustion in an open system produces gaseous products as represented by the following equation:

$$C_xH_{y(g,l,s)} + \left(x + \frac{y}{4}\right)O_{2(g)} \rightarrow xCO_{2(g)} + \frac{y}{2}H_2O_{(g)} + \text{energy}$$

This is an exothermic reaction. In the past, coal fires warmed houses and fuelled steam engines and machinery in factories. By the turn of the twentieth century, hydrocarbon combustion replaced coal combustion for the transportation needs of the world.

PRACTICE EXERCISE

1. List the differences and similarities between the cellular respiration of glucose and the photosynthesis of glucose.

Lesson 3   DEFINING AND COMMUNICATING REACTION ENTHALPIES

Explanation of symbols:

Δ = Change

f = Type of reaction
        (formation)

H = Enthalpy

m = molar (for 1 mole)

° = standard conditions

Enthalpy change (ΔH) is defined as the change in energy or heat content of a system as a result of a process taking place at constant pressure.

Enthalpy change can be communicated in the following four ways:
1. The molar enthalpy of a process, such as formation or combustion, (units kJ/mol)
2. The enthalpy change of a reaction (units kJ)
3. The enthalpy of a reaction written as a reactant or product term in the equation (units kJ)
4. An energy diagram representing a reaction (units kJ)

First, it is important to be familiar with some common definitions:
1. The standard molar enthalpy change of formation of a compound, $\Delta_f H_m{}^\circ$, is the heat energy absorbed or released when 1 mol of compound is formed from its elements in their standard states (298.15 K and 101.325 kPa). Values of $\Delta_f H_m{}^\circ$ can be found on the table of standard molar enthalpies of formation. The variable $\Delta_f H_m{}^\circ$ can also be represented as $\Delta_f H^\circ$.
2. The standard molar enthalpy of formation of elements in their standard states is defined as 0 kJ/mol.

Example

Write the equation representing the reaction for the formation for magnesium carbonate, and determine the standard molar enthalpy of formation for magnesium carbonate.

Solution

From the table of standard molar enthalpies of formation,

$\Delta_f H_m{}^\circ \left(MgCO_{3(s)} \right) = -1\,095.8 \text{ kJ/mol}$.

The following equation represents the formation of $MgCO_{3(s)}$:

$$Mg_{(s)} + C_{(s)} + \frac{3}{2}O_{2(g)} \rightarrow MgCO_{3(s)} + 1\,095.8 \text{ kJ/mol}$$

When 1 mol of magnesium carbonate is formed from its elements, 1 095.8 kJ of heat is released to the surroundings.

Example

Determine the reaction enthalpy change, $\Delta_r H^\circ$, for the equation representing the formation of magnesium carbonate balanced using whole numbers coefficients. Include the value of $\Delta_r H^\circ$ as an energy term in the equation.

Solution

$$Mg_{(s)} + C_{(s)} + \frac{3}{2}O_{2(g)} \rightarrow MgCO_{3(s)} \quad \Delta_f H^\circ = -1\,095.8 \text{ kJ}$$

Fractional reactant-product coefficients for elements are perfectly acceptable when forming or reacting a substance. If whole-number coefficients are desired, multiply the reaction enthalpy by the factor necessary to get rid of the fractions. In this case, multiply the equation and enthalpy change by 2 as follows:

$$2Mg_{(s)} + 2C_{(s)} + 3O_{2(g)} \rightarrow 2MgCO_{3(s)} \quad \Delta_r H^\circ = -2191.6\,kJ$$

The enthalpy change for a reaction is dependent on how the equation is balanced. To balance the equation using whole numbers, all terms were multiplied by 2. The $\Delta_r H^\circ$ variable is also multiplied by 2 because the equation now represents the formation of 2 mol of $MgCO_{3(s)}$.

Note that while the $\Delta_r H^\circ$ for the reaction written this way has doubled, the $\Delta_f H_m^\circ$ is still equal to -1095.85 kJ/mol because the enthalpy of formation is defined for the production of 1 mol of $MgCO_{3(s)}$.

The enthalpy change for a reaction can be included as a reactant or product term in the equation. In an endothermic reaction, which has $\Delta_r H^\circ > 0\,kJ$, heat energy is a reactant. In an exothermic reaction, which has $\Delta_r H^\circ < 0\,kJ$, heat energy is a product.

$$2Mg_{(s)} + 2C_{(s)} + 3O_{2(g)} \rightarrow 2MgCO_{3(s)} + 2191.6\,kJ$$

Example

Draw or sketch the potential energy diagram that represents the formation of magnesium carbonate.

Solution

For an exothermic reaction, like the formation of magnesium carbonate, the potential energy of the products is less than the potential energy of the reactants. The potential energy diagram appears as a step down from the reactants to the products.

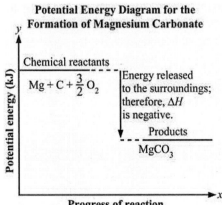

Multiplying an equation by a number changes the value of $\Delta_r H^\circ$ but not the molar enthalpy of formation of a compound $\left(\Delta_f H_m^\circ\right)$.

NOTES

The opposite is true for an endothermic reaction such as the reaction that represents the decomposition of magnesium carbonate.

$$MgCO_{3(s)} \rightarrow Mg_{(s)} + C_{(s)} + \frac{3}{2}O_{2(g)} \quad \Delta_r H° = +1\ 095.8 \text{ kJ}$$

For an endothermic reaction, the potential energy of the products is greater than the potential energy of the reactants; the graph appears as a step up from the reactants to the products.

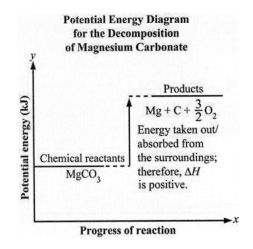

$\Delta_c H_m°\left(\text{or } \Delta_c H°\right)$ stands for the molar enthalpy change for the combustion of a compound. The subscript c indicates that this is a combustion reaction.

Example

Write the standard molar enthalpy of formation for barium sulfate in four different ways.

Solution

1. $\Delta_f H_m°(BaSO_{4(s)}) = -1\ 473.2 \text{ kJ/mol}$

2. $Ba_{(s)} + \frac{1}{8}S_{8(s)} + 2O_{2(g)} \rightarrow BaSO_{4(s)} \qquad \Delta_f H° = -1\ 473.2 \text{ kJ}$

3. $Ba_{(s)} + \frac{1}{8}S_{8(s)} + 2O_{2(g)} \rightarrow BaSO_{4(s)} + 1\ 473.2 \text{ kJ}$

4. When 1 mol of barium sulfate is formed from its elements in their standard states, 1 473.2 kJ of energy is released (that is, the reaction is exothermic), and the products have less potential energy than the reactants.

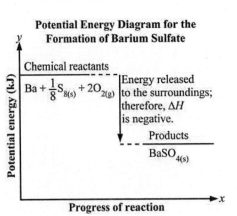

Example

When 1 mol of heptane burns to form carbon dioxide gas and liquid water, it releases 4 816.7 kJ of heat energy to its surroundings. Express this information in four different ways.

Solution

1. $\Delta_c H_m°\left(C_7H_{16(l)}\right) = -4\ 816.7 \text{ kJ/mol}$

2. $C_7H_{16(l)} + 11O_{2(g)} \rightarrow 7CO_{2(g)} + 8H_2O_{(g)}$ $\Delta_c H° = -4\ 816.7 \text{ kJ}$

3. $C_7H_{16(l)} + 11O_{2(g)} \rightarrow 7CO_{2(g)} + 8H_2O_{(g)} + 4\ 816.7 \text{ kJ}$

4. When 1 mol of liquid heptane undergoes combustion, 4 816.7 kJ of energy is released (that is, the reaction is exothermic), and the products have less potential energy than the reactants.

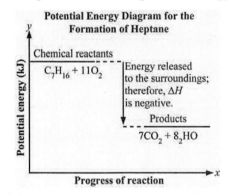

Example

When 1 mol of phenylethene ($C_6H_5C_2H_{3(s)}$) forms from its elements in their standard states, 104.0 kJ of heat energy is absorbed from the surroundings. Write this information in four different ways.

Solution

1. $\Delta_f H_m°(C_6H_5C_2H_{3(s)}) = +104.0 \text{ kJ/mol}$

2. $8C_{(s)} + 4H_{2(g)} \rightarrow C_6H_5C_2H_{3(s)}$ $\Delta_f H° = +104.0 \text{ kJ}$

3. $8C_{(s)} + 4H_{2(g)} + 104.0 \text{ kJ} \rightarrow C_6H_5C_2H_{3(s)}$

4. When 1 mol of solid phenylethene is formed from its elements in their standard states, 104.0 kJ of energy is absorbed (that is, the reaction is endothermic), and the products have more potential energy than the reactants.

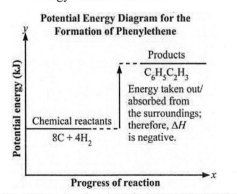

PRACTICE EXERCISES

1. When 1 mol of gasoline $\left(C_8H_{18(l)}\right)$ burns to produce carbon dioxide gas and water vapour, 5 074.1 kJ of energy is released. Write the balanced equation for the combustion of gasoline using whole number coefficients, and include the enthalpy change as a term in the equation.

2. During the formation of 1 mol of urea $\left(\left(NH_2\right)_2 CO_{(s)}\right)$ from its elements under standard conditions, 333 kJ of energy is released to the surroundings. Draw a potential energy diagram to represent this reaction.

3. Write the balanced equation that represents the decomposition of ammonia gas $\left(NH_{3(g)}\right)$ into its elements using whole number coefficients, and include the enthalpy change as a term in the equation.

4. Zinc sulfide is roasted to produce an oxide according to the following reaction equation:
    $$2ZnS_{(s)} + 3O_{2(g)} \rightarrow 2ZnO_{(s)} + 2SO_{2(g)} + 882.6 \text{ kJ}$$

    a) Draw an energy diagram to represent the reaction and enthalpy change.

b) Rewrite the given equation to represent the formation of 1 mol of the metal oxide. Determine the enthalpy change for the reaction represented by the rewritten equation.

5. When 1 mol of ammonium nitrate forms from its elements under standard conditions, 365.6 kJ of heat energy is released to the surroundings. Communicate the enthalpy change that occurs during the decomposition of 1 mol of ammonium nitrate in three different ways.

   •

   •

   •

6. Draw an enthalpy diagram that represents the formation of 2 mol of hydrogen iodide gas from its elements in their standard states.

Lesson 4   CALCULATING ENTHALPY CHANGES

Calculating the enthalpy changes where non-molar quantities of reactants or products are involved requires stoichiometric calculations.

If the molar enthalpy of a reaction is available, use the following equation:

$$\Delta H = n\Delta_r H_m$$

where ΔH = enthalpy change of the reaction that occured
in kilojoules (kJ)
n = amount of reactant used in moles (mol)
$\Delta_r H_m$ = molar enthalpy change of the reaction in kilojoules
per mole of reactant (kJ/mol)

The equation
$\Delta H = n\Delta_r H_m$ uses a naught symbol ($^\circ$) when signifying that the reaction occurs at standard temperature and pressure.

Example

The standard molar enthalpy of combustion of gasoline to give gaseous products is –5 074.1 kJ per mole. What is the enthalpy change for every litre of gasoline (737 g) that burns in an automobile engine? Assume that gasoline is $C_8H_{18(l)}$.

Solution

$$\Delta H = n\Delta_c H_m{}^\circ$$

$$\Delta H = \left(737\ g\right)\left(\frac{1\ mol}{114.26\ g\ C_8H_{18(l)}}\right)\left(-5\ 074.1\ kJ/mol\right)$$

$$\Delta H = -3.27 \times 10^4\ kJ\ or\ -32.7\ MJ$$

The subscript c in the equation $\Delta_c H = n\Delta_c H_m{}^\circ$ stands for combustion.

The enthalpy change per litre of gasoline burned completely is –32.7 MJ. The heat released is 32.7 MJ.

Example

The standard molar enthalpy of neutralization for sodium hydroxide with any monoprotic strong acid is –56.8 kJ/mol. What quantity of heat energy would be released if 750 mL of 1.56 mol/L sodium hydroxide were neutralized with an appropriate quantity of strong acid?

Solution

$$\Delta H = n\Delta_r H_m{}^\circ$$

$$\Delta H = \left(0.750\ L\right)\left(\frac{1.56\ mol}{L}\right)\left(-56.8\ kJ/mol\right)$$

$$\Delta H = -66.5\ kJ$$

The enthalpy change is –66.5 kJ; therefore, 66.5 kJ of heat energy will be released during this reaction.

Example

Heptane burns in a camping stove according to the following reaction equation:

$$C_7H_{16(l)} + 11O_{2(g)} \rightarrow 7CO_{2(g)} + 8H_2O_{(g)} + 4\,816.7 \text{ kJ}$$

What quantity of energy is released for every 1.00 kg of $CO_{2(g)}$ produced?

NOTES

$$\Delta H = n\Delta_c H_m^{\,\circ}$$

Solution

From the balanced equation, the energy-to-mole ratio for each species in the reaction can be calculated.

For every 7 mol of $CO_{2(g)}$ produced, 4 816.7 kJ of energy is released, as seen in the given equation. Therefore, the energy-to-mole ratio for $CO_{2(g)}$ produced is calculated as follows:

$$\left(\frac{4\,816.7 \text{ kJ}}{7 \text{ mol } CO_{2(g)}} \right) = 688.1 \text{ kJ/mol}$$

The amount of energy released for 1.00 kg of $CO_{2(g)}$ can be calculated as follows:

$$\Delta H = n\Delta_c H_m^{\,\circ}$$

$$\Delta H = \left(1.00 \times 10^3 \text{ g}\right)\left(\frac{1 \text{ mol}}{44.01 \text{ g}}\right)\left(\frac{688.1 \text{ kJ}}{1 \text{ mol}}\right)$$

$$\Delta H = 1.56 \times 10^4 \text{ kJ or } 15.6 \text{ MJ.}$$

Thus, 15.6 MJ of heat energy are released per kilogram of $CO_{2(g)}$ released.

Example

Heptane burns in a camping stove according to the following reaction equation:

$$C_7H_{16(l)} + 11O_{2(g)} \rightarrow 7CO_{2(g)} + 8H_2O_{(g)} + 4\ 816.7\ kJ$$

What quantity of energy is released for every 1.0 kg of $C_7H_{16(l)}$ burned?

Solution

To calculate the amount of energy released when 1.00 kg of $C_7H_{16(l)}$ is burned, first calculate the energy-to-mole ratio for $C_7H_{16(l)}$ as follows:

$$\left(\frac{9\ 633.4\ kJ}{1\ mol\ C_7H_{16(l)}} \right) = 4\ 816.7\ kJ/mol$$

$$\Delta H = n\Delta_c H_m{}^\circ$$

$$\Delta H = \left(1.00 \times 10^3\ g \right)\left(\frac{1\ mol}{100.23\ g} \right)\left(\frac{4\ 816.7\ kJ}{1\ mol} \right)$$

$$\Delta H = 4.81 \times 10^4\ kJ\ or\ 48.1\ MJ.$$

Thus, 48.1 MJ of heat energy is released per kilogram of heptane $\left(C_7H_{16(l)} \right)$ burned.

Example

Using the equation that represents the combustion of heptane from the previous example, determine the mass of oxygen that is consumed to produce 1.00 GJ of heat energy.

Solution

The energy-to-mole ratio for $O_{2(g)}$ is calculated as follows:

$$\left(\frac{4\ 816.7\ kJ}{11\ mol\ O_{2(g)}} \right) = 437.9\ kJ/mol$$

$$\Delta H = 1 \times 10^6\ kJ$$

$$\Delta H = n\Delta_c H_m{}^\circ$$

$$1 \times 10^6\ kJ = n\left(\frac{437.9\ kJ}{1\ mol\ O_{2(g)}} \right)$$

$$n = \frac{1 \times 10^6\ kJ}{\left(\dfrac{437.9\ kJ}{1\ mol\ O_{2(g)}} \right)}$$

$$n = 2\ 284\ mol\ O_{2(g)}$$

$$m = \left(2\ 284\ mol \right)\left(\frac{32.00\ g}{mol} \right)$$

$$m = 7.31 \times 10^4\ g\ or\ 73.1\ kg$$

Thus, 73.1 kg of $O_{2(g)}$ is consumed in producing 1.00 GJ of heat energy.

PRACTICE EXERCISES

Formula: $\Delta H = n\Delta_r H$, where ΔH represents the enthalpy change for a reaction

1. Determine the quantity of energy released when 20.0 kg of methane gas $\left(CH_{4(g)}\right)$ is burned.
   $\left(\Delta_c H_m{}^\circ \text{ for } CH_{4(g)} = -802.5 \text{ kJ/mol}\right)$

2. Determine the quantity of energy released when 1.00 kg of liquid octane $C_8H_{18(l)}$ is burned to produce gaseous products. $(\Delta_c H_m{}^\circ \text{ for } C_8H_{18(l)} = -5\ 074.2 \text{ kJ/mol})$

3. **a)** Determine the energy-to-mole ratio for each species consumed or produced in the burning of 1.00 kg of dimethyl ether, an alternative fuel to diesel, as represented by the following equation:
   $$CH_3OCH_{3(g)} + 3O_{2(g)} \rightarrow 2CO_{2(g)} + 3H_2O_{(g)} + 1\ 328.3 \text{ kJ}$$

   b) Determine the quantity of energy released when 1.00 kg of dimethyl ether is consumed.

4. Determine the quantity of energy absorbed per 5.40 kg of aluminum produced in the following unbalanced equation:

    $\underline{1}\ Al_2O_{3(s)} + \underline{2}\ K_{(s)} \rightarrow \underline{2}\ Al_{(s)} + \underline{3}\ K_2O_{(s)}$ $\qquad \Delta_rH = +567.8\ kJ$

Use the following information to answer the next question.

> Fatty acid methyl esters such as methyl oleate ($C_{19}H_{36}O_{2(l)}$) can be burned as biodiesel according to the following reaction equation:
>
> $$C_{19}H_{36}O_{2(l)} + 27O_{2(g)} \rightarrow 19CO_{2(g)} + 18H_2O_{(g)} \qquad \Delta_cH = -11\ 887\ kJ$$

5. Compare the energy produced per kilogram of biodiesel burned with the energy produced per kilogram of petrodiesel burned. Petrodiesel produces 45.8 MJ of energy per kilogram burned.

6. The molar enthalpy of cellular respiration is –2.80 MJ/mol of glucose. Determine the quantity of energy available when 1.00g of glucose is consumed.

Use the following information to answer the next question.

> The combustion of olive oil, triolein $\left(C_{57}H_{104}O_{6(l)} \right)$, is represented by the following net equation:
>
> $C_{57}H_{104}O_{6(l)} + 80\ O_{2(g)} \rightarrow 57CO_{2(g)} + 52H_2O_{(l)} \qquad \Delta_cH = -35\ 099.6\ kJ$

7. Determine the quantity of energy produced per gram of triolein burned.

Lesson 5   PREDICTING ENTHALPY CHANGES

The enthalpy change of any reaction is the difference between the sum of the formation enthalpies of the products and the sum of the formation enthalpies of the reactants.

The following equation is used for predicting enthalpy change of a reaction:

$$\Delta_r H^\circ = \sum_{\text{products}} \left(n\Delta_f H_m{}^\circ \right) - \sum_{\text{reactants}} \left(n\Delta_f H_m{}^\circ \right)$$

where

$\Delta_r H^\circ$ = standard enthalpy change of the reaction

n = amount of chemical reacting in the balanced equation (the coefficient)

$\Delta_f H_m{}^\circ$ = standard molar enthalpy of formation of the reactant or product in kJ/mol

The value of $\Delta_f H_m{}^\circ$ can be found on the table of standard molar enthalpies of formation. For all elements in their standard, stable states, $\Delta_f H_m{}^\circ = 0$.

Example

Determine the enthalpy change for the complete combustion of 1 mol of propane gas.

Solution

The products of a complete hydrocarbon combustion are $CO_{2(g)}$ and $H_2O_{(g)}$. The balanced equation for the combustion of propane is written as follows:

$$C_3H_{8(g)} \qquad +5O_{2(g)} \quad \rightarrow \qquad 3CO_{2(g)} \qquad +4H_2O_{(g)}$$

$\Delta_f H_m{}^\circ$: −103.8 kJ/mol   0 kJ/mol   −393.5 kJ/mol −241.8 kJ/mol

The enthalpy change is calculated as follows:

$$\Delta_r H^\circ = \sum_{\text{products}} \left(n\Delta_f H_m{}^\circ \right) - \sum_{\text{reactants}} \left(n\Delta_f H_m{}^\circ \right)$$

$$\Delta_r H^\circ = \left((3 \text{ mol})(-393.5 \text{ kJ/mol}) + (4 \text{ mol})(-241.8 \text{ kJ/mol}) \right)$$
$$- \left((1 \text{ mol})(-103.8 \text{ kJ/mol}) + (5 \text{ mol})(0 \text{ kJ/mol}) \right)$$
$$\Delta_r H^\circ = 2\,043.0 \text{ kJ}$$

The enthalpy change for the combustion of propane is −2 043.9 kJ under standard conditions. Since 1 mol of propane is burned, the molar enthalpy of combustion of propane is −2 043.9 kJ/mol.

NOTES

The symbol $\sum$ represents the sum of.

$\Delta_f H_m{}^\circ \left(H_2O_{(g)} \right)$
= −241.8 kJ/mol
$\Delta_f H_m{}^\circ \left(H_2O_{(l)} \right)$
= −285.8 kJ/mol
It is very important to determine whether $H_2O_{(g)}$ or $H_2O_{(l)}$ is used.

NOTES

Example

Determine the enthalpy change for the reaction of ethane with water as represented by the following equation: $C_2H_{4(g)} + H_2O_{(g)} \rightarrow C_2H_5OH_{(l)}$

Solution

The balanced equation is written as follows:

$$C_2H_{4(g)} \qquad + H_2O_{(g)} \qquad \rightarrow \qquad C_2H_5OH_{(l)}$$
$$\Delta_f H_m{}^\circ: \quad +52.4\ \text{kJ/mol} \quad -241.8\ \text{kJ/mol} \qquad -277.6\ \text{kJ/mol}$$

The enthalpy change is calculated as follows:

$$\Delta_r H^\circ = \sum_{products} \left(n\Delta_f H_m{}^\circ\right) - \sum_{reactants} \left(n\Delta_f H_m{}^\circ\right)$$

$$\Delta_r H^\circ = (1\ \text{mol})(-277.6\ \text{kJ/mol})$$
$$\qquad - \left((1\ \text{mol})(+52.4\ \text{kJ/mol}) + (1\ \text{mol})(-241.8\ \text{kJ/mol})\right)$$

$$\Delta_r H^\circ = -88.2\ \text{kJ}$$

The addition of water to ethane is exothermic with an enthalpy change of -88.2 kJ.

Example

Determine the enthalpy change when 1 mol of ammonium nitrate decomposes to produce water vapour and dinitrogen monoxide during an explosion.

Solution

The balanced equation is written as follows:

$$NH_4NO_{3(s)} \qquad \rightarrow \qquad N_2O_{(g)} \qquad +2H_2O_{(g)}$$
$$\Delta_f H_m{}^\circ: \quad -365.6\ \text{kJ/mol} \qquad +81.6\ \text{kJ/mol} \quad -241.8\ \text{kJ/mol}$$

The enthalpy change is calculated as follows:

$$\Delta_r H^\circ = \sum_{products} \left(n\Delta_f H_m{}^\circ\right) - \sum_{reactants} \left(n\Delta_f H_m{}^\circ\right)$$

$$\Delta_r H^\circ = \left((1\ \text{mol}) + (81.6\ \text{kJ/mol}) + (2\ \text{mol})(-241.8\ \text{kJ/mol})\right)$$
$$\qquad - (1\ \text{mol})(-365.6\ \text{kJ/mol})$$

$$\Delta_r H^\circ = -36.4\ \text{kJ}$$

The decomposition of 1 mol of ammonium nitrate to water vapour and dinitrogen monoxide is exothermic and has an enthalpy change of -36.4 kJ.

Example

Butane is added to gasoline to make it perform better under the rigorous conditions of the Canadian winter. Approximately how much energy is produced when 1 mol of butane burns in an automobile engine to give gaseous products?

Solution

A balanced equation for 1 mol of butane reacting is written as follows:

$$C_4H_{10(g)} \quad +\frac{13}{2}O_{2(g)} \quad \rightarrow \quad 4CO_{2(g)} \quad +5H_2O_{(g)}$$

$\Delta_f H_m°$: $\quad$ –125.7 kJ/mol $\quad$ 0 kJ/mol $\quad\quad$ –393.5 kJ/mol $\quad$ –241.8 kJ/mol

The enthalpy change is calculated as follows:

$$\Delta_r H° = \sum_{\text{products}} \left(n\Delta_f H_m°\right) - \sum_{\text{reactants}} \left(n\Delta_f H_m°\right)$$

$$\Delta_r H° = \left((4\text{ mol})(-393.5\text{ kJ/mol}) + (5\text{ mol})(-241.8\text{ kJ/mol})\right)$$
$$\quad\quad -\left((1\text{ mol})(-125.7\text{ kJ/mol}) + (0\text{ kJ/mol})\right)$$
$$\Delta_r H° = -2\,657.3\text{ kJ}$$

The combustion of 1 mol of butane is exothermic and has an enthalpy change of –2 657.3 kJ.

PRACTICE EXERCISES

Formulas: $\Delta H = n\Delta_r H_m$ $\qquad \Delta_r H° = \sum_{products} \left(n\Delta_f H_m° \right) - \sum_{reactants} \left(n\Delta_f H_m° \right)$

1. Determine the enthalpy change for the complete combustion of 1 mol of methane gas $\left(CH_{4(g)} \right)$ to give gaseous products.

2. Determine the enthalpy change for the combustion of 1 mol of ethanol ($C_2H_5OH_{(l)}$), a controversial alternative automobile fuel, to give gaseous products.

3. Determine the molar enthalpy of combustion of glucose during cellular respiration, as represented by the following equation: $C_6H_{12}O_{6(s)} + 6O_{2(g)} \rightarrow 6CO_{2(g)} + 6H_2O_{(l)}$

4. In the presence of impurities or other contaminants, liquid hydrogen peroxide decomposes to liquid water and oxygen gas. Determine the enthalpy change for the decomposition of 1 mol of hydrogen peroxide ($H_2O_{2(l)}$). The standard molar enthalpy of formation of $H_2O_{2(l)}$ is –187.8 kJ/mol.

5. During the process of roasting, copper(II) sulfide is heated to produce copper(II) oxide and sulfur dioxide, an acid precipitation pollutant. Determine the enthalpy change for the reaction of roasting 1 mol of copper(II) sulfide.

6. The most promising alternative to diesel fuel is dimethyl ether, $CH_3OCH_{3(g)}$, a compound that can be made from gasification of household waste. Determine the enthalpy change for the complete combustion of 1 mol of dimethyl ether to give gaseous products $\left(\Delta_f H_m^\circ \left(CH_3OCH_{3(g)}\right) = -184.1\,kJ/mol\right)$.

7. Acetylene (also called ethyne) is the fuel source for oxyacetylene welding and cutting of metals. Determine the molar enthalpy of combustion of ethyne to form gaseous products.

Lesson 6 HESS'S LAW

Hess's law can be stated in several ways. The following two ways of stating Hess's law are relevant to this course:

- The total enthalpy change for a chemical reaction is independent of the route by which the reaction takes place, provided initial and final conditions are the same. For example, the energy released per mole of glucose combusted in a bomb calorimeter to produce $CO_{2(g)}$ and $H_2O_{(g)}$ is essentially the same as that released by the cellular respiration of glucose to give the same products.
- The enthalpy change of a net chemical reaction is the arithmetic sum of the enthalpies of the individual reactions combined to make the net reaction. In mathematical terms, this can be expressed as follows:

$$\Delta_{net}H° = \Delta_1H° + \Delta_2H° + \Delta_3H° + \Delta_4H° + ...$$

For example, add together the following four equations:

1.	A	+	B	$\rightarrow$	E + G	$\Delta_rH° = \Delta_1H°$
2.	E	+	G	$\rightarrow$	L + M	$\Delta_rH° = \Delta_2H°$
3.	L	+	M	$\rightarrow$	Q + R	$\Delta_rH° = \Delta_3H°$
4.	Q	+	R	$\rightarrow$	Y + Z	$\Delta_rH° = \Delta_4H°$
5.	A	+	B	$\rightarrow$	Y + Z	$\Delta_{net}H° = \Delta_1H° + \Delta_2H° + \Delta_3H° + \Delta_4H°$

Anything that is both a product and a reactant cancels out when the sums of the coefficients are equal.

For example, adding the following reactions:

$$A + D \rightarrow E + G$$
$$E + G \rightarrow L + M$$
$$A + D \rightarrow L + M$$

Also, anything that appears on the left-hand side of the reactions can be cancelled out or reduced, with like chemicals on the right-hand side.

For example, adding the following reactions:

$$C + R \rightarrow 2B + Q$$
$$B + Q \rightarrow W + Z$$
$$C + R \rightarrow B + W + Z$$

Equations must often be manipulated before they are added together to obtain the desired net equation. When multiplying an equation by a certain factor, each coefficient must be multiplied by that factor. The reaction enthalpy must also be multiplied by the same number.

If the reaction is reversed, multiply the reaction's enthalpy by –1.

When constructing the net reaction, first take care of the compounds in the final reaction, and the rest will usually fall into place.

26

Example

The formation of liquid hexane is represented by the following overall net equation: $6C_{(s)} + 7H_{2(g)} \rightarrow C_6H_{14(l)}$

The enthalpy of reaction for each of the following chemical equations is given.

1. $C_6H_{14(l)} + \dfrac{19}{2}O_{2(g)} \rightarrow 6CO_{2(g)} + 7H_2O_{(l)}$ $\Delta_r H^\circ = -4\,162.9\ kJ$

2. $C_{(s)} + O_{2(g)} \rightarrow CO_{2(g)}$ $\Delta_r H^\circ = -393.5\ kJ$

3. $H_{2(g)} + \dfrac{1}{2}O_{2(g)} \rightarrow H_2O_{(l)}$ $\Delta_r H^\circ = -285.8\ kJ$

Using Hess's law, determine the molar enthalpy of formation for hexane.

Solution

The three given equations need to be manipulated and combined so that the sum of the steps results in the overall net equation

Reversing equation 1 will give hexane as a product, but the sign of the reaction enthalpy must be reversed to positive:

$6CO_{2(g)} + 7H_2O_{(l)} \rightarrow C_6H_{14(l)} + \dfrac{19}{2}O_{2(g)}$ $\Delta_r H^\circ = +4\,162.9\ kJ$

Now, 6 carbon atoms are required. Therefore, the reaction enthalpy and all entities for equation 2 are multiplied by 6 as follows:

$6C_{(s)} + 6O_{2(g)} \rightarrow 6CO_{2(g)}$ $\Delta_r H^\circ = 6 \times (-393.5\ kJ) = -2\,361.0\ kJ$

$\Delta_r H^\circ = -2\,361.0\ kJ$

Now, 7 hydrogen molecules are required for the desired net equation. The reaction enthalpy and all entities in equation 3 are multiplied by 7 as follows:

$7H_{2(g)} + \dfrac{7}{2}O_{2(g)} \rightarrow 7H_2O_{(l)}$ $\Delta_r H^\circ = 7(-285.8\ kJ) = -2\,000.6\ kJ$

$\Delta_r H^\circ = -2\,000.6\ kJ$

Adding equations 1, 2 and 3 gives the following equation:

$6CO_{2(g)} + 7H_2O_{(l)} + 6C_{(s)} + 6O_{2(g)} + \dfrac{7}{2}O_{2(g)} + 7H_{2(g)}$

$\rightarrow C_6H_{14(l)} + \dfrac{19}{2}O_{2(g)} + 6CO_{2(g)} + 7H_2O_{(l)}$

Now, all entities that are both products and reactants must be cancelled or reduced, which leaves the following net equation:

$6C_{(s)} + 7H_{2(g)} \rightarrow C_6H_{14(l)}$

Finally, add the formation and combustion enthalpies as follows:

$$\Delta_{net}H° = +4\,162.9 \text{ kJ} + (-2\,361.0 \text{ kJ}) + (-2\,000.6 \text{ kJ})$$
$$\Delta_{net}H° = -198.7 \text{ kJ}$$

The standard molar enthalpy of formation of hexane, $C_6H_{14(l)}$, is -198.7 kJ/mol.

Example

Determine the enthalpy change for the hydrogenation reaction of benzene to make cyclohexane.

$$C_6H_{6(l)} + 3H_{2(g)} \rightarrow C_6H_{12(l)} \qquad\qquad \Delta_{net}H° = ?$$

Consider the following information:

1. $C_6H_{6(l)} \;+\; \dfrac{15}{2}O_{2(g)} \;\rightarrow\; 6CO_{2(g)} \;+\; 3H_2O_{(l)} \quad \Delta_rH° = -3\,267.0 \text{ kJ}$

2. $C_6H_{12(l)} \;+\; 9O_{2(g)} \;\rightarrow\; 6CO_{2(g)} \;+\; 6H_2O_{(l)} \quad \Delta_rH° = -3\,930.0 \text{ kJ}$

3. $H_{2(g)} \;+\; \dfrac{1}{2}O_{2(g)} \;\rightarrow\; H_2O_{(l)} \qquad\qquad\qquad \Delta_rH° = -285.8 \text{ kJ}$

Solution

Manipulate, and combine the equations to get the net equation and the value of $\Delta_{net}H°$.

$$C_6H_{6(l)} + 3H_{2(g)} \rightarrow C_6H_{12(l)} \qquad\qquad \Delta_{net}H° = ?$$

Equation 1 gives 1 mol of benzene as a reactant needed for the net equation; therefore, this equation does not need to be manipulated.

$$C_6H_{6(l)} + \frac{15}{2}O_{2(g)} \rightarrow 6CO_{2(g)} + 3H_2O_{(l)} \qquad \Delta_rH° = -3\,267.0 \text{ kJ}$$

Reversing the reaction in equation 2 gives cyclohexane as a product in the net equation, so the sign of the enthalpy must be reversed:

$$6CO_{2(g)} + 6H_2O_{(l)} \rightarrow C_6H_{12(l)} + 9O_{2(g)} \qquad \Delta_rH° = +3\,930.0 \text{ kJ}$$

Multiply equation 3 by 3 to give 3 mol of hydrogen gas. When the equations are added, the 3 mol of $H_2O_{(l)}$ will cancel out.

$$3H_{2(g)} + \frac{3}{2}O_{2(g)} \rightarrow 3H_2O_{(l)}$$
$$\Delta_rH° = -857.4 \text{ kJ}$$

Adding these three equations together gives the following net overall equation:

$$C_6H_{6(l)} + 3H_{2(g)} \rightarrow C_6H_{12(l)}$$
$$\Delta_{net}H° = +3\,930.0 \text{ kJ} - 3\,267.0 \text{ kJ} - 857.4 \text{ kJ}$$
$$\Delta_{net}H° = -194.4 \text{ kJ}$$

The standard enthalpy of the hydrogenation of 1 mol of benzene is -194.4 kJ.

PRACTICE EXERCISES

Formulas: $\Delta_{net}H° = \Delta_1 H° + \Delta_2 H° + \Delta_3 H° + \Delta_4 H° + ...$

Use the following to answer the next question.

$$C_{(s)} + 2H_{2(g)} \rightarrow CH_{4(g)} \qquad \Delta_r H° = -74.6 \text{ kJ}$$

$$C_{(s)} \rightarrow C_{(g)} \qquad \Delta_r H° = +715.0 \text{ kJ}$$

$$H_{2(g)} \rightarrow 2H_{(g)} \qquad \Delta_r H° = +436.0 \text{ kJ}$$

1. Determine the enthalpy change for the overall reaction $C_{(g)} + 4H_{(g)} \rightarrow CH_{4(g)}$, $\Delta_{net}H° = ?$.

Use the following to answer the next question.

$$HCl_{(g)} + KOH_{(s)} \rightarrow KCl_{(g)} + H2O_{(l)} \qquad \Delta_r H° = -203.6 \text{ kJ}$$
$$2KOH_{(s)} + 2H_2SO_{4(l)} \rightarrow 2H_2O_{(l)} + K_2SO_{4(aq)} \qquad \Delta_r H° = -342.4 \text{ kJ}$$
$$K_2SO_{4(aq)} \rightarrow K_2SO_{4(aq)} \qquad \Delta_r H° = +23.8 \text{ kJ}$$

The easiest way to produce hydrogen chloride gas ($HCl_{(g)}$) in the laboratory is to add concentrated sulfuric acid to potassium chloride according to the following net equation:

$$2KCl_{(s)} + H_2SO_{4(l)} \rightarrow 2HCl_{(g)} + K_2SO_{4(s)} \qquad \Delta_{net}H° = ?$$

2. Using Hess's law, determine the enthalpy change for the net reaction that forms hydrogen chloride.

Use the following to answer the next question.

The overall net equation that represents the formation of $H_2O_{(g)}$ is written as follows:

$$3H_{2(g)} + O_{3(g)} \rightarrow 3H_2O_{(g)} \quad \Delta_{net}H° = ?$$

3. Determine the enthalpy change for the given overall net reaction.

$1 \cdot 5 \left[2H_{2(g)} + O_{2(g)} \rightarrow 2H_2O_{(g)} \right] \quad \Delta_r H° = \left[-483.6 \text{ kJ} \right] 1 \cdot 5$

$\qquad 3O_{2(g)} \rightarrow 2O_{3(g)} \quad \Delta_r H° = \left[+248.6 \text{ kJ} \right] \begin{bmatrix} -1 \\ /2 \end{bmatrix}$

Use the following to answer the next question.

$$H_{2(g)} + F_{2(g)} \rightarrow 2HF_{(g)} \qquad \Delta_r H° = -546.6 \text{ kJ}$$
$$C_{(s)} + 2F_{2(g)} \rightarrow CF_{4(g)} \qquad \Delta_r H° = -680.0 \text{ kJ}$$
$$2C_{(s)} + 2H_{2(g)} \rightarrow C_2H_{4(g)} \qquad \Delta_r H° = +52.4 \text{ kJ}$$

The overall net equation for the reaction of ethene and fluorine is written as follows:
$$C_2H_{4(g)} + 6F_{2(g)} \rightarrow 2CF_{4(g)} + 4HF_{(g)} \quad \Delta_{net}H° = ?$$

4. Determine the enthalpy change for the overall net reaction of ethene and fluorine.

5. a) Write the balanced reaction for the formation of calcium carbide, $CaC_{2(s)}$, from its elements in their standard states.

b) Use the following equations to determine the molar enthalpy of formation of calcium carbide from its constituent elements.

$$CaO_{(s)} + 3C_{(s)} \rightarrow CaC_{2(s)} + CO_{(g)} \qquad \Delta_r H° = +464.8 \text{ kJ}$$

$$C_{(s)} + \frac{1}{2}O_{2(g)} \rightarrow CO_{(g)} \qquad\qquad \Delta_r H° = -110.5 \text{ kJ} \quad [\times]$$

$$CaO_{(s)} \rightarrow Ca_{(s)} + \frac{1}{2}O_{2(g)} \qquad\qquad \Delta_r H° = +634.9 \text{ kJ} \quad [-]$$

c) Calcium carbide reacts with water to produce acetylene (ethyne), as represented by the following equation:

$$Ca_2C_{(s)} \quad + \quad 2H_2O_{(l)} \quad \rightarrow \quad Ca(OH)_{2(s)} \quad + \quad C_2H_{2(g)}$$

$\Delta_f H_m°$ -285.8 kJ/mol -985.2 kJ/mol 227.4 kJ/mol

Using the $\Delta_f H_m°$ of calcium carbide and the given molar enthalpies of formation, calculate the enthalpy change for the reaction of calcium carbide with water.

Lesson 7 PREDICTING THE ENTHALPY CHANGE OF A REACTION COMPONENT

The enthalpy change of any reaction, given that the molar enthalpies of formation are available, is determined using the following equation:

$$\Delta_r H^\circ = \sum_{products} \left(n\Delta_f H_m{}^\circ\right) - \sum_{reactants} \left(n\Delta_f H_m{}^\circ\right)$$

The equation can be rearranged to calculate the total formation enthalpy of the reactants (or of the products) as follows:

$$\sum_{reactants} \left(n\Delta_f H_m{}^\circ\right) = \sum_{products} \left(n\Delta_f H_m{}^\circ\right) - \Delta_r H^\circ$$

or

$$\sum_{products} \left(n\Delta_f H_m{}^\circ\right) = \sum_{reactants} \left(n\Delta_f H_m{}^\circ\right) + \Delta_r H^\circ$$

When a compound reacts with an element, the sum of the reactant formation enthalpies is a simple multiple of that compound's formation enthalpy. For example, in the combustion of methane gas $\left(CH_{4(g)} + O_{2(g)}\right)$, the $\Delta_f H_m{}^\circ$ for the element is 0.0 kJ/mol. It therefore essentially drops out of the summation equation, which simplifies the equation. The $\sum\left(n\Delta_f H_m{}^\circ\right)$ for the reactants in the combustion of methane gas would simply be $n\Delta_f H_m{}^\circ$ for $CH_{4(g)}$. Combustion enthalpies are ideal for these calculations.

Example

Methylhydrazine burns in a bomb calorimeter according to the following balanced equation:

$$2CH_6N_{2(l)} + 5O_{2(g)} \rightarrow 2CO_{2(g)} + 2N_{2(g)} + 6H_2O_{(l)} \qquad \Delta_c H^\circ = -2\,610.4 \text{ kJ}$$

In bomb calorimeters, $H_2O_{(l)}$ (not $H_2O_{(g)}$) is produced during the combustion reaction because it is a closed system.

Determine the molar enthalpy of formation of methylhydrazine.

Solution

$$\sum_{reactants} \left(n\Delta_f H_m{}^\circ\right) = \sum_{products} \left(n\Delta_f H_m{}^\circ\right) - \Delta_r H^\circ$$

$$\sum_{reactants} \left(n\Delta_f H_m{}^\circ\right) = \left(2 \text{ mol}\right)\left(-393.5 \text{ kJ/mol}\right)$$

$$+\left(6 \text{ mol}\right)\left(-285.8 \text{ kJ/mol}\right) - \left(-2\,610.4 \text{ kJ}\right)$$

$$\sum_{reactants} \left(n\Delta_f H_m{}^\circ\right) = +108.6 \text{ kJ}$$

Because the $\Delta_f H_m{}^\circ$ of $O_2 = 0.00$ kJ, all that is remaining in the sum of reactants is $n\Delta_f H_m{}^\circ$ for $CH_6N_{2(l)}$. However, this is the enthalpy of formation for 2 mol of methylhydrazine. To find the molar enthalpy of formation for the methylhydrazine, divide by 2:

$n\Delta_f H_m{}^\circ = +108.6$ kJ

$$\Delta_f H_m{}^\circ = \frac{+108.6 \text{ kJ}}{2 \text{ mol}}$$
$$= 54.3 \text{ kJ/mol}$$

Example

The standard molar enthalpy of combustion of cyclobutane, $C_4H_{8(l)}$, to gaseous products is $-2\,720.4$ kJ/mol. Determine the standard molar enthalpy of formation of cyclobutane.

Solution

$$C_4H_{8(l)} + 6O_{2(g)} \rightarrow 4CO_{2(g)} + 4H_2O_{(g)} \qquad \Delta_c H^\circ = -2\,720.4 \text{ kJ}$$

$$\sum_{\text{reactants}} (n\Delta_f H_m{}^\circ) = \sum_{\text{products}} (n\Delta_f H_m{}^\circ) - \Delta_r H^\circ$$

$$\sum_{\text{reactants}} (n\Delta_f H_m{}^\circ) = (4 \text{ mol})(-393.5 \text{ kJ/mol})$$

$$+(4 \text{ mol})(-285.8 \text{ kJ/mol}) - (-2\,720.4 \text{ kJ})$$

$$\sum_{\text{reactants}} (n\Delta_f H_m{}^\circ) = +3.2 \text{ kJ}$$

Therefore, the molar enthalpy of formation of $C_4H_{8(l)}$ may be calculated as follows:

$n\Delta_f H_m{}^\circ = +3.2$ kJ

$$\Delta_f H_m{}^\circ = \frac{+3.2 \text{ kJ}}{1 \text{ mol}}$$
$$= +3.2 \text{ kJ/mol}$$

Example

When 1.00 g of diphenylmethanone, $(C_6H_5)_2CO_{(s)}$, burns in a closed system to produce $CO_{2(g)}$ and $H_2O_{(l)}$, 35.74 kJ of heat energy is released.

Determine the molar enthalpy of formation of diphenylmethanone.

Solution

The balanced reaction equation for diphenylmethanone combustion is written as follows:

$$\left(C_6H_5\right)_2CO_{(s)} + 15O_{2(g)} \rightarrow 13CO_{2(g)} + 5H_2O_{(l)}$$
$$? 0 -393.5 \text{ kJ/mol} -285.8 \text{ kJ/mol}$$

Diphenylmethanone releases 35.74 kJ of energy per 1.00 g burned. Diphenylmethanone has a molar mass of 182.23 g/mol. Determine of the molar enthalpy of combustion of $(C_6H_5)_2CO_{(s)}$ as follows:

$$\Delta_c H_m{}^\circ = \frac{-35.74 \text{ kJ}}{1.00 \text{ g}} \times \frac{182.23 \text{ g}}{1 \text{ mol}}$$
$$\Delta_c H_m{}^\circ = -6\,512.9 \text{ kJ/mol}$$

Thus, the given chemical equation may be rewritten as:

$$(C_6H_5)_2CO_{(s)} + 15O_{2(g)} \rightarrow 13CO_{2(g)} + 5H_2O_{(l)} \qquad \Delta_r H^\circ = -6\,512.9 \text{ kJ}$$

Therefore, the molar enthalpy of formation of $(C_6H_5)_2CO_{(s)}$ may be calculated as follows:

$$\sum_{\text{reactants}} (n\Delta_f H_m{}^\circ) = \sum_{\text{products}} (n\Delta_f H_m{}^\circ) - \Delta_r H^\circ$$
$$n\Delta_f H_m{}^\circ((C_6H_5)_2CO_{(s)}) = (13 \text{ mol})(-393.5 \text{ kJ/mol})$$
$$+ (5 \text{ mol})(-285.8 \text{ kJ/mol}) - (-6\,512.9 \text{ kJ})$$
$$n\Delta_f H_m{}^\circ((C_6H_5)_2CO_{(s)}) = -31.6 \text{ kJ}$$

In this case $n = 1$. Therefore, $\Delta_f H_m{}^\circ\left((C_6H_5)_2CO_{(s)}\right) = -31.6$ kJ/mol.

PRACTICE EXERCISES

Formula: $\sum\limits_{\text{reactants}} (n\Delta_f H_m^\circ) = \sum\limits_{\text{products}} (n\Delta_f H_m^\circ) - \Delta_r H^\circ$

1. Determine the enthalpy of formation of decane ($C_{10}H_{22(l)}$) if the complete combustion of 1 mol of decane releases 6 777.9 kJ when gaseous carbon dioxide and liquid water are the products.

2. The standard molar enthalpy of combustion of buta-1,3-diene, $C_4H_{6(l)}$, to produce $CO_{2(g)}$ and $H_2O_{(l)}$ is –2 319.5 kJ/mol. Determine the molar enthalpy of formation of buta-1,3-diene.

Use the following information to answer the next question.

When 6.00 g of urea, $(NH_2)_2CO_{(s)}$, is burned in a bomb calorimeter to produce $CO_{2(g)}$, $N_{2(g)}$, and $H_2O_{(l)}$, 63.3 kJ of heat energy is released.

3. **a)** Determine the energy released in burning 1 mol of urea in a bomb calorimeter.

   b) Determine the molar enthalpy of formation of urea $\left((NH_2)_2CO_{(s)}\right)$.

4. The standard molar enthalpy of combustion of benzoic acid $\left(C_6H_5COOH_{(s)}\right)$ in a closed system is $-3\ 226.7$ kJ/mol. The products are carbon dioxide gas and liquid water. Determine the standard molar enthalpy of formation of benzoic acid.

5. Determine the molar enthalpy of formation of chloroethane given the following reaction and enthalpy change:

$$C_2H_5Cl_{(g)} \rightarrow C_2H_{4(g)} + HCl_{(g)} \qquad\qquad \Delta_r H^\circ = +72.2 \text{ kJ}$$

Lesson 8   USING SIMPLE AND BOMB CALORIMETER DATA TO DETERMINE $\Delta_r H°$

USING SIMPLE CALORIMETER DATA TO DETERMINE $\Delta_r H°$

A simple polystyrene (or foam) cup calorimeter in a high school laboratory is an effective way to measure enthalpy changes of reactions that occur in aqueous environments, such as heat of solution or dilution, neutralizations, single replacement, and other redox reactions.

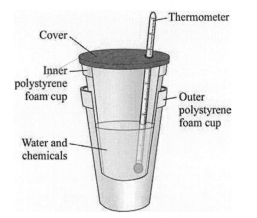

For combustion reactions, an aluminum soft drink can containing water monitored by a thermometer and suspended above the substance undergoing combustion may be used as a calorimeter.

The following assumptions are made when using a simple calorimeter:

- A polystyrene foam cup is assumed to be perfect insulation. Experience shows that the foam cup is not a perfect insulator, and some heat is transferred through the cup to the surroundings. However, this small amount of energy transfer is usually ignored.

- Only the water releases, or absorbs, heat energy to or from the reaction. When a reaction releases heat to the calorimeter, all materials (the water, the thermometer, the foam cup, the lid, and the air above the water) warm up. The heat capacities and masses of each of the components other than the water are all small. It is assumed that no heat is gained or lost to the surroundings unless otherwise indicated.

- $c_{\text{solution}} = c_{H_2O_{(l)}}$ The heat capacity of an aqueous solution used or produced in a reaction, unless otherwise indicated, is assumed to be the same as that of water, $4.19 \text{ kJ/kg} \cdot °C$. (This assumption usually holds provided that the solute concentration is less than 2 mol/L).

- $V_{\text{solution}} = V_{H_2O_{(l)}} = m_{H_2O_{(l)}}$. As with the third assumption, when a solution's concentration is less than 2 mol/L, water constitutes the majority of the solution. Liquid water has a density very close to 1.00 g/mL. This is assumed to be the density of aqueous solutions if no extra information is provided.

NOTES

The given assumptions allow you to calculate the kinetic energy change of the calorimeter, Q_{cal}, given by the following formula: $Q_{cal} = (mc\Delta T)_{cal}$

where Q_{cal} = the kinetic energy change (kJ)
m = the mass of water in the calorimeter (kg)
$c = 4.19$ kJ/kg·°C for the water in the calorimeter
ΔT = the calorimeter temperature change (°C)

A combination of the first and second laws of thermodynamics, where energy is transferred rather than created or destroyed, allows for the assumption that the kinetic energy change of the calorimeter is equal to the enthalpy change of the reaction ΔH, given by the following equation:
$\Delta H = n\Delta_r H_m{}^\circ$
where ΔH = enthalpy change of the reaction that occurred, in kilojoules (kJ)
n = amount of reactant used
$\Delta_r H_m{}^\circ$ = molar enthalpy change of the reaction, in kilojoules per mole of reactant (kJ/mol)

Combining $\Delta H = n\Delta_r H_m{}^\circ$ with the idea that energy gained by the water in a calorimeter equals the energy lost by the reaction, the following equation may be written:
$\Delta H = -Q_{cal} = -(mc\Delta T)_{cal} \Rightarrow n\Delta_r H_m{}^\circ = -(mc\Delta T)_{cal}$

The negative sign denotes that the energy lost by the reaction is gained by the water in the calorimeter and vice-versa.

Example

When 50.0 mL of 1.00 mol/L $NaOH_{(aq)}$, with an initial temperature of 17.4°C, is mixed with 50.0 mL of 1.00 mol/L $HCl_{(aq)}$, with an initial temperature of 17.4°C, the final reaction mixture reaches a temperature of 24.2°C. What is the molar enthalpy change for the neutralization of the base?

Solution
The energy lost by the reaction equals the energy gained by the calorimeter water:
$n\Delta_r H = -(mc\Delta T)_{cal}$
$n_{HCl} = (0.0500$ L$)(1.00$ mol/L$) = 0.0500$ mol
$m = 0.1000$ kg (i.e., the total solution volume of 100.0 mL contains 100.0 g of water)
$c = 4.19$ kJ/kg·°C
$\Delta T = 24.2°C - 17.4°C = 6.80°C$

$(0.0500$ mol$)\Delta_r H_m = -(0.100$ kg$)(4.19$ kJ/kg·°C$)(6.80°C)$
$\Delta_r H_m = -57.0$ kJ/mol

The increase in calorimeter temperature illustrates that the neutralization reaction is exothermic and energy is released during the reaction. This is consistent with the negative enthalpy found in the calculations, $\Delta_r H_m = -57.0 \text{ kJ/mol}$.

Example

When excess zinc is added to 50.0 mL of 0.250 mol/L aqueous copper(II) sulfate, the calorimeter warms by 12.5°C. What is the molar enthalpy of reduction of aqueous copper(II) ions?

Solution

The energy lost by the reaction equals the energy gained by the calorimeter water.

$$n\Delta_r H_m = -(mc\Delta T)_{cal}$$
$$n_{Cu^{2+}} = (0.0500 \text{ L})(0.250 \text{ mol/L}) = 0.0125 \text{ mol}$$
$$m = 0.0500 \text{ kg} \quad (50.0 \text{ mL of solution contains } 50.0 \text{ g of water})$$
$$c = 4.19 \text{ kJ/kg} \cdot °C$$
$$\Delta T = 12.5°C$$

$$(0.0125 \text{ mol})\Delta_r H° = -(0.0500 \text{ kg})(4.19 \text{ kJ/kg} \cdot °C)(12.5°C)$$
$$\Delta_r H° = -210 \text{ kJ/mol}$$

The calorimeter water warmed up, so the reaction is exothermic. This is consistent with the negative enthalpy found in the calculations, $\Delta_r H° = -210 \text{ kJ/mol}$.

THE BOMB CALORIMETER

Professional thermodynamicists use a **bomb calorimeter** to measure the energies released and absorbed by reactions, including combustions. Bomb calorimetry minimizes heat loss with superior insulation, very exact temperature measurements, and a consideration for all possible heat transfers to give more accurate enthalpies of reaction.

If the calorimeter water heats up, it must have gained energy from the reactants. Therefore, the reaction must be exothermic, and ΔH must be negative.

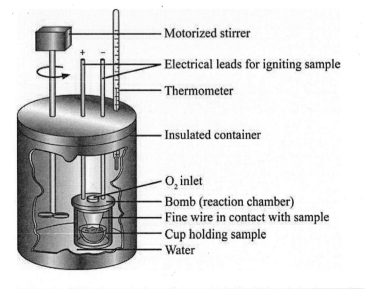

- Motorized stirrer
- Electrical leads for igniting sample
- Thermometer
- Insulated container
- O_2 inlet
- Bomb (reaction chamber)
- Fine wire in contact with sample
- Cup holding sample
- Water

In addition to the large mass of water it contains, the thermometer, the bomb, the stirrer, and the container all absorb energy when an exothermic reaction occurs.

As for simple calorimetry, the enthalpy change of the reaction is equal to the kinetic energy change of the calorimeter:

$$\Delta H = -\left(mc\Delta T\right)_{\text{cal}} \Rightarrow n\Delta_r H_m = -\left(mc\Delta T\right)_{\text{cal}}$$

The kinetic energy change of the calorimeter can now be expressed as the sum of all the kinetic energies of each component as follows:

$$n\Delta_r H_m = -(Q_{H_2O} + Q_{\text{bomb}} + Q_{\text{thermometer}} + Q_{\text{stirrer}} + Q_{\text{container}})$$

Every component experiences the same temperature change, ΔT.

$$n\Delta_r H_m = -(m_{H_2O}c_{H_2O}\Delta T + m_B c_B \Delta T + m_T c_T \Delta T + m_S c_S \Delta T + m_C c_C \Delta T)$$

(In this equation, $m_{H_2O}, m_B, m_T, m_S,$ and m_C are the masses of the water, bomb, thermometer, stirrer, and containers, respectively, and $c_{H_2O}, c_B, c_T, c_S,$ and c_C are their heat capacities)

The equation can be simplified as follows:

$$n\Delta_r H_m = -\left(m_{H_2O}c_{H_2O} + m_B c_B + m_T c_T + m_S c_S + m_C c_C\right)\Delta T$$

The masses and the heat capacities of all the components of the bomb calorimeter are maintained and are, in effect, constants.

The following equation is the simplified form of the equation that is commonly used:

$$\Delta H = n\Delta_r H_m = -C\Delta T$$

In this equation, C is the heat capacity of the bomb calorimeter in kJ/°C.

Example

A 1.00 g sample of benzoic acid $\left(C_6H_5COOH_{(s)}\right)$ is burned in a bomb calorimeter. The initial temperature is 25.00°C, and the heat capacity of the calorimeter is 5.43 kJ/°C. The combustion causes the temperature of the calorimeter to rise to 29.86°C. Using this data, determine the molar enthalpy of combustion of benzoic acid.

Solution

The enthalpy change is calculated as follows:

$$n\Delta_c H_m = -C\Delta T$$

$$n_{C_6H_5COOH_{(s)}} = (1.00 \text{ g})\left(\frac{1 \text{ mol}}{122.13 \text{ g}}\right) = 0.008\,19 \text{ mol}$$

$$C = 5.43 \text{ kJ/°C}$$
$$\Delta T = 29.86°C - 25.00°C = 4.86°C$$

$$\Delta_c H_m = \frac{-C\Delta T}{n} = \frac{-(5.43 \text{ kJ/°C})(4.86°C)}{0.008\,19 \text{ mol}}$$

$$\Delta_c H_m = -3.22 \times 10^3 \text{ kJ/mol}$$

The increase in calorimeter temperature indicates that the neutralization reaction lost energy and is exothermic. This is consistent with the negative molar enthalpy of combustion of $C_6H_5COOH_{(s)}$ calculated, $\Delta_c H_m = -3.22 \times 10^3 \text{ kJ/mol}$.

The equality
$$n\Delta_r H_m = -C\Delta T$$
is used when determining molar enthalpy (kJ/mol) values. The number of moles can be determined or is given.

Example

A reaction in a bomb calorimeter absorbs 22.4 kJ of heat energy. What is the initial temperature of the calorimeter if its final temperature was 24.22°C, and its heat capacity is 28.7 kJ/°C?

Solution

The enthalpy change is calculated as follows:

$$\Delta H = -C\Delta T$$
$$\Delta H = -22.4 \text{ kJ}$$
$$C = 28.7 \text{ kJ/°C}$$
$$\Delta T = ?$$

$$\Delta T = -\frac{\Delta H}{C} = -\frac{22.4 \text{ kJ}}{28.7 \text{ kJ/°C}}$$

$$\Delta T = -0.780°C = T_f - T_i$$
$$T_i = T_f - \Delta T$$
$$T_i = 24.22°C - (-0.780°C)$$
$$T_i = 25.00°C$$

The initial temperature is 25.0°C.

The equality $\Delta H = -C\Delta T$ is used when the quantity of energy (in kJ) gained or lost is to be determined or is given.

PRACTICE EXERCISES

Formulas: $\Delta H = -(mc\Delta T)_{cal} \Rightarrow n\Delta_r H_m = -(mc\Delta T)_{cal}$ and $\Delta H = n\Delta_r H_m = -C\Delta T$

1. Determine the molar enthalpy of a solution of sodium nitrate if dissolving 8.95 g of the salt in 104.52 g of water in a simple calorimeter causes the water temperature to drop from 22.6°C to 18.2°C.

2. Homeowners often buy salt containing calcium chloride in order to melt ice on their driveways in the winter. When 1 mol of calcium chloride dissolves in water, 75.0 kJ of heat energy is released. What is the final temperature expected when 11.35 g of calcium chloride is added to 0.100 kg of water at 22.0°C in a simple calorimeter?

3. The molar enthalpy of solution of the salt potassium iodide is +21.4 kJ/mol. Will water in a calorimeter warm up or cool down when the salt is added? Determine the expected temperature change that will occur when 8.30 g of the salt is added to 50.0 mL of water in a calorimeter.

4. Methylhydrazine ($CH_3(NH)NH_{2(l)}$) burns to produce nitrogen dioxide, carbon dioxide, and liquid water. Burning 2.00 g of methylhydrazine in a bomb calorimeter with a heat capacity of 7.794 kJ/°C raises the temperature of the apparatus from 25.00°C to 32.25°C. Determine the molar enthalpy of combustion of methylhydrazine.

Lesson 9   COMMON APPLICATIONS OF THERMODYNAMIC PRINCIPLES

Every day, water is boiled for cooking or heated for showering, bathing, and washing clothes and dishes. In Alberta, most water is heated by burning natural gas (largely methane) or through electrical means with electricity produced indirectly from burning coal. Water heaters are similar to calorimeters because heat energy from a combustion reaction is transferred directly to water.

Portable stoves that burn all kinds of fuels (methane, propane, butane, isobutane, methanol, ethanol, octane, and kerosene) are available for cooking. Most barbecues burn propane, though models are available that can be hooked up through an outdoor connection to a house's natural gas supply. Calorimeters are used to compare the quantities of energy given off by different fuel sources.

An experiment to determine the molar enthalpy of combustion of a fuel can be accomplished easily using an inexpensive apparatus, but it has its limitations.

A simple calorimeter can be built from a food can, or a 335 mL soft drink can with its lid removed. The can must contain 100 g to 200 g of water and a thermometer. The can is clamped to a stand above the burning fuel (such as a candle, fuel tablet, or burner containing the fuel being investigated). Another can or some aluminum foil can be wrapped around the apparatus to exclude drafts.

An analysis of the experiment must take into account the varying amounts of heat energy that are lost to the immediate surroundings and not actually absorbed by the water. Calculating the energy output of a fuel, $n\Delta_c H$, must incorporate the energy absorbed by those parts of the apparatus that can be measured (the water and the can) as follows:

$$n\Delta_c H_m = -\left(Q_{H_2O_{(l)}} + Q_{can} \right)$$

$$n\Delta_c H_m = -m_{H_2O_{(l)}} c_{H_2O_{(l)}} \Delta T - m_{can} c_{can} \Delta T = -\left(m_{H_2O_{(l)}} c_{H_2O_{(l)}} + m_{can} c_{can} \right) \Delta T$$

$$n\Delta_c H_m = -C\Delta T$$

One way to determine the efficiency of a simple calorimeter is to calculate the energy released from the fuel mass and its standard molar enthalpy of combustion, $\Delta_c H°$ (the actual enthalpy value, the energy input). This value can be compared with the energy increase of the can and water (the experimental enthalpy value, the energy output). The equation to calculate the percent efficiency of a calorimeter is written as follows:

$$\% \text{ efficiency} = \frac{\text{energy output}}{\text{energy input}} \times 100\%$$

Example

The following data was obtained from an experiment to measure the efficiency of a simple combustion calorimeter heated by a stearic acid candle. $(\Delta_c H_m (C_{18}H_{36}O_{2(l)}) = -1.13 \times 10^4$ kJ/mol$)$

Initial temperature of $H_2O_{(l)}$ and $Al_{(s)}$ can	22.0°C
Final temperature of $H_2O_{(l)}$ and $Al_{(s)}$ can	48.0°C
Mass of $H_2O_{(l)}$ and $Al_{(s)}$ can	212.49 g
Mass of $Al_{(s)}$ can	14.3 g
Specific heat capacity for $Al_{(s)}$	$c_{Al} = 0.897$ J/g·°C
Mass of candle burned	1.35 g

Determine the efficiency of the calorimeter.

Solution

The energy absorbed by the calorimeter is (essentially)

$$Q_{cal} = Q_{H_2O_{(l)}} + Q_{can}$$

$$Q_{cal} = Q_{H_2O_{(l)}} + Q_{can} = m_{H_2O_{(l)}} c_{H_2O_{(l)}} \Delta T + m_{can} c_{can} \Delta T$$

$$Q_{cal} = ((212.49 - 14.3) \text{ g})(4.19 \text{ J/g·°C})((48.0 - 22.0)°C)$$
$$+ (14.3 \text{ g})(0.897 \text{ J/g·°C})((48.0 - 22.0)°C)$$

$$Q_{cal} = 2.19 \times 10^4 \text{ J} = 21.9 \text{ kJ}$$

The energy released by the candle wax is calculated as follows:

$$Q_{cal} = -n\Delta H_c$$

$$Q_{cal} = -\left((1.35 \text{ g})\left(\frac{1 \text{ mol}}{284.54 \text{ g}}\right)\right)(1.13 \times 10^4 \text{ kJ/mol})$$

$$Q_{cal} = -53.6 \text{ kJ}$$

Sometimes, the efficiency of a heating apparatus can be used to estimate the actual quantities of fuel needed for the desired heating effect.

The negative sign denotes that energy was released during the reaction, which is consistent with the temperature rise of the calorimeter. Therefore, the percent efficiency of the calorimeter is calculated as follows:

$$\frac{21.9 \text{ kJ}}{53.6 \text{ kJ}} \times 100\% = 40.9\%$$

Example

A particular basement hot-water heater is 70.0% efficient.
What mass of natural gas (assume methane) must burn in order to heat
250 kg of water from 5.0°C to 40.0°C?

Solution

The molar enthalpy of combustion of methane must be calculated from
tabulated values as follows:

$$CH_{4(g)} + 2O_{2(g)} \rightarrow CO_{2(g)} + 2H_2O_{(g)}$$

$$\Delta_r H° = mol(-393.5 \text{ kJ/mol}) + 2 \text{ mol}(-241.8 \text{ kJ/mol})$$
$$-1 \text{ mol}(-74.6 \text{ kJ/mol})$$

$$\Delta_r H° = -802.5 \text{ kJ}$$

$$\Rightarrow \Delta_c H_m° = -802.5 \text{ kJ/mol}$$

Use the calorimetric expression to make the following calculations:

$$n\Delta_c H_m° = -(mc\Delta T)_{H_2O_{(l)}} \Rightarrow n = \frac{-(mc\Delta T)_{H_2O_{(l)}}}{\Delta_c H_m°}$$

$$n_{CH_{4(g)}} = \frac{-(250 \text{ kg})(4.19 \text{ kJ/kg°C})(35.0°C)}{-802.5 \text{ kJ/mol}}$$

$$n_{CH_{4(g)}} = 45.7 \text{ mol}$$

$$\therefore m_{CH_{4(g)}} = (45.7 \text{ mol})(16.05 \text{ g/mol}) = 733 \text{ g}$$

If the heater were 100% efficient, then the mass of methane required
would be 733 g.

Since the heater is only 70.0% efficient, the mass of methane must be
increased by a factor of $\frac{100}{70}$:

$$m = (733 \text{ g})\left(\frac{100}{70}\right) = 1\,048 \text{ g} = 1.05 \text{ kg}$$

PRACTICE EXERCISES

Formulas: $n\Delta_c H_m = -\left(Q_{H_2O_{(l)}} + Q_{can}\right)$ $n\Delta_c H_m = -C\Delta T$

1. **a)** What quantity of water could be heated from 20.0°C to 100°C, without boiling, on a stove that burns 60.0 g of butane ($\Delta_c H_m = -2\,657.4\ kJ/mol$)? Assume that all the heat goes into heating the water only.

   b) List three factors involved in heating the water that may account for the difference between the predicted mass of water that could be heated and the actual mass of water that would be heated.

2. What quantity of methane gas, in moles, would have to burn on an efficient stove top to heat 1.00 kg of water, in a 300 g aluminum pot, from 10.0°C to 90.0°C, without boiling? $\left(\Delta_c H_m = -802.5\ kJ/mol\right)$

3. **a)** Which automotive fuel—natural gas (assume methane) or propane—releases more energy per kilogram of fuel burned? $\left(\left(\Delta_c H_m\right)_{CH_{4(g)}} = -802.5\ kJ/mol,\ \left(\Delta_c H_m\right)_{C_3H_{8(g)}} = -2\,043.9\ kJ/mol\right)$

b) Which automotive fuel—natural gas (assume methane) or propane—releases more energy per kilogram of $CO_{2(g)}$ produced?

c) Based on the energy released per kilogram of fuel burned and the energy released per kilogram of $CO_{2(g)}$ produced, which fuel is the best in terms of energy?

Lesson 10   ENERGY EXCHANGES IN CHEMICAL REACTIONS

NOTES

Chemical reactions can produce energy, in exothermic reactions, or absorb energy, in endothermic reactions. The energy released or absorbed by chemical reactions must in some way be linked with formation or breaking bonds. In fact, all chemical reactions involve bond breaking (energy absorbing) steps and bond making (energy releasing) steps. In most cases, the bonds in the reactants are no longer present in the products, so they had to be broken, and the new bonds in the products had to be formed.

Consider the combustion of methane gas to make gaseous products, which is an exothermic reaction:

Methane + Oxygen ⟶ Carbon dioxide + Water
$CH_{4(g)}$ $2O_{2(g)}$ (excess) $CO_{2(g)}$ $2H_2O_{(g)}$

$$-\overset{|}{\underset{|}{C}}-$$ O=O
O=O   O=C=O

O
/\
H H

O
/\
H H

Energy is always absorbed to break bonds in the reactants, as separated atoms have more chemical potential energy to react than bonded atoms.

All the C-H bonds in $CH_{4(g)}$ and the O=O bonds in $O_{2(g)}$ are broken as the reaction proceeds. Energy E_{in} has to be absorbed when the bonds are broken.

Similarly, both the C=O double bonds in $CO_{2(g)}$ and all the O-H bonds in $H_2O_{(g)}$ have to be formed in the products. Energy E_{out} has to be released when bonds are formed.

Energy is always released to form bonds in the products, as bonded atoms have less chemical potential energy than separated atoms.

The net change in enthalpy of a reaction ($\Delta_r H$) is shown in the following equation:
$$\Delta_r H = E_{in} - E_{out}$$

When methane burns, $\Delta_r H$ is negative because the reaction is exothermic. In this case, forming bonds in the products releases more energy than what is absorbed to break the bonds in the reactants; that is, $E_{out} > E_{in}$.

In general, the following rules regarding the energy of reactions apply:
- If the total energy input is greater than the total energy output, $\Delta_r H$ is positive, and the reaction is endothermic (the reaction absorbs energy from the surroundings).
- If the total energy output is greater that the total energy input, $\Delta_r H$ is negative, and the reaction is exothermic (the reaction releases energy to the surroundings).

This information can also be represented diagrammatically in a potential energy diagram, where the change in enthalpy is shown as the reaction progresses.

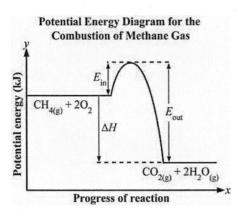

In an energy diagram, all parts of the graph are labelled, including the reactants and the products, each axis, and the step up or down in terms of enthalpy change. In the given diagram, the products possess less potential energy than the reactants. Thus, the reaction is exothermic.

Consider the formation of hydrogen iodide gas from its gaseous elements:

$$H_{2(g)} \quad + \quad I_{2(g)} \quad \rightarrow \quad 2HI_{(g)}$$
$$H{-}H \quad + \quad I{-}I \quad \rightarrow \quad 2\ H{-}I$$

This reaction is endothermic, so the products possess more total potential energy than the reactants do. This reaction absorbs energy from its surroundings.

The energy absorbed to break the H-H and the I-I bonds in the reactants (E_{in}) is greater than the energy released to form the H-I bond in the product (E_{out}).

This reaction has the following potential energy diagram:

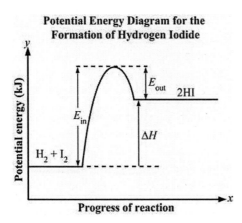

NOTES

In both the enthalpy diagrams for the combustion of methane and the formation of HI, there is a prominent high peak in the middle that corresponds to the activation energy. The activation energy of a reaction, E_a, is the minimum amount of energy needed for reactant particles to successfully react and form product entities. This amount of energy can be very low: a single spark can make a natural gas leak explode. In other cases, the amount of energy is very high: a lit match will not start a strip of magnesium burning, but a Bunsen burner will. The rate at which a reaction proceeds is determined in part by the reaction's activation energy. The higher a reaction's value of E_a, the slower the reaction proceeds.

The energy profiles of an endothermic and an exothermic reaction are shown in the following potential energy diagrams:

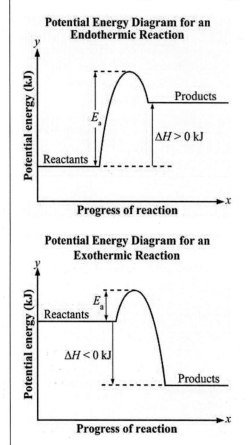

A catalyst can be defined as a chemical that, when added to a reaction, speeds up the reaction and also remains when the reaction is over.

What effect does a catalyst have on the enthalpy change of a reaction? Hess's law suggests that the enthalpy of a reaction depends only on the enthalpies of the initial and final states, no matter what series of steps exist between the products and the reactants. A catalyst has no effect on the enthalpy change, $\Delta_r H$, of a reaction. A catalyzed reaction will either lose heat energy more rapidly if it is exothermic, or absorb heat energy more rapidly if it is endothermic.

Catalysts speed up a reaction by providing an alternate reaction pathway that has lower activation energy than the uncatalyzed reaction.

The energy profiles of a catalyzed and an uncatalyzed exothermic reaction are shown in the following graph:

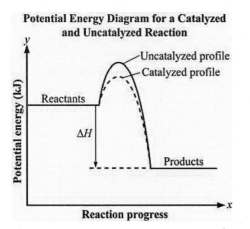

When ionic compounds or salts dissolve in water, they give off or absorb energy. Three processes occur when an ionic compound dissolves:
1. Energy is absorbed to break the ionic bonds of the salt.
2. Energy is absorbed to break the hydrogen bonds between water molecules.
3. Energy is released when bonds form between the dissociated ions and the water molecules that now surround them (these are called ion-dipole bonds).

If the first two processes absorb more energy than is released in forming the ion-dipole bonds, the heat of solution is endothermic; that is., the reaction cools its surroundings. This is what happens in a chemical cold pack, such as those for treating athletic injuries.

Should the first two processes absorb less energy than is released upon forming the ion-dipole bonds, the heat of solution is now exothermic; that is, the reaction warms its surroundings. This is what happens in a chemical hot pack, such as hand warmers.

Never assume that a reaction with a large $\Delta_r H$ value is likely to be faster than an endothermic or less exothermic reaction. The rate of a reaction is mostly determined by the activation energy.

Another misconception is that an endothermic reaction proceeds when energy is added. An endothermic reaction absorbs energy as it proceeds.

Adding or removing any amount of energy to or from a reaction can never change it from an endothermic to an exothermic reaction or vice versa.

PRACTICE EXERCISES

Formulas: $\Delta_r H = E_{in} - E_{out}$

Use the following information to answer the next question.

Molecules A-A and B-B combine to form 2 A-B. The bond in A-B is stronger than the bond in A-A or B-B.

1. Draw an energy diagram to represent the given reaction.

2. Sodium nitrate dissolves endothermically. Describe what is happening in terms of energy in the bond-making and bond-breaking steps of this reaction?

3. Potassium hydroxide dissolves exothermically. Describe what is happening in terms of energy in the bond-making and bond-breaking steps of this reaction.

Use the following information to answer the next question.

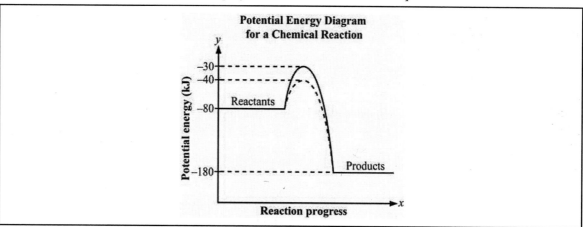

4. **a)** What is the E_a of the catalyzed reaction?

    b) What is the E_a of the uncatalyzed reaction?

    c) Is the catalyzed or uncatalyzed reaction faster? Explain your answer.

    d) What is the enthalpy change of the forward reaction?

    e) What is the enthalpy change of the reverse reaction?

    f) For the forward reaction, how does the energy absorbed in bond breaking compare with the energy released in bond making?

5. Chlorine atoms catalyze the destruction of ozone in the stratosphere. For each chlorine atom present, 1000 ozone molecules are destroyed. Describe what the chlorine atom catalyst does for this reaction, and how or if the chlorine atoms are affected by this reaction.

REVIEW SUMMARY

- The quantity of kinetic energy lost or gained when something with mass undergoes a change of temperature is given by the equation $Q = mc\Delta T$. Specific heat capacity is a measure of the amount of energy required to raise the temperature of one gram of a substance by one degree Celsius ($\text{J/g} \cdot {}^\circ\text{C}$).

- Photosynthesis is an endothermic process that stores solar radiation as potential chemical energy.

- Cellular respiration is an exothermic process that releases chemical potential energy as kinetic or thermal energy through the decomposition of chemical structures.

- The combustion of hydrocarbons is similar to cellular respiration in terms of the release of energy and the production of carbon dioxide and water as byproducts.

- The standard molar enthalpy change of formation of a substance is a measure of the amount of energy required to create that substance from its elements. Elements found in standard states are a reference level for bond energies and are defined as having zero energy of formation.

- The enthalpy of a reaction can be expressed as a term in a chemical equation:
  – Endothermic reactions contain heat energy as a reactant.
  – Exothermic reactions contain heat energy as a product.

- When non-molar quantities of reactants and products are specified, stoichiometry is required to translate the amounts from mass or volume to molar quantities.

- The molar enthalpy of a reaction can be determined using the formula $\Delta H = n\Delta_r H_m$.

- The change in enthalpy in any reaction is equal to the difference between the sum of the formation enthalpies of the products and the sum of the formation energies of the reactants. The equation that is used to express this concept is $\Delta_r H^\circ = \sum_{\text{products}} (n\Delta_f H_m) - \sum_{\text{reactants}} (n\Delta_f H_m)$.

- Hess's law states that provided that the conditions of the initial and final states of a chemical reaction are the same, then only the starting and ending phases are important when calculating total energy change. As a result, chemical equations can be added, with identical substances cancelling out when they appear as both reactants and products.

- When a compound reacts with an element in standard state, the sum of the reactant formation enthalpies is a simple multiple of that compound's formation enthalpy.

- A calorimeter can be any container that insulates a reaction and does not allow energy to leave or enter the confines of the container.

- The equation for the amount of energy exchanged in a simple water calorimeter is as follows:
$$\Delta H = -\left(mc\Delta T\right)_{\text{cal}} \quad \Rightarrow \quad n\Delta_r H_m{}^\circ = -\left(mc\Delta T\right)_{\text{cal}}$$

- Bomb calorimetry can be used to calculate the sum of all the kinetic energy changes of the components involved in the experiment, and can therefore isolate a more precise result of a chemical reaction.

- One way to determine the efficiency of a calorimeter or an engine is to burn a hydrocarbon and then divide the amount of heat received in the calorimeter by the ideal $\Delta_c H$ of the hydrocarbon.

- The expression that indicates whether a reaction is endothermic or exothermic is $\Delta_r H = E_{\text{in}} - E_{\text{out}}$.

- Energy diagrams are used to explain reaction coordinates of a reaction's activation energy, net energy transfer, catalytic effects, and reaction energy profiles.

- Catalysts increase the rate of a reaction by lowering its activation energy, but they do not affect the net change in enthalpy of the reaction.

PRACTICE TEST

1. Photosynthesis is a process that is vital to life on Earth. Write the balanced chemical equation representing the photosynthesis reaction, and determine the enthalpy change for the reaction.

Use the following information to answer the next question.

The following equation represents the decomposition of dinitrogen pentoxide:
$$2N_2O_{5(g)} \rightarrow 4NO_{2(g)} + O_{2(g)} \qquad \Delta H = +110.2 \text{ kJ}$$

2. Draw a potential energy diagram to represent the given decomposition reaction. Include a label indicating the ΔH value for the reaction.

3. Determine the molar enthalpy of combustion when 1.00 mol of $C_2H_{4(g)}$ is burned to produce gaseous products.

4. For each of the reactions represented by the following equations, identify whether the reaction is endothermic or exothermic, and determine whether energy is absorbed or released.

    A. $2KClO_{3(s)} + \text{Heat} \longrightarrow 2KCl_{(s)} + O_{2(g)}$

    B. $2SO_{2(g)} + O_{2(g)} \longrightarrow 2SO_{3(g)} + \text{heat}$

    C. $N_{2(g)} + O_{2(g)} + 180 \text{ kJ} \longrightarrow 2NO_{(g)}$

    D. $H_{2(g)} + S_{(s)} \longrightarrow H_2S_{(g)} + 20 \text{ kJ}$

5. Describe how the energy of the products compares with the energy of the reactants for the reaction represented by the following equation:
    $$N_{2(g)} + 3H_{2(g)} \rightleftharpoons 2NH_{3(g)} + 92.4 \text{ kJ}$$

6. Write the balanced equation for the formation of $MgCO_{3(s)}$ from its elements. Using the molar enthalpy of formation of $MgCO_{3(s)}$, determine the amount of energy released when 1.00 g of $MgCO_{3(s)}$ is produced from its elements.

Use the following information to answer the next question.

Hydrogen and iodine react to form hydrogen iodide according to the following reaction:
$$H_{2(g)} + I_{2(g)} \rightarrow 2HI_{(g)}$$

7. Determine the enthalpy change $(\Delta_r H^\circ)$ for the given reaction, and describe what effect adding a catalyst will have on the reaction and the $\Delta_r H^\circ$.

Use the following information to answer the next question.

The reaction between nitrogen and oxygen, which yields nitric oxide, is represented by the following equation: $N_{2(g)} + \frac{1}{2}O_{2(g)} \rightleftharpoons NO_{(g)}$

8. When 1 mol of nitrogen monoxide gas forms from its elements, 91.3 kJ of energy is absorbed from the surroundings. Communicate this information in four different ways.

Use the following information to answer the next question.

The partial decomposition of $PCl_{5(g)}$ is represented by the following equation:
$$PCl_{5(g)} \rightarrow PCl_{3(g)} + Cl_{2(g)} \qquad \Delta_r H = 124.0 \text{ kJ}$$

9. Determine the quantity of energy absorbed when 5.00 g of $Cl_{2(g)}$ is produced during the given partial decomposition reaction.

Use the following information to answer the next question.

When 50.0 mL of 1.00 mol/L $AgNO_{3(aq)}$ and 50.0 mL of 1.00 mol/L $HCl_{(aq)}$ are mixed in a calorimeter, the temperature rises by 8.1°C.

10. Determine the molar enthalpy change per mole of acid for the given reaction.

Use the following information to answer the next question.

When a 1.173 g sample of lactic acid, $C_3H_6O_{3(s)}$, burns in a bomb calorimeter with a heat capacity of 9.624 kJ/°C, the temperature changes from 23.90°C to 25.75°C. $n\Delta H = -[C\Delta T] = -17.8044$

11. Determine the enthalpy change for the combustion of lactic acid in MJ/mol and kJ/g.

Use the following information to answer the next question.

The combustion of propane gas is represented by the following overall equation:
$$C_3H_{8(g)} + 5O_{2(g)} \rightarrow 3CO_{2(g)} + 4H_2O_{(g)} \qquad \Delta_r H = ?$$

12. Use the following information to determine the $\Delta_r H$ for the given combustion reaction.

1. $3C_{(s)} + 4H_{2(g)} \rightarrow C_3H_{8(g)}$ $\Delta H = -104$ kJ
2. $2H_{2(g)} + O_{2(g)} \rightarrow 2H_2O_{(g)}$ $\Delta H = -242$ kJ
3. $C_{(s)} + O_{2(g)} \rightarrow CO_{2(g)}$ $\Delta H = -394$ kJ

Use the following information to answer the next question.

The formation of $SO_{3(g)}$ is represented by the following overall equation:

$$2S_{(s)} + 3O_{2(g)} \rightarrow 2SO_{3(g)} \qquad \Delta_r H = ?$$

The following information is available:

∂ $S_{(s)} + O_{2(g)} \rightarrow SO_{2(g)}$ $\qquad \Delta H = -297$ kJ $[2]$

$2SO_{3(g)} \rightarrow 2SO_{2(g)} + O_{2(g)}$ $\qquad \Delta H = +198$ kJ $[-]$

13. Use the given equations to determine the enthalpy change for the overall equation representing the formation of $SO_{3(g)}$.

Use the following information to answer the next question.

The given diagram represents the plotting of potential energy against the progress of a reaction.

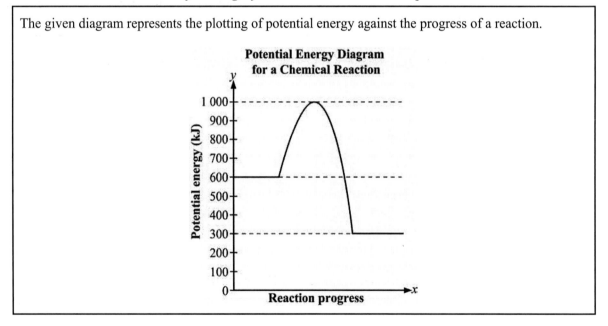

14. Describe the type of reaction the given diagram represents, and determine the values of ΔH and E_a for the reaction.

15. Draw a potential energy diagram to represent an endothermic reaction. In the diagram, label the E_a and ΔH for the endothermic (forward) reaction, as well as the E_a for the reverse reaction. Based on the diagram, write an equation that represents the relationship between the E_a forward, E_a reverse, and ΔH.

Use the following information to answer the next question.

In separate reaction vessels, 2.0 g of copper was added to some amount of sulfuric acid. The following reaction took place in both the vessels:

$$Cu_{(s)} + H_2SO_{4(aq)} \longrightarrow CuSO_{4(aq)} + H_{2(aq)}$$

The entire quantity of copper took only two minutes to react in the first experiment and four minutes to react in the second experiment.

16. Provide an explanation that might account for the difference between the rates of the given two experiments.

17. Explain how a catalyst affects the activation energy of a reaction.

Use the following information to answer the next question.

The decomposition of ozone is represented by the following equation:

$$O_{3(g)} + O_{(g)} \longrightarrow O_{2(g)} + O_{2(g)}$$

Chlorine atoms act as catalysts for the given reaction.

18. Which of the following potential energy diagrams correctly compares the energies in catalyzed and uncatalyzed decomposition?

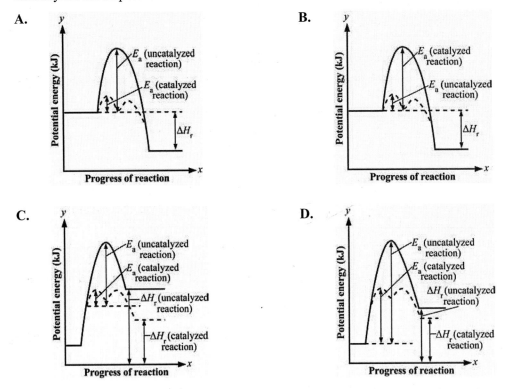

A.

B.

C.

D.

ELECTROCHEMICAL CHANGES

When you are finished this unit, you will be able to...
• Define oxidation and reduction operationally and theoretically
• Define oxidizing agent, reducing agent, oxidation number, half-reaction, and disproportionation
• Differentiate between redox reactions and other reactions, using half-reactions and/or oxidation numbers
• Identify electron transfer, oxidizing agents, and reducing agents in redox reactions that occur in everyday life, in both living systems and nonliving systems
• Describe the methods and devices used to prevent corrosion; i.e., physical coatings and cathodic protection
• Compare the relative strengths of oxidizing and reducing agents using empirical data
• Predict the spontaneity of a redox reaction based on standard reduction potentials, and compare the predictions to experimental results
• Write and balance equations for redox reactions in acidic and neutral solutions by
  – Using half-reaction equations obtained from a standard reduction potential table
  – Developing simple half-reaction equations from information provided about redox changes
  – Assigning oxidation numbers, where appropriate, to the species undergoing chemical change
• Perform calculations to determine quantities of substances involved in redox titrations
• Define anode, cathode, anion, cation, salt bridge/porous cup, electrolyte, external circuit, power supply, voltaic cell and electrolytic cell
• Identify the similarities and differences between the operation of a voltaic cell and that of an electrolytic cell
• Predict and write the half-reaction equation that occurs at each electrode in an electrochemical cell
• Identify the products of electrochemical cells
• Recognize that predicted reactions do not always occur
• Explain that the values of standard reduction potential are all relative to 0 volts, as set for the hydrogen electrode at standard conditions
• Calculate the standard cell potential for electrochemical cells
• Explain the discrepancies between the theoretical and actual cell potentials
• Predict the spontaneity or nonspontaneity of redox reactions, based on standard cell potential and the relative positions of half-reaction equations on a standard reduction potential table
• Calculate mass, amounts, current and time in single voltaic and electrolytic cells by applying Faraday's law and stoichiometry

PREREQUISITE SKILLS AND KNOWLEDGE

Prior to starting this unit, you should be able to

- Find and verify solutions of rational equations
- Rewrite linear expressions in terms of the dependant variables
- Plot linear and non-linear data using appropriate scales
- Understand the concepts of energy transformation, energy transmission, the generation of electrical energy, electrical charge and current, circuits, electrical resistance, and Ohm's law
- Describe the different forms of energy
- Understand the different types of chemical bonding
- Draw electron dot diagrams and Lewis structures
- Write chemical reaction equations, net ionic equations, and perform reaction stoichiometry

Lesson 1 OXIDATION AND REDUCTION

Oxidation and reduction reactions are reactions that involve an exchange of electrons. Redox reactions are involved in a number of processes, including cellular respiration, photosynthesis, combustion, and corrosion. Redox reactions are also used in industrial processes, such as electroplating metals and creating electrochemical cells.

Redox reactions must involve both oxidation reactions and reduction reactions. Historically, the term oxidation referred to the chemical reaction of oxygen with other substances, such as the reactions that occur in combustion. Reduction was historically defined as the process of reducing metal compounds to pure, elemental, metal components.

As the redox theory of electron transfer developed, the definitions of oxidation and reduction were refined. In terms of electron transfer, reduction refers to the gain of electrons in a reaction, and oxidation refers to the loss of electrons in a reaction. The overall oxidation-reduction reaction, therefore, involves the transfer of electrons.

A common mnemonic to help remember oxidization and reaction is "LEO the lion says GER." In this mnemonic, LEO stands for **L**oss of **E**lectrons = **O**xidation, and GER stands for **G**ain of **E**lectrons = **R**eduction.

Half-reactions can be used to illustrate the gain or loss of an electron by one reactant in an overall reaction. For example, the following net reaction can be written as two half-reactions:

Net reaction: $Cu_{(s)} + 2Ag^+_{(aq)} \rightarrow Cu^{2+}_{(aq)} + 2Ag_{(s)}$
Half-reaction 1: $Cu_{(s)} \rightarrow Cu^{2+}_{(aq)} + 2e^-$ Loss of electron (oxidation)
Half-reaction 2: $2\,[Ag^+_{(aq)} + e^- \rightarrow Ag_{(s)}]$ Gain of electron (reduction)

In the net redox reaction, the substance that gains an electron *(reduction)* causes the oxidation of another substance; therefore, it is called an oxidizing agent. The substance that loses an electron causes the reduction of another substance; therefore, it is called a reducing agent. In the net reaction for the given example, each $Cu_{(s)}$ atom loses two electrons, resulting in the reduction of two $Ag^+_{(aq)}$ ions. Therefore, $Cu_{(s)}$ is the reducing agent. In the net reaction, two $Ag^+_{(aq)}$ ions gain one electron each, resulting in the oxidation of one $Cu_{(s)}$ atom. Therefore, $Ag^+_{(aq)}$ is the oxidizing agent.

OXIDATION NUMBERS

The reducing agent and the oxidizing agent in a reaction can be identified by examining the oxidation numbers of atoms in a molecule. For example, in a molecule of water, H_2O, oxidation numbers need to be assigned to the hydrogen atoms and the oxygen atom. In a covalently bonded molecule such as H_2O, the shared pair of electrons in the covalent bond is counted as if it belongs to the more electronegative atom in the bond.

NOTES

For example, elemental oxygen has 8 protons and 8 electrons. Elemental hydrogen has 1 electron and 1 proton. In H_2O, the electrons shared between hydrogen and oxygen are counted as a part of oxygen, which has a higher electronegativity (3.5) than hydrogen (2.1).

$$H \overset{\cdot\cdot}{\underset{\cdot\cdot}{\overset{\cdot\cdot}{O}}} H$$

Therefore, in calculating oxidation numbers for H_2O, oxygen is considered to have 8 protons and 10 electrons, giving it an oxidation number of –2. Each hydrogen in H_2O is considered to have 1 proton and no electrons; therefore, each hydrogen has an oxidation number of +1.

$$\overset{+1}{H_2}\overset{-2}{O}$$

The sum of the oxidation numbers must equal the overall electrical charge of the molecule. For molecules that are electrically neutral, the oxidation numbers must equal zero. For molecules that have an electrical charge of –1, the sum of the oxidation numbers must equal –1, and so on.

Since H_2O is an electrically neutral molecule, the oxidation numbers must add up to zero.

2 atoms hydrogen + 1 atom oxygen = neutral molecule of water
$$2(+1) + 1(-2) \qquad = 0$$

In general, the oxidation number of free elemental atoms is 0, H in compounds is +1, and O in compounds is –2.

(Note: Exceptions include hydrides, in which H is –1; peroxides, in which O is –1; and OF_2, in which O is +2.)

Example

What are the oxidation numbers of Al and O in Al_2O_3?

Solution

The sum of the oxidation numbers must add up to 0, as this is a neutral compound. The oxidation number of oxygen in compounds is –2, and there are 3 oxygens present. This totals –6. This means the oxidation number of the two Al atoms together must be +6. Therefore, each Al atom must be +3.

$$\overset{+3}{Al_2}\overset{-2}{O_3}$$

DISPROPORTIONATION REACTIONS

Disproportionation reactions occur when the same entity is both oxidized and reduced in a redox reaction. Usually, one entity is reduced, and the other is oxidized, but when one entity can act as both an oxidizing agent and a reducing agent, it can undergo both oxidation and reduction. In terms of oxidation numbers, this can be described as an entity's oxidation number both increasing and decreasing over the course of a reaction.

NOTES (side note): The oxidation number of an atom in its elemental form is zero. For example, H in H_2 would have an oxidation number of 0.

The reaction of hydrogen peroxide to form water and oxygen is an example of disproportionation.

$$2\overset{+1}{H}_2\overset{-1}{O}_{2(aq)} \rightarrow 2\overset{+1}{H}_2\overset{-2}{O}_{(l)} + \overset{0}{O}_{2(aq)}$$

Disproportionation is also commonly known as self-oxidation–reduction or autooxidation.

Oxygen has an oxidation number of –1 in $H_2O_{2(aq)}$, –2 in $H_2O_{(l)}$, and 0 in $O_{2(g)}$. Its oxidation number both decreases and increases over the course of the reaction. Because a change in oxidation number indicates a loss or gain of electrons, $H_2O_{2(aq)}$ is both reduced and oxidized in this reaction.

The two half-reactions can be written with $H_2O_{2(aq)}$ on the left side of both half-reactions.

Reduction: $H_2O_{2(aq)} + 2H^+_{(aq)} + 2e^- \rightarrow 2H_2O_{(l)}$

Oxidation: $H_2O_{2(aq)} \rightarrow O_{2(g)} + 2H^+_{(aq)} + 2e^-$

Net: $2H_2O_{2(aq)} \rightarrow 2H_2O_{(l)} + O_{2(g)}$

RECOGNIZING REDOX REACTIONS

Redox reactions are characterized by a transfer of electrons from a reducing agent to an oxidizing agent. If no electron transfer occurs in a reaction, it is not a redox reaction. In terms of oxidation numbers, there must be a change in oxidation numbers over the course of a reaction. One entity must show a decrease in oxidation number and another entity must show an increase in oxidation number from one side of the equation to the other (or in the case of disproportionation reactions, the same entity both increases and decreases in oxidation number). If there is no change in oxidation number, a redox reaction has not taken place.

Example

In the reaction of solid iron with chlorine gas, the following reaction occurs:

$$2\overset{0}{Fe}_{(s)} + 3\overset{0}{Cl}_{2(g)} \rightarrow 2\overset{+3}{Fe}\overset{-1}{Cl}_{3(s)}$$

Determine if the reaction is a redox reaction.

Solution

In this reaction, there is a change in the oxidation numbers of iron and chlorine; therefore, this is a redox reaction.

Using half-reactions of $Fe_{(s)}$ and $Cl_{2(g)}$ gives the following equations:

$$2 \times (Fe_{(s)} \rightarrow Fe^{3+}_{(aq)} + 3e^-)$$
$$3 \times (Cl_{2(g)} + 2e^- \rightarrow 2Cl^-_{(aq)})$$

Net: $2Fe_{(s)} + 3Cl_{2(g)} \rightarrow 2Fe^{3+}_{(aq)} + 6Cl^-_{(aq)}$

NOTES

EVERYDAY EXAMPLES OF ELECTRON TRANSFER: LIVING SYSTEMS

Electron transfers that occur in redox reactions are not limited to laboratory experiments and fuel cells (non-living systems); they are found in living systems as well. Without redox reactions, producers like plants and algae would not be able to use the sun's energy in photosynthesis. Without photosynthesis, entire food chains would collapse, and there would be no oxygen to breathe.

Recall the basic chemical equation of photosynthesis, in which light energy converts carbon dioxide and water into sugar and oxygen in the presence of chlorophyll:

light energy $+ 6CO_2 + 6H_2O \rightarrow C_6H_{12}O_6 + 6O_2$

This equation is the net equation for photosynthesis, taking into account the initial reactants and the final products. In fact, a series of smaller reactions, called the electron transport chain, occur in which electrons are passed between donors and acceptors. When sunlight strikes a molecule of chlorophyll, it provides the energy needed to excite an electron and release it. The electron is captured by the primary electron acceptor, which is reduced; the chlorophyll loses an electron and is oxidized. The electron continues to be moved between compounds until it finally reduces the complex molecule $NADP^+$ into its higher energy form, NADPH. The movement of the electrons through the electron transport chain is governed by the same principles as simple laboratory redox reactions.

EVERYDAY EXAMPLES OF ELECTRON TRANSFER: NON-LIVING SYSTEMS

Corrosion is the oxidation of a metal in the environment as a result of the effects of oxygen, moisture, and salt.

Photosynthesis releases oxygen to the atmosphere, creating an oxidizing environment. It is this oxygen, in combination with moisture, that provides the conditions for a commonly recognized spontaneous redox reaction: corrosion.

Corrosion is commonly thought of as the breakdown of metals. When a metal is exposed to the environment, electrons are pulled away from the metal atoms by oxygen, and the metal is oxidized. The metal acts as a reducing agent; the tendency for a metal to corrode depends on its strength as a reducing agent, or oxidation potential. Some metals, like gold and silver, are very weak reducing agents. They corrode very slowly, if at all. Other metals, like aluminum and iron, are strong reducing agents and corrode easily.

The corrosion of metal creates structural and economic problems. Knowledge of electrochemical principles can help reduce and prevent corrosion. For example, consider a homeowner who wants to build a metal fence around his or her garden plot and could use iron or aluminum posts.

$4Al_{(s)} + 3O_{2(g)} \rightarrow 2Al_2O_{3(s)}$ or

$Fe_{(s)} + O_{2(g)} + H_2O_{(l)} \rightarrow Fe_2O_3 \times H_2O_{(s)}$

Note: The equation for iron is not balanced because rust, $Fe_2O_3 \cdot xH_2O_{(s)}$, can vary in its formula.

Aluminum oxide, formed when aluminum corrodes, adheres tightly to the aluminum metal, preventing the oxygen from further reaching the aluminum. Iron oxide, on the other hand, flakes away easily from the iron metal, further exposing the iron metal.

There are many methods of preventing corrosion. If oxygen is prevented from reaching the metal, oxidation cannot occur. A coat of paint, sealant, or even a thin layer of a second metal will protect the metal. Galvanization is a special term given to the coating of iron with zinc; nails used in construction projects that will be exposed to air are usually galvanized. Although they cost more than regular nails, they will last a lot longer.

Another popular method of preventing corrosion is cathodic protection. As will be seen with electrochemical cells, oxidation occurs at the anode; in the spontaneous corrosion of a large iron storage tank, the iron acts as the anode. By connecting the iron tank to another metal, such as magnesium, the electron flow is reversed, and the iron acts as the cathode. The magnesium is oxidized instead of the iron and is called a sacrificial anode. As long as some magnesium remains, the iron is protected. In North America, millions of kilograms of magnesium are used in sacrificial anodes each year.

NOTES

Cathodic protection involves preventing oxidation by forcing the metal to become a cathode at the site of reduction.

RELATIVE STRENGTHS OF OXIDIZING AND REDUCING AGENTS

The relative strengths of oxidizing and reducing agents can be found through experimental evidence. By placing one substance in direct contact with another and observing whether or not a reaction occurs, the relative reducing or oxidizing strengths of the two substances can be determined.

If a redox reaction occurs, one substance will be oxidized and will lose electrons. The other substance will be reduced and will gain electrons. The substance that is reduced is the stronger oxidizing agent, as it has a greater affinity for electrons and is able to attract them from the other substance.

Example

When solid copper is placed in a solution of $AgNO_{3(aq)}$, an observable reaction occurs. As $Ag_{(s)}$ is deposited onto the $Cu_{(s)}$, the solution turns blue as a result of the presence of $Cu^{2+}_{(aq)}$ ions. Identify the strongest oxidizing agent present in the solution. (Note: $NO_3^-_{(aq)}$ and $SO_4^{2-}_{(aq)}$ ions are spectator ions and will not react.)

Solution

The $Ag^+_{(aq)}$ is reduced, gaining electrons to form $Ag_{(s)}$, while $Cu_{(s)}$ is oxidized, losing electrons to form $Cu^{2+}_{(aq)}$. This means that $Ag^+_{(aq)}$ is a stronger oxidizing agent than $Cu^{2+}_{(aq)}$, and it has a greater tendency to be reduced.

Example

When solid silver is placed into a solution of $CuSO_{4(aq)}$, no reaction occurs. Identify the strongest oxidizing agent present in the solution.

Solution

That fact that no reaction occurs means that $Cu^{2+}_{(aq)}$ is a weaker oxidizing agent than $Ag^+_{(aq)}$ and has a lesser tendency to be reduced. It is not strong enough to attract electrons from $Ag_{(s)}$, and no electron exchange would occur. The strongest oxidizing agent present is $Ag^+_{(aq)}$.

HALF-REACTIONS

In the reaction of $Cu_{(s)}$ with $Ag^+_{(aq)}$, electrons were said to be transferred from $Cu_{(s)}$ to the $Ag^+_{(aq)}$, forming $Ag_{(s)}$. As with any redox reaction, this can be written as two half-reactions showing the oxidation or reduction of each entity by adding the electron exchange that occurs.

For each half-reaction, electrons are added to balance the charge on both sides of the equation.

Reduction: $Ag^+_{(aq)} + e^- \rightarrow Ag_{(s)}$

Oxidation: $Cu_{(s)} \rightarrow Cu^{2+}_{(aq)} + 2e^-$

The number of electrons in both half-reactions must also be equal because the number of electrons lost must equal the number of electrons gained. In this example, every term of the silver half-reaction is multiplied by 2.

Reduction: $2\left(Ag^+_{(aq)} + e^- \rightarrow Ag_{(s)}\right)$

Oxidation: $Cu_{(s)} \rightarrow Cu^{2+}_{(aq)} + 2e^-$

Once the equations are balanced, the net reaction can be determined.

Net: $2Ag_{(s)} + Cu_{(s)} \rightarrow 2Ag_{(s)} + Cu^{2+}_{(aq)}$

The electrons cancel out, leaving the net reaction and the appropriate molar ratios.

REDOX TABLES

By conducting a series of experiments testing the relative oxidizing and reducing strengths of various substances, a redox table can be constructed. A redox table lists half-reactions as reductions by placing the strongest oxidizing agent at the top of the table and the weakest oxidizing agent at the bottom of the table.

Since $Ag^+_{(aq)}$ was seen to be a stronger oxidizing agent than $Cu^{2+}_{(aq)}$, the silver half-reaction would be above the copper half-reaction on a redox table.

$Ag^+_{(aq)} + e^- \rightarrow Ag_{(s)}$

$Cu^{2+}_{(aq)} + 2e^- \rightarrow Cu_{(s)}$

If another experiment were conducted testing the oxidizing strength of another element compared with silver or copper, it could be added to the redox table based on the observations.

For example, if solid tin were immersed in a $CuSO_{4(aq)}$ solution, a reaction producing $Cu_{(s)}$ would be observed. $Cu^{2+}_{(aq)}$ is reduced, gaining electrons to form $Cu_{(s)}$, while $Sn_{(s)}$ is oxidized to $Sn^{2+}_{(aq)}$. $Cu^{2+}_{(aq)}$ is therefore the stronger oxidizing agent, pulling electrons away from the $Sn_{(s)}$. The tin half-reaction would occur below the copper half-reaction on a redox table. A redox table composed of these three elements would appear as follows:

Strongest oxidizing agent $\quad Ag^+_{(aq)} + e^- \rightarrow Ag_{(s)}$

$$Cu^{2+}_{(aq)} + 2e^- \rightarrow Cu_{(s)}$$

$$Sn^{2+}_{(aq)} + 2e^- \rightarrow Sn_{(s)} \quad \text{Strongest reducing agent}$$

The right side of the equations can be seen as the reducing agents, with the strongest reducing agent being at the bottom right of a redox table and the weakest reducing agent at the top right of a redox table.

SPONTANEOUS REACTIONS

A reaction is said to be spontaneous if it does not require an input of energy to proceed. The reaction of $Ag^+_{(aq)}$ with $Cu_{(s)}$ to form $Ag_{(s)}$ and $Cu^{2+}_{(aq)}$ is an example of a spontaneous reaction. Here, the oxidizing agent is strong enough to attract electrons, causing the reaction to proceed spontaneously.

If $Ag_{(s)}$ is immersed in a solution containing $Cu^{2+}_{(aq)}$, no reaction will be observed, but this does not mean that it is impossible for a reaction to occur.

The reaction $2Ag_{(s)} + Cu^{2+}_{(aq)} \rightarrow 2Ag^+_{(aq)} + Cu_{(s)}$ is a non-spontaneous reaction. This means that it requires an input of energy to proceed (as will be seen in electrolytic cells).

A spontaneous reaction can be predicted based on the positions of the half-reactions on a table of standard electrode potentials. If the strongest oxidizing agent is above the strongest reducing agent, the reaction will be spontaneous. If the strongest oxidizing agent is below the strongest reducing agent, the reaction will be non-spontaneous. Experimental evidence accumulated and verified over many years has allowed for the creation of a table of half-reactions and their standard electrode potentials. It can be consulted to find the positions of half-reactions relative to each other.

PRACTICE EXERCISES

Use the following information to answer the next question.

The practice of metallurgy (turning metals into a practical and useable form) was one of the most important developments in the advancement of human society. Metals have served as tools, weapons, and currency since the earliest stages of civilization. Metals exist in nature most often in an oxidized state (as ore) as a result of the largely oxidizing environment of Earth. However, in order to be useful, metals must be extracted into their pure forms.

1. In terms of oxidation and reduction, describe what is necessary to change Fe_2O_3 (iron ore) into the pure form of Fe.

2. Explain corrosion in terms of oxidation-reduction chemistry and compare it with combustion. How are the reactions of corrosion and combustion similar?

Use the following chemical reaction to answer the next question.

$$Cu_{(s)} + 2Ag^+{}_{(aq)} \rightarrow Cu^{2+}{}_{(aq)} + 2Ag_{(s)}$$

3. In the given reaction, identify the oxidizing agent and the reducing agent, and write the equations representing the half-reactions that occur during the reaction.

4. Explain the difference between the ionic charge of a substance and its oxidation number.

Use the following information to answer the next question.

The diversity of life on Earth and the existence of life in nearly every environment attests to the adaptability of organisms. Some of the most adaptable organisms are bacteria, which can exist in the most extreme environments. These environments often do not have the normal nutrients that humans require. For instance, certain bacteria are able to use elemental sulfur as an energy source, as represented by the following equation:

$$4S_{(s)} + 4H_2O_{(l)} \rightarrow SO_4{}^{2-}{}_{(aq)} + 3HS^-{}_{(aq)} + 5H^+{}_{(aq)}$$

This reaction is a disproportionation reaction.

5. Show that the given reaction is a disproportionation reaction by identifying the oxidation numbers, the atom oxidized, and the atom reduced during the reaction.

Use the following information to answer the next question.

The following two equations represent reactions involving compounds made up of hydrogen and oxygen.

$$2H_2O_{(l)} \rightarrow H_3O^+{}_{(aq)} + OH^-{}_{(aq)}$$
$$2H_2O_{2(aq)} \rightarrow 2H_2O_{(l)} + O_{2(g)}$$

6. Identify which of the given reactions is a redox reaction by using oxidation numbers.

Use the following information to answer the next question.

Four unknown substances are being analyzed in oxidation-reduction studies. Each substance has a form that acts as an oxidizing agent (for example, "A^+") and a reducing agent (for example, "A"). All reactions involve only one electron. The following table was constructed with an asterisk (*) indicating when a reaction was observed.

	A	B	C	D
A^+				
B^+	*		*	*
C^+	*			
D^+	*		*	

7. Construct a redox table of the four given substances, giving the full reduction half-reactions.

Use the following information to answer the next question.

Copper wire decomposes when exposed to chlorine gas. This implies that copper is reactive with chlorine. However, when copper wire is placed in a solution of sodium chloride, no reaction occurs.

8. Explain this outcome using the relative strengths of oxidizing and reducing agents.

Use the following information to answer the next question.

In student chemistry sets, a common experiment involves placing iron shavings in a solution of copper(II) sulfate.

9. Predict whether or not a spontaneous reaction would occur.

10. If a solution of potassium perchlorate is added to an acidic solution of sodium iodide, does a redox reaction occur, and if so, between what? Write the half-reactions for any reactions that occur. (Hint: the term "acidic solution" suggests to look for combinations on the table of standard electrode potentials, as $H^+_{(aq)}$ ions can react with a polyatomic ion.)

11. "LEO the lion says GER" is often used as a study aid to remember the definitions of oxidation and reduction. What do "LEO" and "GER" stand for?

12. Is it possible for an ion to act as an oxidizing agent in one reaction and as a reducing agent in a different reaction? Explain, using the definitions of oxidizing agent and reducing agent.

13. Photosynthesis and cellular respiration are redox reactions. Identify each of the following equations as either photosynthesis or cellular respiration, and identify the entity in each reaction that is oxidized and the one that is reduced.

$$C_6H_{12}O_6 + 6O_2 \rightarrow 6CO_2 + 6H_2O + energy$$
$$6CO_2 + 6H_2O + energy \rightarrow C_6H_{12}O_6 + 6O_2$$

Use the following information to answer the next question.

The following four reactions between metals are observed.
$$3Pd^{2+} + 2Ga \rightarrow 2Ga^{3+} + 3Pd$$
$$Cd + Ga^{3+} \rightarrow \text{no reaction}$$
$$Hg^{2+} + Pd \rightarrow Pd^{2+} + Hg$$
$$Pd^{+2} + Cd \rightarrow Cd^{2+} + Pd$$

14. Arrange the given metals in order of their reduction half-reactions from strongest oxidizing agent to weakest oxidizing agent, and identify the strongest reducing agent.

15. Describe how to use the table of standard electrode potentials to predict whether or not a reaction will be spontaneous.

Lesson 2   REDOX REACTIONS IN SOLUTION

PREDICTING REDOX REACTIONS IN SOLUTION

One method for predicting the net equation of a redox reaction is to consult a table of standard electrode potentials to determine the appropriate half-reactions involved.

First, identify all the substances present in the solution, and decide which are oxidizing agents and which are reducing agents. The table of standard electrode potentials can be helpful in identifying oxidizing and reducing agents, as the oxidizing agents are on the left side of the table, and the reducing agents are on the right side. Some substances, such as $Sn^{2+}_{(aq)}$ or $H_2O_{(l)}$, can act as reducing agents and oxidizing agents. They will be present on both sides of the table of standard electrode potentials. Also, some substances, such as $MnO_4^-_{(aq)}$, only react in the presence of $H^+_{(aq)}$. $H^+_{(aq)}$ will be present in the half-reaction.

Identify the strongest oxidizing agent and the strongest reducing agent present. Write the oxidation and reduction half-reactions that occur during the reaction. If the number of electrons in the half-reactions are not equal, multiply one or both of the equations with a number to balance the electrons.

Once the electrons are balanced, the equations can be added together to produce a net equation for the reaction.

Example

If solid copper is placed in nitric acid, what is the net ionic equation?

Solution

The following substances are present in the solution:
$Cu_{(s)}$, $H^+_{(aq)}$, $NO_3^-_{(aq)}$, $H_2O_{(l)}$

The reducing agents are $Cu_{(s)}$ and $H_2O_{(l)}$.
The strongest reducing agent is $Cu_{(s)}$.
The oxidizing agents are $H^+_{(aq)}$ and $NO_3^-_{(aq)}$.
The strongest oxidizing agent is $NO_3^-_{(aq)}$ in the presence of $H^+_{(aq)}$.

The following half-reactions occur:
$$2NO_3^-_{(aq)} + 4H^+_{(aq)} + 2e^- \rightarrow N_2O_{4(g)} + 2H_2O_{(l)}$$
$$Cu_{(s)} \rightarrow Cu^{2+}_{(aq)} + 2e^-$$

Balance the electrons.
$$2NO_3^-_{(aq)} + 4H^+_{(aq)} + 2e^- \rightarrow N_2O_{4(g)} + 2H_2O_{(l)}$$
$$Cu_{(s)} \rightarrow Cu^{2+}_{(aq)} + 2e^-$$

Combine the two half-reactions as follows:

$$2NO_3^-{}_{(aq)} + 4H^+{}_{(aq)} + Cu_{(s)} \rightarrow N_2O_{4(g)} + 2H_2O_{(l)} + Cu^{2+}{}_{(aq)}$$

The reaction proceeds spontaneously.

BALANCING REDOX REACTIONS IN ACIDIC SOLUTIONS

By knowing the starting materials, the products, and the conditions of a reaction, a skeleton equation can be constructed. This skeleton can then be used to predict a net ionic equation without needing the table of standard electrode potentials.

In an acid solution, remember the following steps:
1. Balance everything but O and H first.
2. To balance O, add H_2O.
3. To balance H, add H^+.
4. Finally, balance the electrons.

In an acidic solution, after writing out the half-reactions of oxidation and reduction, each half-reaction must be completed. The atoms of all elements other than O and H must first be balanced. O is then balanced by adding $H_2O_{(l)}$ where necessary, and H is balanced by adding $H^+{}_{(aq)}$. Electrons are then added to balance the charge.

Each half-reaction must have the same number of electrons, so one or both of the half-reactions may need to be multiplied by a number to balance the electrons.

Once all the components are balanced, the half-reactions can be combined to form a net equation. If the same entity occurs on both sides of the equation, subtract the lower number from both sides so that it is only left on one side of the equation.

Example

Given that the following reaction occurs in an acidic solution, predict the net equation.

$$MnO_4^-{}_{(aq)} + Cu_{(s)} \rightarrow Mn^{2+}{}_{(aq)} + Cu^{2+}{}_{(aq)}$$

Solution
The skeleton half-reactions, based on the given equation, are as follows:

$$MnO_{4(aq)} \rightarrow Mn^{2+}{}_{(aq)}$$
$$Cu_{(s)} \rightarrow Cu^{2+}{}_{(aq)}$$

Balance the half-reactions by adding H_2O and H^+, if needed.

i) $\qquad\qquad MnO_4^-{}_{(aq)} \rightarrow Mn^{2+}{}_{(aq)}$

ii) $\qquad\qquad MnO_4^-{}_{(aq)} \rightarrow Mn^{2+}{}_{(aq)} + 4H_2O_{(l)}$

iii) $\qquad MnO_4^-{}_{(aq)} + 8H^+{}_{(aq)} \rightarrow Mn^{2+}{}_{(aq)} + 4H_2O_{(l)}$

iv) $MnO_4^-{}_{(aq)} + 8H^+{}_{(aq)} + 5e^- \rightarrow Mn^{2+}{}_{(aq)} + 4H_2O_{(l)}$

Balance the electrons.

$$2\left(MnO_4^-{}_{(aq)} + 8H^+{}_{(aq)} + 5e^- \rightarrow Mn^{2+}{}_{(aq)} + 4H_2O_{(l)}\right)$$
$$5\left(Cu_{(s)} \rightarrow Cu^{2+}{}_{(aq)} + 2e^-\right)$$
$$2MnO_4^-{}_{(aq)} + 16H^+{}_{(aq)} + 10e^- \rightarrow 2Mn^{2+}{}_{(aq)} + 8H_2O_{(l)}$$
$$5Cu_{(s)} \rightarrow 5Cu^{2+}{}_{(aq)} + 10e^-$$

The net equation is

$$2MnO_4^-{}_{(aq)} + 16H^+{}_{(aq)} + 5Cu_{(s)} \rightarrow 5Cu^{2+}{}_{(aq)} + 2Mn^{2+}{}_{(aq)} + 8H_2O_{(l)}.$$

By following the steps for constructing a net equation in an acidic solution, the same net equation is reached as that found by consulting a table of standard electrode potentials. This step-wise construction is needed if the reactants cannot be found in the table.

BALANCING REDOX REACTIONS USING OXIDATION NUMBERS

Remember that oxidation numbers are numbers that are arbitrarily assigned to atoms in compounds as a means of tracking electrons. The oxidation numbers of the atoms in a neutral molecule will always add up to zero, while the oxidation numbers of the atoms in polyatomic ion will always add up to the net charge of the ion.

Oxidation numbers can be assigned to every atom in each substance on both sides of an equation in a redox reaction. If the oxidation number of an atom changes during a reaction, electrons have been transferred, meaning a redox reaction has occurred. If an oxidation number increases, the substance has been oxidized, and if an oxidation number decreases, it has been reduced.

If you know the reactants, products, and conditions of a reaction, you can identify which substances undergo a change in oxidation numbers and write a balanced redox equation for the reaction. Because the electrons gained by an oxidizing agent are the same electrons that are lost by a reducing agent, the numbers of electrons and the change in oxidation numbers must be equal for the two reactants. The change in oxidation number refers to each atom; therefore, the number of atoms in a compound must be taken into account. Once the number of electrons transferred is established, the coefficients for the reactants are known. The rest of the equation can then be balanced based on the conditions of the reaction.

Remember that the oxidation numbers of an atom in its elemental form is zero. For example, P in P_4 would have an oxidation number of 0.

The oxidation number of H in compounds is usually +1, and the oxidization number of O in compounds is usually –2.

Example

Balance the net equation for the reaction of solid copper with nitric acid using oxidation numbers.

$$NO_3^-{}_{(aq)} + Cu_{(s)} \rightarrow NO_{2(g)} + Cu^{2+}{}_{(aq)}$$
$$\,\,\,\,+5\,\,-2 \qquad\quad 0 \qquad\quad +4\,\,-2 \qquad +2$$

Solution

The oxidation number of N decreases from +5 to +4; it is reduced.
The oxidation number of Cu increases from 0 to +2; it is oxidized.

The change in oxidation number for nitrogen in NO_3 is −1.
The change in oxidation number for Cu is +2.
To balance the number of electrons transferred, multiply the N atoms by 2.

$$2NO_3^-{}_{(aq)} + Cu \rightarrow 2NO_{2(g)} + Cu^{2+}{}_{(aq)}$$

Because this reaction takes place in an acidic solution (nitric acid is present), you must add H_2O and then H^+ to balance the O and H in the equation.

add H_2O: $\qquad 2NO_3^-{}_{(aq)} + Cu_{(s)} \rightarrow 2NO_{2(g)} + Cu^{2+}{}_{(aq)} + H_2O_{(l)}$

add H^+: $\,\,2NO_3^-{}_{(aq)} + Cu_{(s)} + 4H^+{}_{(aq)} \rightarrow 2NO_{2(g)} + Cu^{2+}{}_{(aq)} + 2H_2O_{(l)}$

Note: The number of electrons were balanced when the N atoms were multiplied by 2.

PRACTICE EXERCISES

1. Write the balanced redox equation for the reaction of solid aluminum with a solution of silver nitrate.

2. The following half-reactions occur in an acidic solution. Write the balanced net redox equation that represents the reaction that occurs when these two half-reactions are combined.

    $$ClO_4^-{}_{(aq)} + 8H^+{}_{(aq)} + 8e^- \rightarrow Cl^-{}_{(aq)} + 4H_2O_{(l)}$$
    $$2I^-{}_{(aq)} \rightarrow I_{2(s)} + 2e^-$$

3. Balance the following redox equation using oxidation numbers.

    $$Cu_{(s)} + HNO_{3(aq)} \rightarrow Cu(NO_3)_{2(aq)} + NO_{(g)} + H_2O_{(l)}$$

4. Balance the following redox equation for the reaction that occurs in an acidic solution.

    $$Fe^{2+}{}_{(aq)} + MnO_4^-{}_{(aq)} \rightarrow Fe^{3+}{}_{(aq)} + Mn^{2+}{}_{(aq)}$$

5. Balance the following redox equation for the reaction that occurs in an acidic solution.

    $$UO^{2+}{}_{(aq)} + Cr_2O_7^{2-}{}_{(aq)} \rightarrow UO_2^{2+}{}_{(aq)} + Cr^{3+}{}_{(aq)}$$

Lesson 3 *REDOX TITRATIONS*

Stoichiometry can be used in redox reactions to determine quantities of substances in the same way as it is used for other types of chemical reactions. Establishing stoichiometric ratios in net ionic equations, along with concentration equations, allows you to find unknown values.

A titration is a process used to determine an unknown quantity in a reaction. The process involves slowly adding one solution, called a titrant, to another solution, the sample. As the titrant is added to the sample, the two solutions will react. The titrant is added to the sample until the equivalence point—the point at which both solutions have reacted completely—is reached. The endpoint, the point at which the titration is stopped, is often determined visually by using an indicator, which is a substance that will change colour near the equivalence point. The amount of titrant required to reach the equivalence point can then be used to perform calculations and determine an unknown quantity.

The endpoint of a titration is the point at which the indicator changes colour, at which point the titration is complete.

In redox titrations, the titrant is a strong oxidizing or reducing agent. As the titrant is added to the sample, a redox reaction occurs until it reaches completion and can no longer proceed. Two strong oxidizing agents that are often used in redox titrations are solutions containing permanganate or dichromate ions, as they both change colour as they are reduced; they are self-indicating, meaning no additional indicator is needed. The endpoint can be seen when the addition of one drop of titrant causes a permanent colour change in the sample. At that point, no more of the sample is available to react with the titrant.

Example

Find the concentration of $Fe^{2+}_{(aq)}$ in a 10.0 mL sample that requires 14.0 mL of a 0.050 mol/L acidic permanganate solution to reach the endpoint.

Solution

Determine the half-reactions involved, and write the balanced equation representing the reaction.

Reduction: $MnO_4^-{}_{(aq)} + 8H^+_{(aq)} + 5e^- \rightarrow Mn^{2+}_{(aq)} + 4H_2O_{(l)}$

Oxidation: $5(Fe^{2+}_{(aq)} \rightarrow Fe^{3+}_{(aq)} + e^-)$

Net: $5Fe^{2+}_{(aq)} + MnO_4^-{}_{(aq)} + 8H^+_{(aq)} \rightarrow 5Fe^{3+}_{(aq)} + Mn^{2+}_{(aq)} + 4H_2O_{(l)}$

Find the number of moles of $MnO_4^-{}_{(aq)}$ as follows:

$c = \dfrac{n}{V}$

$$n_{MnO_4^-{}_{(aq)}} = cV$$
$$= (0.050 \text{ mol/L}) \times (0.0140 \text{ L})$$
$$= 7.0 \times 10^{-4} \text{ mol}$$

80

$Fe^{2+}_{(aq)}$ occurs in a 5:1 ratio to $MnO_4^-{}_{(aq)}$. Find the number of moles of $Fe^{2+}_{(aq)}$ as follows:

$$n_{Fe^{2+}_{(aq)}} = n_{MnO_4^-{}_{(aq)}} \times \frac{5}{1}$$
$$= 7.0 \times 10^{-4} \text{ mol} \times \frac{5}{1}$$
$$= 3.5 \times 10^{-3} \text{ mol}$$

From the number moles of $Fe^{2+}_{(aq)}$, the concentration of $Fe^{2+}_{(aq)}$ can be found.

$$c_{Fe^{2+}_{(aq)}} = \frac{n}{V}$$
$$= \frac{3.5 \times 10^{-3} \text{ mol}}{0.010 \text{ L}}$$
$$= 0.35 \text{ mol/L}$$

The concentration of $Fe^{2+}_{(aq)}$ in the sample used in this titration was 0.35 mol/L.

PRACTICE EXERCISES

Use the following balanced redox equation to answer the next two questions.

$$Cr_2O_7^{2-}{}_{(aq)} + 6Fe^{2+}{}_{(aq)} + 14H^+{}_{(aq)} \rightarrow 6Fe^{3+}{}_{(aq)} + 2Cr^{3+}{}_{(aq)} + 7H_2O_{(l)}$$

1. Explain how the concentration of a solution of potassium dichromate could be calculated using a solution of iron(II) chloride with a known concentration. Include an explanation of molar ratios.

2. The titration of a 15.0 mL sample of 0.0700 mol/L potassium dichromate solution is completed by the addition of 0.100 mol/L iron(II) chloride solution. Fill in the following titration chart.

Trial	1
Final burette reading (mL)	
Initial burette reading (mL)	1.0
Volume of FeCl₂ added	

Use the following information to answer the next question.

A titration is performed with a 20.0 mL sample of SnCl₂ in an acidic solution. The titration requires 15.0 mL of 0.0300 M K₂Cr₂O₇. The following balanced equation represents the reaction:

$$Cr_2O_7^{2-}{}_{(aq)} + 14H^+{}_{(aq)} + 3Sn^{2+}{}_{(aq)} \rightarrow 3Sn^{4+}{}_{(aq)} + 2Cr^{3+}{}_{(aq)} + 7H_2O_{(l)}$$

3. Determine the original concentration of the SnCl₂(aq) sample.

Use the following information to answer the next question.

The concentration of ethanol in a sample can be determined by titration with potassium dichromate, according to the following balanced equation:

$$2Cr_2O_7^{2-}{}_{(aq)} + 16H^+{}_{(aq)} + 3C_2H_5OH_{(l)} \rightarrow 4Cr^{3+}{}_{(aq)} + 11H_2O_{(l)} + 3CH_3COOH_{(aq)}$$

4. A 10.0 mL sample of ethanol of unknown concentration is titrated with 3.20 mL of 0.0200 mol/L potassium dichromate solution. Determine the concentration of the ethanol sample.

5. An iron nail with a mass of 1.635 g is dissolved in an acidic solution, yielding $Fe^{2+}{}_{(aq)}$, which is then titrated with 24.87 mL of $KMnO_{4(aq)}$. Assume the entire mass of the iron nail is converted to $Fe^{2+}{}_{(aq)}$.

   a) Write the equations representing the half-reactions involved in the given titration reaction.

   b) Balance the half-reaction equations, and write the net balanced redox equation representing the reaction.

   c) Determine the concentration of the $KMnO_{4(aq)}$ solution.

Lesson 4   VOLTAIC CELLS

NOTES

A voltaic cell is an electrochemical cell that spontaneously produces energy (voltage). It has two electrodes, an anode and a cathode, which are solid electrical conductors. The anode is the electrode where oxidation, the loss of electrons, occurs; it is the negative electrode of a voltaic cell. The cathode is the electrode where reduction, the gain of electrons, occurs; it is the positive electrode of a voltaic cell.

When the cell is operating, the anode releases electrons (oxidation) that flow through an external circuit, such as a wire, to the cathode, causing reduction. Electrons must have an external circuit to flow through. Each electrode is immersed in an aqueous solution that can conduct electricity. This aqueous solution is called an electrolyte. One electrode and one electrolyte make up a half-cell, and each voltaic cell consists of two half-cells.

A battery, such as the ones used in watches, some toys, calculators, and cameras, is a set of voltaic cells connected in series.

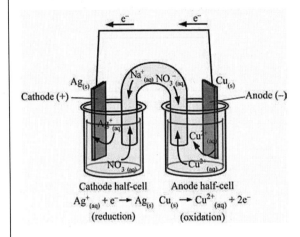

Cathode half-cell   Anode half-cell
$$Ag^+_{(aq)} + e^- \rightarrow Ag_{(s)} \quad Cu_{(s)} \rightarrow Cu^{2+}_{(aq)} + 2e^-$$
(reduction)   (oxidation)

Remember that only ions (not electrons) flow in the solution.

The two half-cells are separated by a porous boundary that allows the movement of ions between the two half-cells while keeping the electrolytes separated. The cations (the positively charged ions) flow toward the cathode, and the anions (the negatively charged ions) flow toward the anode during the operation of the cell. This maintains electric neutrality of the solution. The porous boundary can be either a salt bridge containing an unreactive aqueous electrolyte or a porous porcelain cup containing one electrolyte immersed in a container containing the second electrolyte.

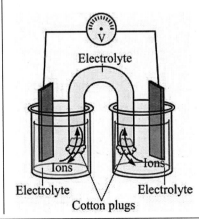

84

To predict the reactions that occur in a voltaic cell, the strongest oxidizing agent and the strongest reducing agent need to be identified. Oxidation occurs at the anode, where the strongest reducing agent in the cell will lose electrons. The strongest oxidizing agent will always undergo reduction at the cathode, where it will gain electrons.

The half-reactions of the strongest oxidizing and reducing agents can then be stoichiometrically balanced and combined to predict the net reaction.

Example

A silver-copper voltaic cell consists of a copper half-cell with a $Cu_{(s)}$ electrode and a 1.0 mol/L $Cu(NO_3)_{2\ (aq)}$ electrolyte, as well as a silver half-cell with an $Ag_{(s)}$ electrode and a 1.0 mol/L $AgNO_{3(aq)}$ electrolyte. The two half-cells are connected by a salt bridge containing $KNO_{3(aq)}$. Describe the reaction that occurs while the cell is operating.

Solution

$Cu_{(s)}$ is the strongest reducing agent present, so it will undergo oxidation at the anode. $Ag^+_{(aq)}$ is the strongest oxidizing agent present and will undergo reduction at the cathode. The two half-reactions are as follows:

Reduction (cathode): $2[Ag^+_{(aq)} + e^- \rightarrow Ag_{(s)}]$

Oxidation (anode): $\qquad\qquad Cu_{(s)} \rightarrow Cu^{2+}_{(aq)} + 2e^-$

Net: $\qquad\qquad Cu_{(s)} + 2Ag^+_{(aq)} \rightarrow Cu^{2+}_{(aq)} + 2Ag_{(s)}$

As $Cu_{(s)}$ undergoes oxidation at the anode to produce $Cu^{2+}_{(aq)}$, the electrons that are released travel through an external circuit to the silver cathode, where $Ag_{(s)}$ is produced. To maintain the electric neutrality of the solution, $Na^+_{(aq)}$ from the salt bridge moves into the cathode half-cell, while $NO_3^-_{(aq)}$ moves into the anode half-cell.

The strongest oxidizing agent and strongest reducing agent can be identified from their positions on the table of standard electrode potentials.

Cell notation is a shorthand way of representing a voltaic cell. The anode is represented on the left, and the cathode is represented on the right. A single vertical line (|) is used to separate the electrode from the solution it is placed in. Two vertical lines (||) are used to represent the salt bridge or porous cup.

The following cell notation represents the silver-copper voltaic cell used in the given example:

$Cu_{(s)} | Cu^{2+}_{(aq)} || Ag^+_{(aq)} | Ag_{(s)}$

CELL POTENTIALS

A voltaic cell is defined as a cell that spontaneously produces energy. A spontaneous reaction can be recognized by the value of the standard cell potential, E°_{cell}. A positive value of E°_{cell} indicates that the reaction will occur spontaneously. E°_{cell} is the potential difference (the voltage) between two standard electrodes at standard atmospheric, temperature, and pressure (SATP) conditions. E°_{cell} is determined from the standard reduction potential (E°_r) of each half-cell.

$E^\circ_{cell} = E^\circ_{r\ cathode} - E^\circ_{r\ anode}$

NOTES

The following equations apply to the silver-copper voltaic cell:

Cathode: $2[Ag^+_{(aq)} + e^- \rightarrow Ag_{(s)}]$ $\quad E^\circ_r = 0.80$ V

Anode: $\quad\quad Cu_{(s)} \rightarrow Cu^{2+}_{(aq)} + 2e^-$ $\quad E^\circ_r = 0.34$ V

$$\begin{aligned} E^\circ_{cell} &= E^\circ_{r\,cathode} - E^\circ_{r\,anode} \\ &= 0.80 \text{ V} - 0.34 \text{ V} \\ &= 0.46 \text{ V} \end{aligned}$$

The E°_{cell} value is positive, meaning the reaction will proceed spontaneously. Note that multiplying a half-reaction by a number does not change the value of E°_r for the half-reaction.

A spontaneous reaction can also be determined based on the relative positions of the half-reaction equations on the table of standard electrode potentials. If the strongest oxidizing agent present in a cell is found higher on a redox table than the strongest reducing agent present, the reaction will proceed spontaneously. If the strongest oxidizing agent is lower than the strongest reducing agent, the reaction is non-spontaneous, as is found with electrolytic cells.

THE STANDARD HYDROGEN HALF-CELL

A half-cell cannot operate on its own. In order to determine its reduction potential, it must be measured by comparing it with the standard hydrogen half-cell (at SATP conditions). This half-cell is used as the reference half-reaction when determining the E°_r for each half-reaction.

The standard hydrogen half-cell uses an inert metal electrode, such as platinum, in a solution of 1.00 mol/L $H^+_{(aq)}$, with $H_{2(g)}$ passing over the surface of the electrode. As the $H^+_{(aq)}$ is reduced to $H_{2(g)}$, the potential that results is arbitrarily considered to be 0.00 V.

$2H^+_{(aq)} + 2e^- \rightarrow H_{2(g)}$ $\quad\quad E^\circ_r = 0.00$ V

The standard hydrogen half-cell (at SATP conditions) is used as the reference half-reaction when determining the E°_r for each half-reaction.

$2H^+_{(aq)} + 2e^- \rightarrow H_{2(g)}$

$\quad\quad E^\circ_r = 0.00$ V

The ° symbol indicates that the half-reaction or electrochemical cell is operating at standard state.

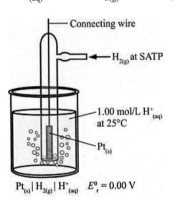

Connecting wire

$H_{2(g)}$ at SATP

1.00 mol/L $H^+_{(aq)}$ at 25°C

$Pt_{(s)}$

$Pt_{(s)} | H_{2(g)} | H^+_{(aq)}$ $\quad E^\circ_r = 0.00$ V

Because the standard reduction potential (E°_r) measures the tendency to undergo a reduction, a half-cell with a greater tendency to be reduced (a stronger oxidizing agent) than hydrogen ions is assigned a positive E°_r. A half-cell with a lesser tendency to be reduced (a weaker oxidizing agent) than hydrogen ions is assigned a negative E°_r. A voltmeter is used to measure the flow of electrons between half-cells and to find the cell potential.

PRACTICE EXERCISES

1. Label the following diagram of a voltaic cell. Label the cathode, anode, and salt bridge, and show the direction of electron flow and the flow of cations and anions.

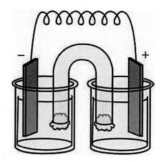

2. Explain the purpose of a salt bridge in a voltaic cell.

3. What is the purpose of the external wire in a voltaic cell? What would happen if this were removed?

4. A voltaic cell has a tin electrode placed in a solution of $SnCl_2$ and a copper electrode placed in a solution of $Cu(NO_3)_2$. Identify the electrode that is the anode and the electrode that is the cathode, and write the equations representing the half-reactions that occur in each half-cell.

5. For the following cell notation, write the equations representing the half-reactions that occur during the operation of this cell.

$Ag_{(s)} \,|\, Ag^+_{(aq)} \,\|\, Cr_2O_7^{2-}_{(aq)}, H^+_{(aq)} \,|\, Pt_{(s)}$

6. Explain what the reading on a voltmeter means in a voltaic cell and how it relates to the standard reduction potentials and $E°_{cell}$.

7. Why are some standard reduction potentials positive and others negative, and how does this relate to the standard hydrogen half-cell?

8. Write the cell notation and the standard cell potential for a voltaic cell with a copper electrode immersed in a solution of copper(II) nitrate and a cobalt electrode immersed in a solution of cobalt(II) chloride.

9. A half-cell is created with a strip of metal (M) immersed in a solution containing ions of the same metal (M^{n+}). Describe the two types of reactions that might occur between the metal atoms on the electrode and the metal ions in the solution when the half-cells are connected.

10. Write the balanced equation, and determine the standard cell potential for the reaction that occurs in the cell represented by the following cell notation:

$$Zn_{(s)} \,|\, Zn^{2+}_{(aq)} \,\|\, Cu^{2+}_{(aq)} \,|\, Cu_{(s)}$$

11. Determine the value of $E°_{cell}$ for the reaction in which $Cl_{2(g)}$ oxidizes $Fe^{2+}_{(aq)}$ to $Fe^{3+}_{(aq)}$.

12. Consider two reactions: one with an $E°_{cell} = 0.46$ V and one with $E°_{cell} = -0.46$ V. Which one of the two reactions will proceed spontaneously? Explain your answer.

Lesson 5   ELECTROLYTIC CELLS

The value of $E°_{cell}$ in an electrolytic cell is negative.

For reactions that occurs in an electrolytic cell, the reduction half-reaction will be below the oxidation half-reaction on the table of standard electrode potentials.

Electrolytic cells require an input of electricity to force a non-spontaneous reaction to occur. The cell potential ($E°_{cell}$) is negative. An electrolytic cell consists of an electrolyte and two electrodes attached to an external power supply. The process of supplying energy to force a non-spontaneous reaction is called electrolysis. The power supply forces an electron transfer inside the cell, causing electrons to move away from the entity they are most attracted to.

As in the voltaic cell, the strongest oxidizing agent undergoes a reduction at the cathode, and the strongest reducing agent undergoes an oxidation at the anode. In a voltaic cell, the flow of electrons originates at an electrode (the anode), while in an electrolytic cell, the electron transfer is forced by an external power supply. In electrolytic cells, the cathode is the negative electrode, and the anode is the positive electrode.

An electrolytic cell can look similar to voltaic cell, but most often the reactants are not separated, and there is no salt bridge or porous cup. There is no need to separate the reactants because no spontaneous reaction occurs between them. An electrolytic cell consists of two electrodes immersed in an electrolyte (either aqueous or liquid). The electrodes are connected to a power source by external wires.

The minimum voltage required to initiate the reaction can be determined by writing the half-reaction equations of the cell and calculating the cell potential. The strongest oxidizing and reducing agents present are found using a redox table. If the strongest oxidizing agent is positioned lower on the redox table than the strongest reducing agent, the cell potential is negative, and the reaction is non-spontaneous.

The minimum voltage required for the reaction to occur is the absolute value of $E°_{cell}$. This means that a greater input of energy (a higher voltage) is required as the value of $E°_{cell}$ becomes more negative.

ELECTROLYSIS

In the electrolysis of water, only the entities present in the electrolyte react to form products. Electrodes of an inert metal, such as platinum, are used because they do not react with the other components of the cell, but they provide a surface to attach the power source to. The electrodes are immersed in water, and $Na_2SO_{4(aq)}$ is added to the solution to provide a sufficient amount of $Na_2SO_{4(aq)}$.

Using $H_2SO_{4(aq)}$ as the electrolyte is even more effective as a result of the presence of H^+ ions.

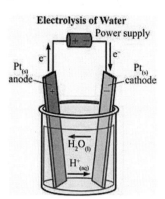

Electrolysis of Water

Cathode: $4H^+_{(aq)} + 4e^- \rightarrow 2H_{2(g)}$ $E°_r = 0.00$ V

Anode: $2H_2O_{(l)} \rightarrow O_{2(g)} + 4H^+_{(aq)} + 4e^-$ $E°_r = 1.23$ V

Net: $2H_2O_{(l)} \rightarrow O_{2(g)} + 2H_{2(g)}$

$$E°_{cell} = E°_{r\,cathode} - E°_{r\,anode}$$
$$= 0.00 \text{ V} - 1.23 \text{ V}$$
$$= -1.23 \text{ V}$$

$$E°_{cell} = E°_{r\,cathode} - E°_{r\,anode}$$

In an acidified solution, the minimum voltage required to power the electrolysis of water is 1.23 V. As the reaction proceeds, $O_{2(g)}$ is produced at the anode, and $H_{2(g)}$ is produced at the cathode.

Without the hydrogen ions present, $H_2O_{(l)}$ would be both the oxidizing and reducing agent, and the following cathode reaction would exist:

$2H_2O_{(l)} + 2e^- \rightarrow H_{2(g)} + 2OH^-_{(aq)}$ $E°_r = -0.83$ V

$$\therefore E°_{cell} = -2.06 \text{ V}$$
$$E°_{cell} = E°_{r\,cathode} - E°_{r\,anode}$$
$$= -0.83 \text{ V} - 1.23 \text{ V}$$
$$= -2.06 \text{ V}$$

ELECTROPLATING

One practical commercial use of electrolysis is electroplating. A metal that is relatively inexpensive, such as steel or copper, can be coated with a layer of a more expensive metal, such as silver or gold. Metals with desirable qualities, such as conductance or strength, can also be plated onto other metals.

The metal or object to be coated is the cathode of an electrolytic cell, and the ions of the metal that will be deposited onto the cathode are present in the electrolyte. Supplying the minimum voltage will allow the reaction to proceed, causing the desired metal ions to be reduced and deposited onto the cathode. A voltage greater than the minimum can allow the reaction to proceed more efficiently.

NOTES

If more than one non-spontaneous reaction is possible, then the reaction requiring the least amount of voltage will proceed for as long as the reactants are present.

Remember that if an aqueous solution is the electrolyte, then $H_2O_{(l)}$ is also present and must be considered when determining the oxidizing and reducing agents.

Consider the following example of electroplating.

The copper strip that is to be plated is made the cathode, the anode is an inert electrode, and the electrolyte is an aqueous solution of 1.0 mol/L of silver nitrate.

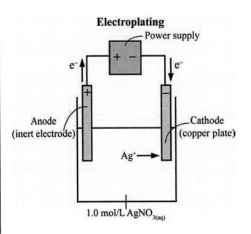

Electroplating

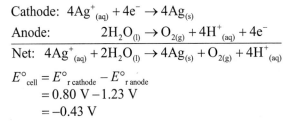

Cathode: $4Ag^+_{(aq)} + 4e^- \rightarrow 4Ag_{(s)}$

Anode: $2H_2O_{(l)} \rightarrow O_{2(g)} + 4H^+_{(aq)} + 4e^-$

Net: $4Ag^+_{(aq)} + 2H_2O_{(l)} \rightarrow 4Ag_{(s)} + O_{2(g)} + 4H^+_{(aq)}$

$E^\circ_{cell} = E^\circ_{r\,cathode} - E^\circ_{r\,anode}$
$\quad = 0.80\ V - 1.23\ V$
$\quad = -0.43\ V$

The minimum voltage required is 0.43 V. $Ag^+_{(aq)}$ will be reduced at the cathode, forming a coating of $Ag_{(s)}$ (a silver plate) on top of the copper cathode.

ELECTROREFINING

Another commercial use of electrolysis is electrorefining, in which a desired metal can be retrieved from a sample containing metal impurities. Using the impure metal as the anode, several of the metals present are oxidized, but the desired metal can be preferentially reduced at the cathode, allowing it to be recovered. The remaining undesirable metals form a sludge called anode mud that drops to the bottom of the cell and can be disposed of. A similar method called electrowinning involves recovering a desired metal from a molten or aqueous electrolyte through electrolysis.

THE CHLORIDE ANOMALY

Reactions can generally be predicted by finding the strongest oxidizing and reducing agents in a redox table then adding the half-reactions together, but some exceptions do exist. The chloride anomaly occurs during the electrolysis of solutions containing the chloride ion. Because the strongest reducing agent usually reacts at the anode, water would be expected to react, producing $O_{2(g)}$. Instead, chloride ions react, and chlorine gas ($Cl_{2(g)}$) is produced at the anode.

PRACTICE EXERCISES

1. Describe the differences between the reaction that occurs in a voltaic cell and the reaction that occurs in an electrolytic cell. List some common uses for voltaic and electrolytic cells.

2. Describe the main differences between a voltaic cell and an electrolytic cell in terms of how they are constructed.

Use the following information to answer the next question.

The half-reactions that occur in an electrochemical cell are represented by the following equations:

At the cathode: $2H_2O_{(l)} + 2e^- \rightarrow H_{2(g)} + 2OH^-_{(aq)}$

At the anode: $2Cl^-_{(aq)} \rightarrow Cl_{2(g)} + 2e^-$

3. Write the balanced equation that represents the reaction that occurs in the cell, and determine the E°_{cell}. Is this electrochemical cell a voltaic cell or an electrolytic cell? Explain your answer.

4. Identify the products of an electrolytic cell in which water and chloride ions are the only reducing agents present. Explain your answer.

5. Are the batteries used to power MP3 players, calculators, and cellphones voltaic or electrolytic cells? Explain your answer.

6. Complete the following table comparing voltaic and electrolytic cells.

Characteristic	Voltaic Cell	Electrolytic Cell
Reaction type		
Energy input/output		
Reduction occurs at		
Electrons flow from/to		
$E°_{cell}$		

Use the following information to answer the next question.

The following half-reactions represent the reactions that occur in a lead-acid storage battery found in cars.

Cathode: $PbO_{2(s)} + 4H^+_{(aq)} + SO_4^{2-}_{(aq)} + 2e^- \rightarrow PbSO_{4(s)} + 2H_2O_{(l)}$ $E°_r = 1.69$ V

Anode: $PbSO_{4(s)} + 2e^- \rightarrow Pb_{(s)} + SO_{4(aq)}^{2-}$ $E°_r = -0.36$ V

7. a) Determine the $E°_{cell}$ for the reaction that occurs in the battery.

b) Will the reaction proceed spontaneously? For what reason is this important for a car battery?

Lesson 6 *FARADAY'S LAW AND ELECTRICAL ENERGY*

According to the electron transfer theory, oxidation and reduction occur because of the exchange of electrons from the reducing agent to the oxidizing agent. The movement of electrons, such as those carried through a wire, produce an electric current (I), which is measured in amperes. One ampere equals the passage of one coulomb of charge per second (C/s) past a given point. Charge (Q) is the product of current and time, and it is calculated using the following formula:

$$Q = It$$

In this formula, Q is the charge in Coulombs, I is the current in amperes, and t is the time in seconds.

The Faraday constant (F) is the value of the electric charge carried by one mole of electrons, or the molar charge of electrons.
$$F = 9.65 \times 10^4 \text{ C/mol e}^-$$

The number of moles of electrons can be found using electric charge and Faraday's constant:

$$n_{e^-} = \frac{Q}{F}$$

Because $Q = It$, this formula can be rewritten as follows:

$$n_{e^-} = \frac{It}{F}$$

By finding the moles of electrons, the mass of the product produced in an electrolytic cell can be found using stoichiometric ratios.

Example

Determine the mass of copper that could be produced by an electrolytic cell in one hour when a current of 4.0 A is applied.

Solution
Determine the number of moles of e$^-$ transferred during the reaction.

$$Cu^{2+}_{(aq)} + 2e^- \rightarrow Cu_{(s)}$$

$$
\begin{aligned}
n_{e^-} &= \frac{It}{F} \\
&= \left(4.0 \text{ C/s} \times 60.0 \text{ min} \times 60.0 \text{ s/min} \right) \times \frac{1 \text{ mol e}^-}{9.65 \times 10^4 \text{ C}} \\
&= 0.149 \text{ mol}
\end{aligned}
$$

Determine the number of moles of $Cu_{(s)}$. There are 2 mol of electrons for every mole of Cu. To find the number of moles of Cu, multiply the number of moles by $\frac{1}{2}$.

$$
\begin{aligned}
n_{Cu_{(s)}} &= 0.149 \text{ mol} \times \frac{1}{2} \\
&= 0.0746 \text{ mol}
\end{aligned}
$$

Calculate the mass of $Cu_{(s)}$ can from its molar mass.

$$m_{Cu_{(s)}} = 0.075 \text{ mol} \times 63.55 \text{ g/mol}$$
$$= 4.7 \text{ g}$$

Example

In the electrolysis of silver, the electrolytic cell is operating at 5.00 A. How long must it run to produce 4.00 g of $Ag_{(s)}$ at the cathode?

Solution

$$Ag^+_{(aq)} + e^- \rightarrow Ag_{(s)}$$

Since the mass produced is known, the moles of $Ag_{(s)}$ can be determined based on the molar mass.

$$n_{Ag_{(s)}} = \frac{m}{M}$$
$$= \frac{4.00 \text{ g}}{107.87 \text{ g/mol}}$$
$$= 0.0371 \text{ mol}$$

There is 1 mol of e^- for every 1 mol $Ag_{(s)}$.

$$n_{e^-} = n_{Ag_{(s)}}$$
$$= 0.0371 \text{ mol}$$

The moles of electrons can now be used to find time by using Faraday's constant.

$$n_{e^-} = \frac{It}{F}$$
$$t = \frac{n_{e^-}F}{I}$$
$$= \frac{0.0371 \text{ mol} \times \left(9.65 \times 10^4 \text{ C/mol e}^-\right)}{5.00 \text{ A}}$$
$$= 7.16 \times 10^2 \text{ s}$$
$$= 11.9 \text{ min}$$

PRACTICE EXERCISES

1. What does Faraday's constant represent, and what is it used to calculate in an analysis of an electrolysis?

2. Determine the mass of copper that could be generated in an electrolytic cell using a 1.00 A power source for 10.0 min. The following equation represents the half-reaction for copper:

    $$Cu^{2+}_{(aq)} + 2e^- \rightarrow Cu_{(s)}$$

3. Determine the number of moles of electrons that are transferred in a cell that operates for 1.5 h at a current of 0.175 A.

4. Determine the current that would be required to transfer 0.100 mol of electrons in 35 min.

Use the following information to answer the next question.

A silverware manufacturer electroplates its spoons with silver.
$$Ag^+_{(aq)} + e^- \rightarrow Ag_{(s)}$$

5. If each spoon requires 0.150 g of silver plating, and the company runs its cells at 0.247 A, how long does it take to plate 100 spoons?

REVIEW SUMMARY

- Reduction refers to the gain of electrons; oxidation refers to the loss of electrons.
- A reducing agent causes the reduction of another substance by losing an electron; an oxidizing agent causes the oxidation of another substance by gaining an electron.
- The oxidation number of a substance is its assigned electrical charge (for tracking purposes).
- Disproportionation reactions occur when a substance is both oxidized and reduced.
- If the oxidation numbers do not change, the reaction is not a redox reaction.
- Photosynthesis, corrosion, and galvanization are examples of redox reactions.
- Spontaneous reactions occur without the additional input of energy.
- In an ionic equation, if the strongest oxidizing agent is higher on the redox table than the strongest reducing agent, the reaction will proceed spontaneously.
- Titration is when one solution (the titrant) is slowly added to another (the sample). In redox reactions, the titrant is a strong oxidizing or reducing agent.
- A voltaic cell is an electrochemical cell that spontaneously produces electrical energy.
- A voltaic cell has two electrodes (solid electrical conductors): the anode (negative) and the cathode (positive).
- Electrodes are immersed in aqueous electrical conductors called electrolytes.
- Oxidation occurs at the anode; reduction occurs at the cathode.
- A half-cell consists of one electrode and one electrolyte. Half-cells are separated by a porous boundary.
- The standard cell potential, or E°_{cell}, is the potential difference (or voltage) between two electrodes.
- The standard cell potential is calculated with the formula $E^\circ_{cell} = E^\circ_{r\,cathode} - E^\circ_{r\,anode}$. If E°_{cell} is positive, the reaction will occur spontaneously.
- The reduction potential of a half-cell is determined by comparing it with the standard hydrogen half-cell, which has an $E^\circ_r = 0.00$ V.
- An electrolytic cell is an electrochemical cell that requires an input of electricity to force a non-spontaneous reaction to occur.
- The minimum voltage required for electrolysis is the absolute value of E°_{cell}.
- Electroplating and electrorefining are two commercial uses of electrolysis.
- Charge is calculated using the formula $Q = It$, where Q is the charge in coulombs, I is the current in amperes, and t is the time in seconds.
- Faraday's constant, F, is 9.65×10^4 C/mol e⁻. It is the value of the electric charge carried by one mole of electrons.
- The number of moles of electrons is the electric charge divided by Faraday's constant: $n_{e^-} = \dfrac{It}{F}$.

PRACTICE TEST

Use the following information to answer the next question.

The following four unbalanced half-reactions are given:

$$\text{I.} \qquad 2MnO_{4}^{-}{}_{(aq)} \rightarrow Mn^{2+}{}_{(aq)}$$

$$\text{II.} \qquad IO_{3}^{-}{}_{(aq)} \rightarrow I^{-}{}_{(aq)}$$

$$\text{III.} \qquad Cl^{-}{}_{(aq)} \rightarrow Cl_{2(l)}$$

$$\text{IV.} \qquad ClO_{3}^{-}{}_{(aq)} \rightarrow ClO_{4}^{-}{}_{(aq)}$$

1. Identify which of the given half-reactions represent reduction half-reactions and which of the half-reactions represent oxidation half-reactions.

2. Calculate the oxidation number of iodine in each of the following compounds:

   a) $IF_{5(s)}$

   b) $KI_{(s)}$

   c) $I_{2(g)}$

3. List four characteristics that describe a reducing agent.

4. List four characteristics that describe an oxidizing agent.

Use the following information to answer the next question.

Manganese dioxide reacts with hydrochloric acid to produce manganese chloride, chlorine gas, and water. The balanced chemical equation of this process is represented as follows:

$$MnO_{2(s)} + 4HCl_{(aq)} \rightarrow MnCl_{2(aq)} + Cl_{2(g)} + 2H_2O_{(l)}$$

5. Determine the oxidation numbers of manganese and chlorine in the reaction represented by the given equation. What is the change in the oxidation numbers of chlorine and manganese during the reaction?

6. For each of the following reactions, identify if the reaction is a redox reaction.

   A. $NO_3^-{}_{(aq)} + 4H^+{}_{(aq)} \rightarrow NO_{(g)} + 2H_2O_{(l)}$

   B. $MnO_4^-{}_{(aq)} + 8H^+{}_{(aq)} \rightarrow Mn^{2+}{}_{(aq)} + 4H_2O_{(l)}$

   C. $2CuO_{(s)} + C_{(s)} \rightarrow 2Cu_{(s)} + CO_{2(g)}$

   D. $AgNO_{3(aq)} + HCl_{(aq)} \rightarrow AgCl_{(aq)} + HNO_{3(aq)}$

7. For each of the following reactions, identify if the reaction is a redox reaction.

   A. $2Zn_{(s)} + O_{2(g)} \rightarrow 2ZnO_{(s)}$

   B. $CuO_{(s)} + H_{2(g)} \rightarrow Cu_{(s)} + H_2O_{(l)}$

   C. $2Al_{(s)} + 3CuCl_{2(aq)} \rightarrow 2AlCl_{3(aq)} + 3Cu_{(s)}$

   D. $Fe_2O_{3(s)} + 6HCl_{(aq)} \rightarrow 2FeCl_{3(aq)} + 3H_2O_{(l)}$

Use the following information to answer the next question.

Hydrogen sulfide reacts with bromine water to produce hydrogen bromide and sulfur, as represented by the following equation:

$$H_2S_{(g)} + Br_{2(l)} \rightarrow 2HBr_{(g)} + S_{(s)}$$

8. Identify the oxidizing and reducing agents in the given reaction.

Use the following information to answer the next question.

The following equation represents a redox reaction.

$$2MnO_4^-{}_{(aq)} + 10Cl^-{}_{(aq)} + 16H^+{}_{(aq)} \rightarrow 2Mn^{2+}{}_{(aq)} + 5Cl_{2(g)} + 8H_2O_{(l)}$$

9. Identify the species that is oxidized and the species that is reduced during the given reaction.

Use the following information to answer the next question.

The following equation represents a redox reaction.

$$Cr_2O_7^{2-}{}_{(aq)} + 6Fe^{2+}{}_{(aq)} + 14H^+{}_{(aq)} \rightarrow 2Cr^{3+}{}_{(aq)} + 6Fe^{3+}{}_{(aq)} + 7H_2O_{(l)}$$

10. Identify the species that acts as a reducing agent in the given reaction.

Use the following information to answer the next question.

A solution of $FeCl_{3(aq)}$ reacts readily with $Cu_{(s)}$ metal, while a solution of $FeCl_{2(aq)}$ does not react with $Cu_{(s)}$.

11. List the oxidizing agents in the given reactions in order from weakest to strongest.

Use the following information to answer the next question.

A strip of zinc metal is placed in four different solutions. The first solution contains $Cu^{2+}_{(aq)}$, the second solution contains $Mg^{2+}_{(aq)}$, the third solution contains $Ba^{2+}_{(aq)}$, and the fourth solution contains $Ca^{2+}_{(aq)}$.

12. Identify in which of the given solutions a spontaneous reaction will occur, and write the net ionic equation representing the reaction.

13. For each of the following pairs of reactants, predict if a spontaneous reaction will occur.

A. $Ni_{(s)}$ and $Mn^{2+}_{(aq)}$

B. $Fe_{(s)}$ and $Cu^{2+}_{(aq)}$

C. $Zn_{(s)}$ and $Mg^{2+}_{(aq)}$

D. $Al_{(s)}$ and $Ca^{2+}_{(aq)}$

Use the following information to answer the next question.

The following equation represents a redox reaction:
$$Cr_2O_7^{2-}{}_{(aq)} + Fe^{2+}{}_{(aq)} \rightarrow Cr^{3+}{}_{(aq)} + Fe^{3+}{}_{(aq)} + H_2O_{(l)}$$

14. Write the reduction half-reaction that occurs during the reaction, and determine the number of electrons gained by the atom being reduced.

Use the following information to answer the next question.

The following equation represents a redox reaction.
$$MnO_{2(aq)} + 2Cl^-{}_{(aq)} + 4H^+{}_{(aq)} \rightarrow Mn^{2+}{}_{(aq)} + Cl_{2(g)} + 2H_2O_{(l)}$$

15. Write the balanced equation that represents the reduction half-reaction that occurs during the given reaction.

Use the following information to answer the next question.

A 10.0 mL sample of oxalate solution is titrated with 10.0 mL of a 0.10 mol/L $KMnO_{4(aq)}$ solution, as represented by the following equation:

$$2MnO_4^-{}_{(aq)} + 5C_2O_4^{2-}{}_{(aq)} + 16H^+{}_{(aq)} \rightarrow 2Mn^{2+}{}_{(aq)} + 10CO_{2(g)} + 8H_2O_{(l)}$$

16. Determine the concentration of oxalate solution used in the titration.

Use the following information to answer the next question.

The given diagram represents a voltaic cell.

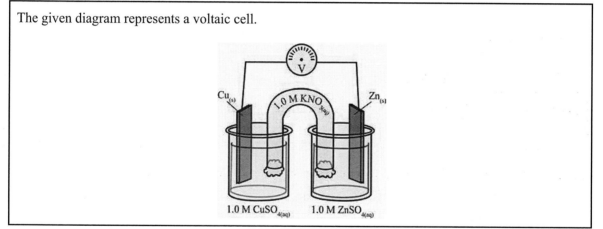

17. For the given voltaic cell, identify the anode and the cathode, and describe the flow of electrons that occurs during the operation of the cell.

18. Describe the type of reaction that occurs in an electrolytic cell and the resulting cell potential ($E°_{cell}$).

Use the following information to answer the next question.

The given diagram represents a voltaic cell.

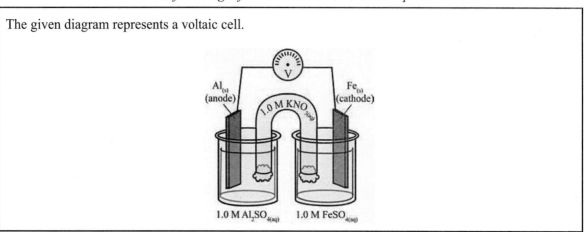

19. Describe what happens to the mass of the cathode and the mass of the anode during the operation of the given cell.

Use the following information to answer the next question.

The given diagram represents an electrolytic cell in which the electrolysis of molten LiCl is carried out using platinum electrodes.

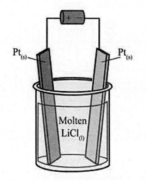

20. Write the balanced equations for the reactions that occur at the cathode and the anode while the cell is operating.

Use the following information to answer the next question.

The given diagram represents an electrolytic cell in which molten sodium chloride is electrolyzed using inert electrodes.

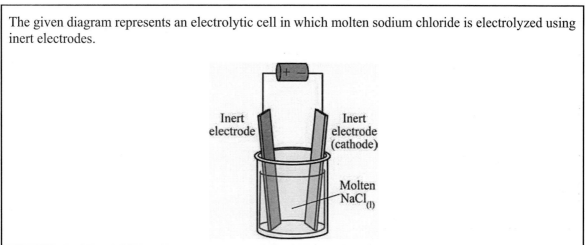

21. Describe the movement of anions and cations during the operation of the cell, and write the balanced equation for the half-reaction that occurs at the cathode.

Use the following information to answer the next question.

The given diagram represents a voltaic cell.

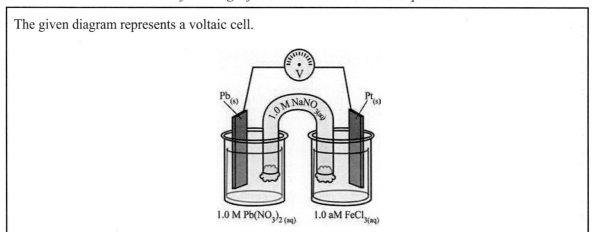

22. Describe what happens to the concentrations of $Fe^{3+}_{(aq)}$ and $Pb^{2+}_{(aq)}$ ions during the operation of the given cell.

Use the following information to answer the next question.

The given diagram represents a voltaic cell.

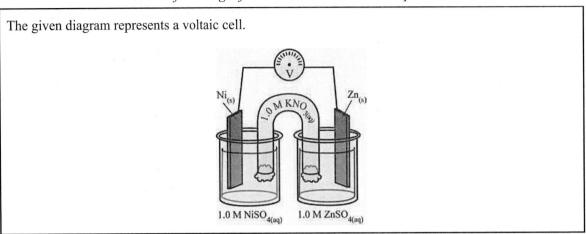

23. Write the balanced net equation and $E°_{cell}$ for the reaction that occurs in the given cell.

Use the following information to answer the next question.

An iron rod is dipped into a solution of $SnCl_{2(aq)}$ under standard conditions.

24. Write the balanced equation that represents the reaction that will occur.

25. A solution containing $Cu^{2+}_{(aq)}$ ions was electrolyzed by a 5.0 A current for 10.0 min. Determine the mass of copper metal that was electroplated during the operation of this cell.

ORGANIC CHEMISTRY

When you are finished this unit, you will be able to…

• Define organic compounds, and differentiate between organic and inorganic compounds

• Identify and describe the origins, structure, and applications of significant organic compounds in daily life

• Name and draw saturated and unsaturated aliphatic and aromatic carbon compounds using structural diagrams, condensed structural diagrams, line diagrams, and formulas

• Use IUPAC naming conventions to classify and organize:

  – Compounds containing up to 10 carbon atoms in the parent chain or cyclic structure

  – Carbon compounds containing only one type of functional group, including simple halogenated hydrocarbons, alcohols, carboxylic acids, and esters

  – Halogenated halogens and alcohols with multiple occurrences of a functional group

• Identify types of compounds from the hydroxyl, carboxyl, ester linkage and halogen functional groups, given the structural formula

• Define structural isomerism and relate the structures to variations in the properties of the isomers

• Compare the boiling points and solubility of examples of aliphatics, aromatics, alcohols and carboxylic acids

• Describe, in general terms, the physical, chemical and technological processes used to separate organic compounds from natural mixtures or solutions

• Define, illustrate and provide examples of simple addition, substitution, elimination, esterification and combustion reactions

• Define, illustrate, describe and provide examples of monomers, polymers and polymerization in living systems and nonliving systems

• Investigate the uses of greenhouse gases; identify some greenhouse gases, including methane, carbon dioxide, water, and dinitrogen oxide and analyze their contribution to climate change

PREREQUISITE SKILLS AND KNOWLEDGE

Prior to starting this unit, you should be able to…

• Contrast and compare the different types of chemical bonds

• Give examples of oxidation and reduction reactions

• Discuss hydrocarbon combustion

Lesson 1 ORGANIC CHEMISTRY AND ALKANES

Carbon is found naturally in both elemental and compound forms.

Organic chemistry is the study of molecular, covalently-bonded compounds of carbon. The number and variety of carbon-containing compounds is huge, and the range in their properties is wide.
Elemental forms of carbon-containing compounds include charcoal, graphite, and diamond. Two examples of hydrocarbon compounds are methane, which is the biggest component of natural gas, and octane, which is found in both gasoline and crude oil.

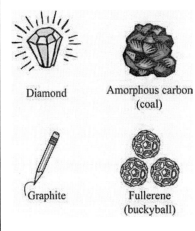

Diamond   Amorphous carbon
                 (coal)

Graphite   Fullerene
                 (buckyball)

Other carbon compounds have different functional groups attached to the carbon atoms that give them special properties. The following substances are examples of such compounds:

• Formaldehyde—a preservative

• Polyethylene—the primary component in plastic milk jugs

• Kevlar—commonly found in bulletproof vests

• Ethanol—in beer, wine, and spirits

• Esters responsible for fruit flavours

• Explosives, such as TNT

• CFCs that are associated with refrigeration and ozone depletion

• Ethanoic acid in vinegar

PREVALENCE OF CARBON COMPOUNDS

There are four principle reasons why carbon compounds are so prevalent.

• Carbon has four bonding electrons.

$$\cdot \overset{\displaystyle \cdot}{\underset{\displaystyle \cdot}{C}} \cdot \quad \text{or} \quad -\overset{\displaystyle |}{\underset{\displaystyle |}{C}}-$$

• Carbon can bond to itself in chains or rings.

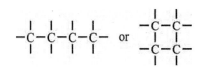

- Carbon can form single, double, and triple bonds.

$$-\overset{|}{\underset{|}{C}}-\overset{|}{\underset{|}{C}}-,\quad \overset{\diagdown}{\diagup}C=C\overset{\diagup}{\diagdown},\quad -C\equiv C-$$

- Carbon can form isomers, which are substances with the same molecular formulas but different structures. As a result, these substances have different names, characteristics, and properties.

These are two isomers of C_2H_6O:

Ethanol (drinking alcohol found in beer and wine)	Diethyl Ether (a general anesthetic)
Complete structural diagram	Complete structural diagram
H H | | H–C–C–O–H | | H H	H H | | H–C–O–C–H | | H H
Condensed structural diagram	Condensed structural diagram
CH_3-CH_2-OH	CH_3-O-CH_3
Properties • Will hydrogen bond • Polar • Dissolves in water and other polar substances	**Properties** • Will not hydrogen bond • Non-polar • Insoluble in water and other polar substances

ORGANIC COMPOUNDS

Organic compounds contain carbon and hydrogen and have a carbon-hydrogen bond. All organic compounds can be divided into two categories: aliphatic (those not containing a benzene ring) and aromatic (those containing a benzene ring).

Organic compounds include all compounds of carbon **except** the following compounds:

- Oxides
- Carbides
- Carbonates and bicarbonates
- Cyanides

Examples of inorganic compounds include carbon dioxide, carbonic acid, calcium carbonate, gold(II) cyanide, and sodium bicarbonate.

Organic molecules can be shown using three different types of diagrams: a complete structural diagram, a condensed structural diagram, and a line structural diagram.

NOTES

Complete Structural Diagram
2-methylhexane

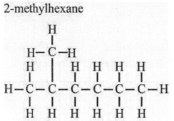

Sometimes, the hydrogen atoms are not drawn in the structural diagram for simplicity's sake. The carbon atoms and any atoms other than hydrogen are still written out in full. The structural diagram of 2-methylhexane can therefore also look like the following diagram.

2-methylhexane

$$\overset{\displaystyle |}{\underset{\displaystyle |}{-\mathrm{C}-}}$$

$$-\overset{\displaystyle |}{\underset{\displaystyle |}{\mathrm{C}}}-\overset{\displaystyle |}{\underset{\displaystyle |}{\mathrm{C}}}-\overset{\displaystyle |}{\underset{\displaystyle |}{\mathrm{C}}}-\overset{\displaystyle |}{\underset{\displaystyle |}{\mathrm{C}}}-\overset{\displaystyle |}{\underset{\displaystyle |}{\mathrm{C}}}-\overset{\displaystyle |}{\underset{\displaystyle |}{\mathrm{C}}}-$$

Condensed Structural Diagram
2-methylhexane

$$\underset{\displaystyle CH_3-\overset{}{CH}-CH_2-CH_2-CH_2-CH_3}{\overset{\displaystyle CH_3}{\overset{\displaystyle |}{}}}$$

In this type of diagram, all of the carbon-bonding groups are shown attached to one another in a line, with branches representing attached chains of atoms.

Line Structural Diagram (Skeletal Diagram)
2-methylhexane

In this type of diagram, every junction between lines and the endpoint of each line indicates a carbon atom. There are enough hydrogen atoms bonded to each carbon to make the total number of carbon bonds equal to four.

ALKANES

Three characteristics define organic compounds called alkanes. First, alkanes are hydrocarbon compounds. This means that they contain only carbon and hydrogen atoms. Second, all of the carbon atoms in an alkane are saturated, which means that each of them forms four single bonds. Finally, all alkanes are aliphatic, meaning they do not contain a benzene ring.

The general formula for an alkane is C_nH_{2n+2}.

The members of the family of alkanes differ from one another by a constant relative atomic mass of 14 (one carbon and two hydrogen atoms). According to IUPAC, International Union of Pure and Applied Chemistry, naming conventions, alkanes are named using the following steps:

1. The root of the compound is named by using the longest continuous chain of carbon atoms and applying the standard naming rules.
2. Every side chain is named by subtracting the "-ane" suffix and adding a "-yl" suffix.
3. Every side chain is then numbered by its distance from the first carbon in the chain in such a way that the sum of the numbers is a minimum.
4. If there are multiple side chains of the same type, Greek-language prefixes are used to designate the number of those chains found in the molecule.

Example

Name the following alkane.

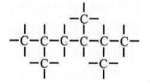

Solution

The longest continuous chain of carbon atoms is six, so given the Greek-language numeric prefix for six, this is hexane. There are three side chains attached, each of which consists of one carbon, so these are methane chains. Numbering from left to right, they are attached to the second, fourth, and fifth carbons. However, these are not the lowest possible numbers; if you count from right to left, they are attached to the second, third, and fifth carbons.

The compound is therefore 2,3,5-trimethylhexane.

The following three characteristics define the organic group of alkanes:
- Hydrocarbons
- Saturated
- Aliphatic

The general formula for an alkane is C_nH_{2n+2}.

IUPAC stands for the International Union of Pure and Applied Chemistry.

The following Greek-language prefixes are used in naming alkanes:
1—mono-
2—di-
3—tri-
4—tetra-
5—penta-
6—hexa-
7—hepta-
8—octo-
9—nona-
10—deca-

The following table lists the first 10 alkanes, in order of increasing number of carbon atoms in the compound chain. Notice that only the first four alkanes are gases. The remaining alkanes are found in liquid form at standard temperature and pressure. As the number of carbon atoms in the alkane compound increases, the substances become denser because the intermolecular forces (London forces) increase, changing the natural state from gas to liquid to solid. As a result, the boiling point also increases as the length of the chain increases.

Name	Formula	Structural Diagram
Methane	$CH_{4(g)}$	
Ethane	$C_2H_{6(g)}$	
Propane	$C_3H_{8(g)}$	
Butane	$C_4H_{10(g)}$	
Pentane	$C_5H_{12(l)}$	
Hexane	$C_6H_{14(l)}$	
Heptane	$C_7H_{16(l)}$	
Octane	$C_8H_{18(l)}$	
Nonane	$C_9H_{20(l)}$	
Decane	$C_{10}H_{22(l)}$	

These hydrocarbons have a very low solubility in water and are not very chemically or biologically active. They are practically inert in alkaline and acidic solutions, but all alkanes are combustible when in an oxygenated environment. The greater the number of carbon molecules in the alkane, the more difficult the substance is to ignite.

The following table shows the condensed structural diagrams and line structural diagrams for the first 10 alkanes.

Alkane	Structural Diagrams
Methane	CH_4
Ethane	CH_3-CH_3
Propane	$CH_3-CH_2-CH_3$
Butane	$CH_3-CH_2-CH_2-CH_3$
Pentane	$CH_3-CH_2-CH_2-CH_2-CH_3$
Hexane	$CH_3-CH_2-CH_2-CH_2-CH_2-CH_3$
Heptane	$CH_3-CH_2-CH_2-CH_2-CH_2-CH_2-CH_3$
Octane	$CH_3-CH_2-CH_2-CH_2-CH_2-CH_2-CH_2-CH_3$
Nonane	$CH_3-CH_2-CH_2-CH_2-CH_2-CH_2-CH_2-CH_2-CH_3$
Decane	$CH_3-CH_2-CH_2-CH_2-CH_2-CH_2-CH_2-CH_2-CH_2-CH_3$

NOTES

Example

Given the following skeletal diagram, name the alkane.

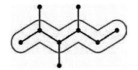

Solution

Begin by finding the longest continuous carbon chain.

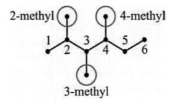

Since there are six carbons in the parent chain, the compound is hexane. The next step is to find the carbons that are not part of the parent chain. Each of these carbon strings is called a branch. This compound has three branches, each with one carbon. Therefore, it is a trimethyl hexane.

2-methyl ● ● 4-methyl

1 3 5
2 4 6

3-methyl

Once the branches have been numbered so that the sum of the numbers is a minimum, the names of the branches are arranged in ascending alphabetical order. For example, a two-carbon chain (ethyl) would be listed before a single carbon chain (methyl), but after a four-carbon chain (butyl). Any prefixes, such as di-, tri-, and tetra-, are not considered alphabetically. Triethyl would precede dimethyl. This compound is a trimethyl hexane, with methyl chains attached to the 2, 3, and 4 carbons. The IUPAC name would therefore be 2,3,4-trimethylhexane.

CYCLOALKANES

Alkanes that have a cyclical or ring-like structure are known as cycloalkanes. Like other alkanes, they are saturated aliphatic compounds. In other words, all of the chemical bonds in a cycloalkane compound are single bonds, and there are no extra valence electrons or empty orbitals. The general formula for a cycloalkane is C_nH_{2n}, where n is a number equal to or greater than 3.

The following table gives some examples of cycloalkanes.

	Structural Diagrams		
Cyclopropane (C_3H_6)	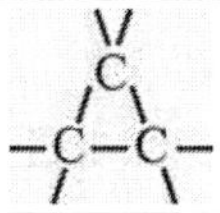	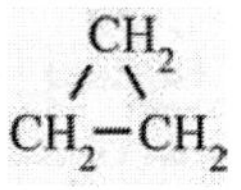	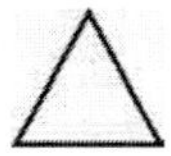
Cyclobutane (C_4H_8)	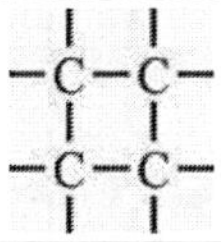	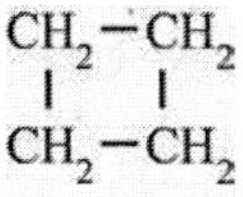	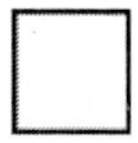
Cyclopentane (C_5H_{10})	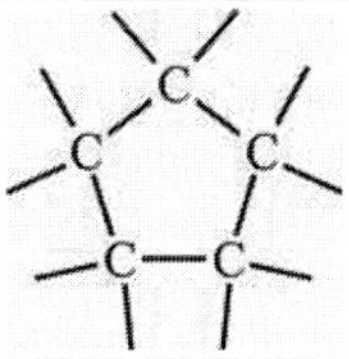	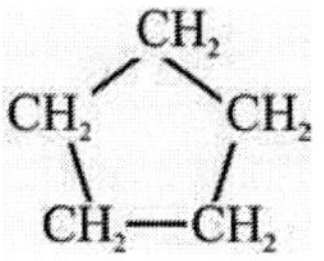	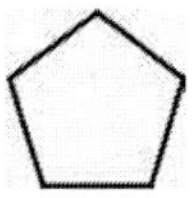
Cyclohexane (C_6H_{12})	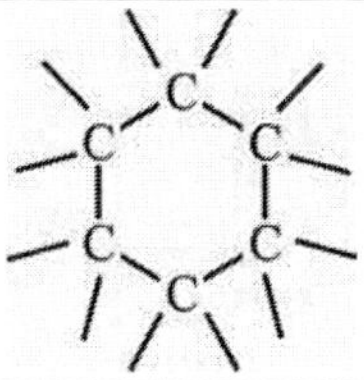	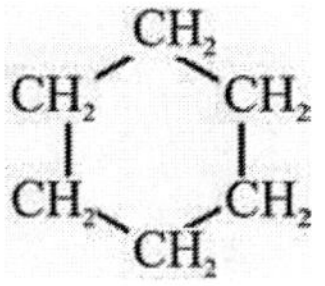	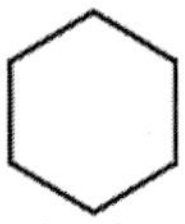

According to IUPAC naming conventions, the parent molecule is determined by the carbons that form the ring structure. Any branches that are bonded with those carbons are numbered in the same way as alkanes, in that the sum of the numbers should always be a minimum. If there is only one branch, then the carbon atoms are not numbered.

Example

Name the following cycloalkanes:

a)

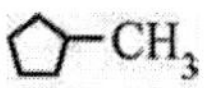

$\bigcirc$—CH_3

Solution

Since the ring has five carbon atoms, the parent chain is cyclopentane. There is only one branch (a methyl group), so the carbon atoms are not numbered. The name of this cycloalkane is methylcyclopentane.

b)

Solution

Since the ring has four carbon atoms, the parent chain is cyclobutane. There are two methyl branches, so the carbons are numbered so that the branches are on the lowest numbers. The name of this cycloalkane is 1,2-dimethylcyclobutane.

COMMERCIAL IMPORTANCE OF ALKANES

Natural Gas

The main component of natural gas, which is used to heat homes in some places, is methane. It can also have varying quantities of ethane, propane, butane, and pentane. In order to prepare natural gas for commercial use, it is heated in a fractional distillation tower to separate its components based on their different boiling points. A mixture can be heated to a gaseous state and then cooled in a distillation tower where the components of the mixture will condense to a liquid at different temperatures. In the fractional distillation of natural gas, the deadly gas hydrogen sulfide ($H_2S_{(g)}$) must be removed from the natural gas. Elemental sulfur is recovered through this process.

Petroleum

Petroleum (crude oil) has a variety of alkane components that are also separated by fractional distillation. Some fractions are separated for use as fuel sources, such as diesel, fuel oil, kerosene, and gasoline. Other non-alkane components obtained are waxes, asphalt, tar, and sulfur. Petroleum is also the starting material for products like some pharmaceuticals, fertilizers, pesticides, and plastics.

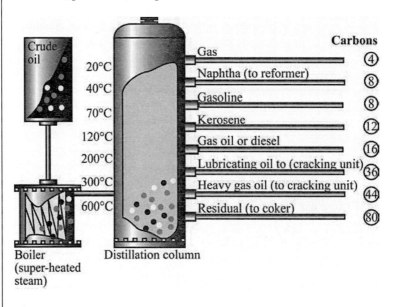

PRACTICE EXERCISES

1. Which of the following compounds are organic compounds?

   a) $HCN_{(g)}$ b) $Na_2CO_{3(s)}$ c) $C_3H_6O_{2(l)}$

   d) $NaHCO_{3(s)}$ e) $CH_3COOH_{(l)}$ f) $C_6H_{12}O_{6(s)}$

   g) $CO_{(g)}$ h) $HClO_{(aq)}$

2. a) As the number of the carbons in the chains of an alkane increases, what happens to the natural state of the alkane?

   b) What effect does the number of carbon atoms in the main chain of an alkane have on the boiling point?

3. a) Explain how the process of fractional distillation can be used to separate a mixture of methane gas (natural gas) and propane gas.

   b) Explain how polarity or other physical properties can be used to separate a mixture of water and crude oil.

4. Many alkanes are used as fuel sources and burned for energy. List a common or commercial use for three different alkanes.

5. When alkanes undergo complete combustion, energy is released. What are the other products of hydrocarbon combustion? Write a balanced equation representing the complete combustion of an alkane.

6. Complete the following chart:

	Structural Diagram	IUPAC Name
a)		2-methylhexane
b)	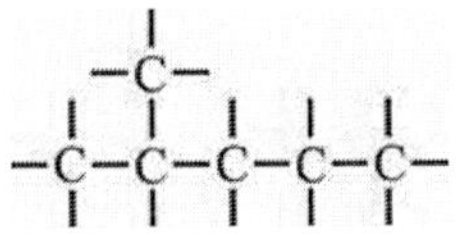 (structure: a carbon chain $-C-C-C-C-C-$ with a $-C-$ branch on the second carbon)	
c)		3,5,5-triethyl-2,4-dimethyloctane
d)		2,3,3,4-tetramethyloctane
e)	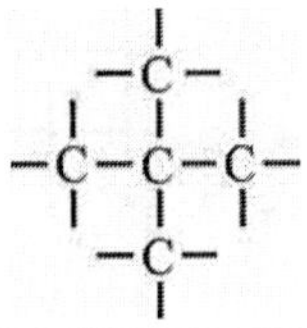 (structure: a central $-C-C-C-$ chain with a $-C-$ above and a $-C-$ below the central carbon)	
f)		2-methyl-4-propyloctane
g)	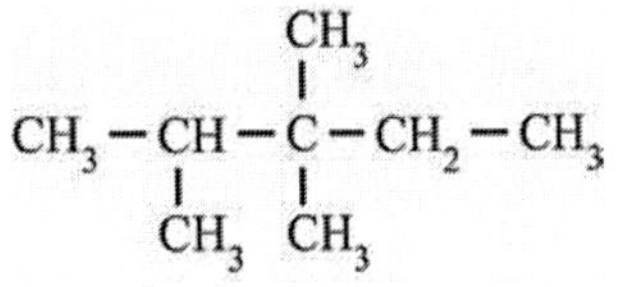 $CH_3-CH-C-CH_2-CH_3$ with CH_3 above the third carbon and CH_3, CH_3 below the second and third carbons	
h)	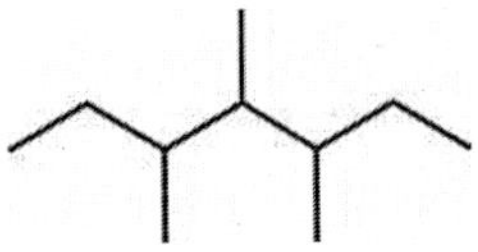 (skeletal structure)	
i)		6-ethyl-4-methyl-4,6,7-tripropyldecane

7. Draw, and correct each of the following improperly named alkanes.

   a) 4,5-dimethyl pentane

   b) 4-ethyl-2-methyl pentane

   c) 3,4-dimethyl pentane

   d) 4-methyl pentane

8. Draw the structural formulas for all reactants and products in each of the following reactions.

   a) propane + pentane → octane + hydrogen

   b) 2-methylbutane + oxygen $\xrightarrow{\text{burned}}$?

9. Draw the structural diagram of 1-ethyl-1,2-dimethylcyclobutane.

10. Name the compound indicated by the following structural diagram:

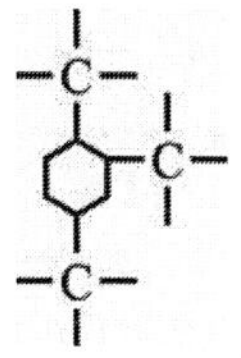

Lesson 2 ALKENES AND ALKYNES

NOTES

Alkenes are unsaturated aliphatic hydrocarbons.

Like alkanes, alkenes are aliphatic hydrocarbon molecules. What makes them distinct is that they have at least one carbon-carbon double bond. This means they are unsaturated. One way of remembering the difference between saturated and unsaturated hydrocarbons is to recall that saturation occurs when no more hydrogen atoms can be added to the compound, and all carbon atoms have formed four bonds with other atoms. In the case of alkenes, a carbon-carbon double bond can be broken down to a single bond, and two more hydrogen atoms can be added to the molecule with covalent bonds.

The general formula for an alkene molecule is C_nH_{2n}, where n is a number greater than 1.

NOMENCLATURE OF ALKENES

Alkenes are named using much the same conventions as alkanes. In order to name an alkene according to IUPAC, use the following steps:
1. Find the parent chain; that is, the longest contiguous chain of carbon atoms that includes all of the carbon-carbon double bonds in the molecule.
2. Change the ending of the parent name to "-ene."
3. Number the parent chain so that the double bonds have the lowest possible numbers.
4. If there is more than one double bond, use the Greek language prefixes to indicate the quantity (such as di- or tri-).

Example

Name the following alkene.

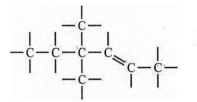

Solution

Start by identifying the parent chain in the molecule.

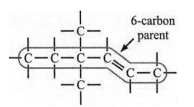

A six-carbon alkene is called hexene, and because the double bond is attached to the second carbon in the chain, it is called hex-2-ene. There are two methane branches attached to the fourth carbon in the chain, so the full name of the molecule is 4,4-dimethylhex-2-ene.

CYCLOALKENES

It is important to note that cycloalkenes are unsaturated aliphatic hydrocarbons. They are classified as unsaturated because they contain a double bond between two carbon atoms. Cycloalkenes contain a carbon ring structure and have a general formula of C_nH_{2n-2}.

NOTES

Aromatic compounds are different from cycloalkenes.

When naming a cycloalkene according to IUPAC conventions, use the following rules.

• The parent chain is always the ring structure.

• The double bond is always given the lowest possible number.

• The branches are always given the lowest possible values and are numbered in order, following the assignment of the double-bond number.

Example

Name the following compound.

Solution

There are six carbon atoms in the ring structure, so the parent is cyclohexene. The lowest possible numbers for the double bond would indicate that the double bond is between atoms 1 and 2. The carbon atoms would therefore be numbered as shown in the following illustration:

There are two methyl groups—one attached to the first carbon and one attached to the sixth carbon in the ring—so the name of this compound is 1,6-dimethylcyclohexene.

Example

Draw a structural diagram of propylcyclobutene.

Solution

Cyclobutene has four carbon atoms in a ring that resembles a square. The propyl group does not have a number, so it is attached to the first carbon in the ring, as shown in the following diagram

NOTES

ALKYNES

Alkynes are unsaturated aliphatic hydrocarbons that contain a carbon-carbon triple bond. The general formula for an alkyne is C_nH_{2n-2}.

The triple bond in the molecule causes alkynes to exhibit different chemical properties than alkanes or alkenes. Alkynes tend to be very volatile and reactive, and they very rarely form cyclic molecules. The simplest alkyne, C_2H_2, is ethyne, which is commonly known as acetylene.

The following rules for naming alkyne compounds are very similar to those used to name alkenes:

- The parent is defined as the longest continuous carbon chain that contains both carbon atoms that are triple bonded to one another.

- The suffix of the parent is "-yne."

- The parent chain is numbered so that the triple bond joins the lowest possible numbers.

- If there is more than one triple bond, Greek language prefixes are used to number them (such as di- or tri).

Example

Name the alkyne shown in the following structural diagram.

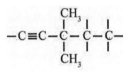

Solution

The longest continuous chain of carbon atoms that includes the triple bond are the five horizontal carbons found in a row. Starting with the far left, number the carbon atoms as follows:

Since there are two methyl groups that branch off from the third carbon atom, the IUPAC name for this compound is 3,3-dimethylpent-1-yne.

Example

Draw a structural diagram to represent buta-1,3-diyne.

Solution

The parent root of butyne indicates that this is a hydrocarbon compound composed of four carbon atoms. The prefix di- indicates that there are two triple bonds in the molecule. Since each carbon atom forms four bonds, the diagram looks like this:

$$-C \equiv C - C \equiv C-$$

PHYSICAL PROPERTIES OF ALKANES, ALKENES, AND ALKYNES

Melting and Boiling Points

As the number of carbon atoms in a hydrocarbon molecule increases, so does the number of electrons and the strength of London dispersion forces. As a result, it takes an increasing amount of energy to break these forces. The boiling and melting points of organic compounds increase in accordance with the amount of carbon found in the molecular structure.

More carbon atoms leads to higher boiling and melting points.

Solubility

Aliphatics are non-polar molecules that are immiscible (they do not mix) and insoluble in polar substances like water.

Potential Energy

Because double and triple bonds contain more stored energy than single bonds, the more double and triple bonds that exist within a molecule, the greater the potential energy the hydrocarbon has. For example, acetylene (ethyne) has more energy stored in its bonds than ethene does, which in turn has more energy than ethane. This is the reason that welders use acetylene (ethyne) torches to manipulate metal. The combustion of acetylene releases much more heat than ethene or ethane because of the energy stored in the triple bond.

Viscosity

The alkanes with fewer than five carbons are found in a gaseous state, while those with five or more are found in a liquid state. As a general rule, as the number of carbon atoms in an aliphatic hydrocarbon increases, the substance becomes denser and has a deeper colour and a higher viscosity, or resistance to flow.

HALOGENATION TEST FOR SATURATION

A saturated hydrocarbon contains only single bonds. A relatively easy way to test if an aliphatic carbon compound is saturated is to mix it with a reactive halogen. The individual types of halogenation reactions are named for the specific halogen involved in the reaction. The four halogens used in this way are fluorine, chlorine, bromine, and iodine. Therefore, the four main types of halogenation reactions are fluorination, chlorination, bromination, and iodination.

Alkanes, alkenes, and alkynes are all aliphatic molecules.

The central principle behind halogenation is that a saturated hydrocarbon will participate in a substitution reaction with a halogen, while an unsaturated hydrocarbon will participate in an addition reaction. In other words, a saturated hydrocarbon will slowly replace hydrogen atoms with halogen atoms and produce hydrogen gas. Unsaturated hydrocarbons will break a carbon-carbon double bond, and the halogens will attach to those bonding sites.

Alkanes are saturated and will produce slow substitution reactions with halogens. Alkenes and alkynes are unsaturated and will generate rapid addition reactions with halogens.

Adding reddish-brown liquid bromine to a clear six-carbon liquid will create a fluid that will either gradually become more transparent or immediately lose all colour. These reactions are described by the following illustrations:

Cyclohexane	Cyclohexene
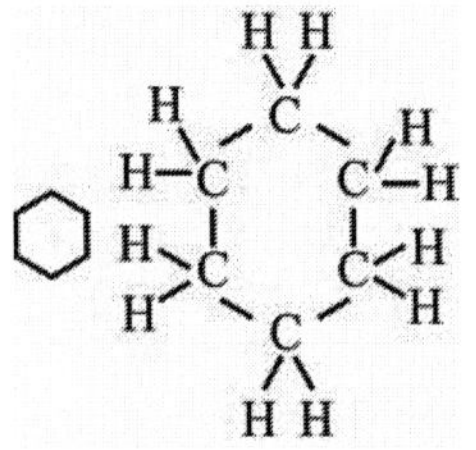	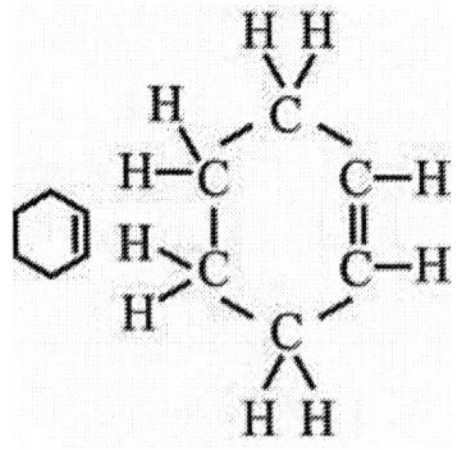
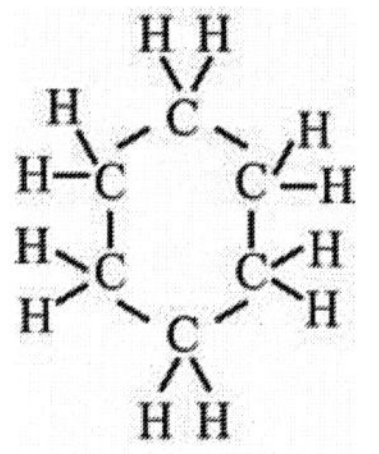 + Br—Br	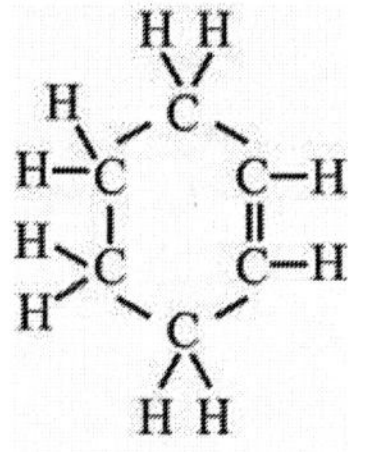 + Br—Br
(substitution)	(addition)
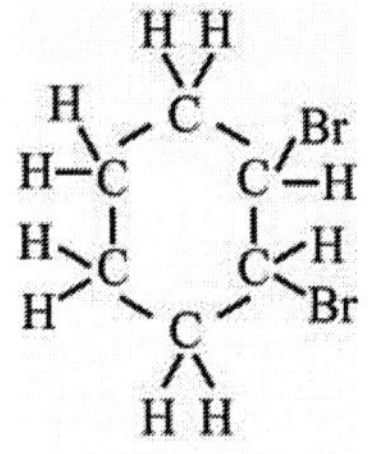 + H—H	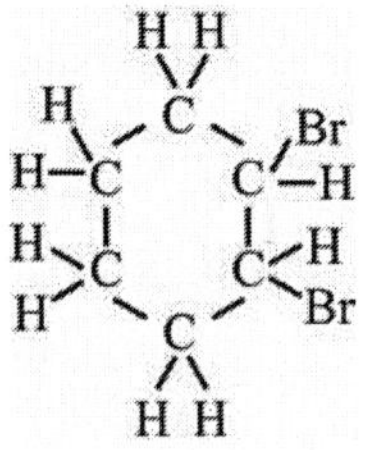

PRACTICE EXERCISES

1. Draw the structural diagram for 3,4-diethyl-2,6-dimethyloct-4-ene.

2. Draw the structural diagram for 2,4-dimethylpenta-1,3-diene.

3. Name and draw the three alkene isomers of C_4H_8.

4. Name and draw the three alkyne isomers of C_5H_8.

5. Name the molecule in each of the following diagrams.

a)

b)

6. Draw, or give the name for each of the following hydrocarbon compounds.

a) 1-methylcycloprop-1-ene

b) $CH_3—CH=CH—CH_2—CH_3$

c)

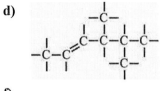

d)

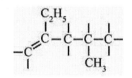

e) Ethyne

f)

g) C_3H_4

h) 4-methylpent-2-yne

Lesson 3 ISOMERS

Isomers are compounds with the same number of carbon and hydrogen atoms but different structures. Isomers share identical molar masses but have different names, characteristics, and chemical properties.

Example

Draw and name both isomers of $C_4H_{10(l)}$.

Solution

	Butane	**2-methylpropane**
Complete structural diagram	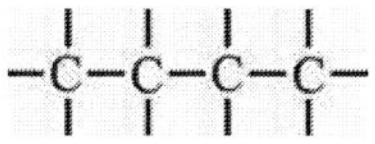	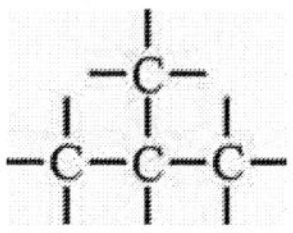
Condensed structural diagram	$CH_3-CH_2-CH_2-CH_3$	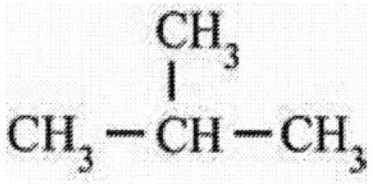
Line diagram		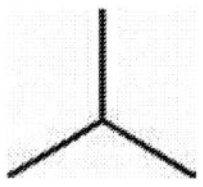

Example

Draw the complete structural diagram for each of the three isomers of $C_5H_{12(l)}$, and name them.

Solution

Pentane	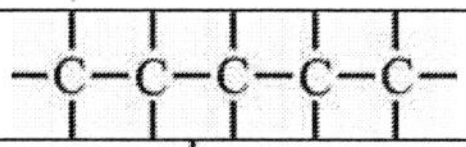
2-methyl butane	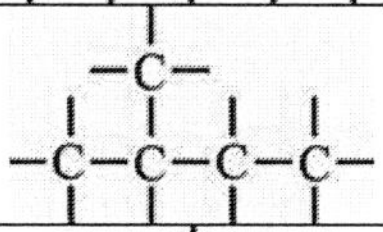
2,2-dimethyl propane	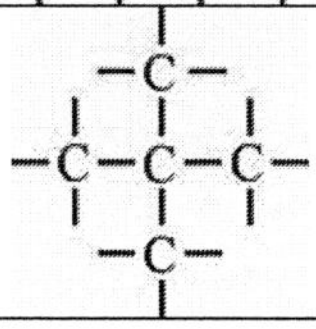

NOTES

CIS- AND *TRANS-*ISOMERS

Whenever a hydrocarbon has two identical branches that point in the same direction, the compound is known as a *cis*-isomer of the molecular formula. If the branches are oriented in opposite directions, the molecule is known as a *trans*-isomer of the molecular formula. *Cis-* and *trans*-isomers generally contain double bonds, which restrict the molecules ability to rotate. The *cis-* and *trans*-isomers for $C_2H_2Cl_2$ are shown in the following diagrams:

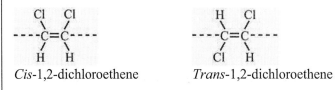

Cis-1,2-dichloroethene   *Trans*-1,2-dichloroethene

Above the dotted line in the *cis*-isomer, the chlorine branches are pointing in the same direction, whereas in the *trans*-isomer, the chlorine branches are pointing in opposite directions (above and below the dotted line).

PRACTICE EXERCISES

1. **a)** What is the molar mass of ethanol ($C_2H_5OH_{(l)}$)?

    b) What is the molar mass of dimethyl ether ($CH_3–O–CH_{3(l)}$)?

    c) Why are these two molecules considered to be isomers of each other?

2. Name and draw 11 isomers of C_6H_{12} that do **not** contain double or triple bonds.

Lesson 4 AROMATICS

Aromatics are complex carbon compounds that contain cyclical structures called benzene rings or derivatives of benzene rings. Benzene is the simplest primary aromatic compound because it does not have true single and double bonds. Instead, the electrons travel around a six-carbon ring, which causes the bonds between the carbon atoms to oscillate, or flip-flop, between being single and double.

The following structural diagrams can be used to show benzene:

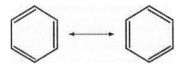

The double-headed arrow symbolizes the fact that benzene alternates back and forth between these states. A diagram of this sort is called a resonance diagram because neither of the structures exists exactly as it is depicted. A resonance diagram is an approximation of molecular shape.

Conjugated means having alternating single and double bonds

The easiest way to think about this sort of structure is to envision the electrons moving freely around the ring of carbon atoms, creating a more stable mutual bond between the atoms than any one individual set of bonds. Because the bonds alternate between single and double bonds, the compound is said to be conjugated.

The more conventional way of showing a benzene ring of carbon atoms is to use a circle to represent the constant movement of electrons around the ring, as shown in the following diagram:

Benzene

$C_6H_{6(l)}$

When a benzene ring loses a hydrogen atom and uses that bond to join other molecular structures, it is known as a phenyl group. If a benzene ring is attached to a long chain of carbons (more than six) it is considered a branch on the carbon chain and would be referred to as a phenyl group.

Other aromatic structures found in organic compounds include C_4H_4O, which is also known as furan. Furan is shown in the following structural diagram:

Furan

$C_4H_4O_{(l)}$

A benzene ring that has one methyl group attached to it is known as toluene and is shown in the following diagram:

Toluene
$C_7H_{8(l)}$

Toluene can technically be designated as methylbenzene.

Aromatic compounds are found in a number of common applications. As a phenyl group, benzene appears in a number of pharmaceutical products, such as morphine, birth control pills, amphetamines, and pain relievers like acetylsalicylic acid (the ASA in Aspirin). Toluene is perhaps most often associated with 2,4,6-trinitrotoluene, otherwise known as the explosive TNT.

Aromatics were first given their name because of the strong smell so many aromatic compounds have.

Aromatic compounds are found in the following substances:
- Particularly flavourful or odoriferous foods, such as chocolate, vanilla, and cinnamon

- Hormones such as testosterone, estrogen, and cortisol

- All five nucleotides that make up the DNA/RNA genetic code of all living things

- Polymers such as polyester and polystyrene

NOMENCLATURE OF AROMATICS
When benzene is the parent of the chain, the system used to name the molecule is similar to the one used for alkanes. The molecular suffix is –benzene, and any attached structures are numbered starting from the largest attached chain or the branch containing the greatest number of carbons.

The sum of all the numbers must be a minimum.

When benzene is not the parent of the chain, it becomes a phenyl branch. This happens when there is a double or triple bond in the remainder of the molecule or when the benzene ring is attached to a carbon chain with more than six carbons.

Example

Name the compound in the following structural diagram:

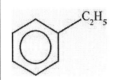

Solution

The aliphatic group that is attached to the benzene ring is ethane, and since there is only one branch from the parent chain, there is no need to number it. Every carbon in a benzene ring has an equal probability of bonding with another compound. The name of this molecule is ethylbenzene.

The sum of the numbers in the chemical name must be a minimum.

Example

Draw a structural diagram for 2-ethyl-1,4-dimethyl benzene.

Solution

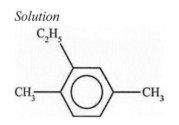

The largest chain attached to the benzene ring is an ethane group, and numbering from that carbon gives the term 1-ethyl-2,5-dimethylbenzene. However, IUPAC conventions also require that the sum of the numbers must be a minimum, so it is necessary to make an exception and number from left to right in the diagram shown. The correct name for this molecule is 2-ethyl-1,4-dimethylbenzene. Note that the longer chain is mentioned first in the formula.

Example

Name the compound in the following structural diagram using IUPAC conventions:

$$-\overset{|}{\underset{|}{C}}-\overset{|}{\underset{|}{C}}-\overset{\overset{\bigcirc}{|}}{\underset{|}{C}}-\overset{|}{\underset{|}{C}}-\overset{|}{\underset{|}{C}}-\overset{|}{\underset{|}{C}}-\overset{|}{\underset{|}{C}}-$$

Solution

The parent chain has seven carbons, so it is a heptane base. The benzene ring is bonded to the third carbon, so the name for the given molecule is 3-phenylheptane.

Example

Draw a structural diagram for phenylethene.

Solution

The parent chain is the last term in the name of the compound, so the parent chain will have two carbons joined with a double bond. Since there is only one branch, there is no need to number it, and anything bonding with a two-carbon molecule must be at an end site. The compound has the following structural diagram:

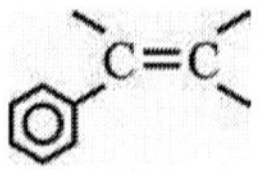

PRACTICE EXERCISES

1. Draw the structural diagram for each of the following aromatic compounds.

   a) 1,2-dimethylbenzene

   b) 1-ethyl-2-methylbenzene

   c) 1-ethyl-2,3-dimethylbenzene

   d) 2-methyl-2-phenylheptane

   e) 2-phenylpropane

   f) 1-methyl-3-propylbenzene

2. Name each of the following compounds, given its structural diagram.

   a)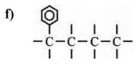

   b)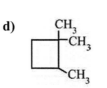

   c)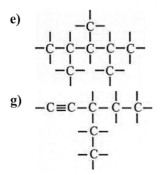

   d)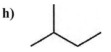

   e)

   f)

   g)

   h)

Lesson 5 FUNCTIONAL GROUPS

HALOGENATED HYDROCARBONS (ORGANIC HALIDES)

An organic compound that contains one or more halogen atoms is known as a halogenated hydrocarbon, or an organic halide.

The general formula for a halide is R-X, where R represents a hydrocarbon chain, and X represents at least one atom of fluorine, chlorine, bromine, or iodine.

As the number of halogens on the hydrocarbon increases, the number of hydrogen atoms decreases; therefore, there is an increase in electrons. This increases the London dispersion forces and the boiling point.

NOMENCLATURE OF HALOCARBONS

Halogens are numbered like an ordinary branch from a parent chain, and they are arranged in alphabetical order. There are two types of halides: aryl halides, which contain an aromatic ring, and alkyl halides, which do not contain an aromatic ring.

There are two types of halides: aryl halides and alkyl halides.

Example

Name the organic compound in the following structural diagram:

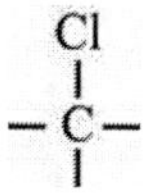

Solution

The given diagram shows a methane molecule with an attached chlorine atom. The IUPAC name for this molecule is chloromethane.

Example

Draw the structural diagram for 2-bromo-2-methylpropane.

Solution

The parent chain of this molecule will be a three-carbon propane chain. The second carbon in the chain is bonded to a bromine atom and a methane group. The molecule has the following structural diagram:

NOTES

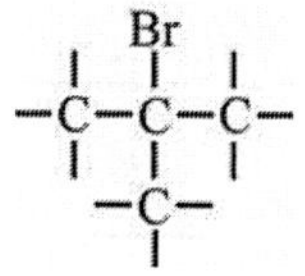

NOTES

Example

Name the organic compound in the following structural diagram.

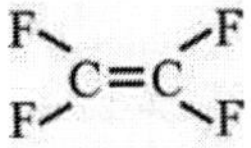

Solution

The parent carbon chain in the given diagram is a double-bonded ethene molecule. There are four fluorine atoms bonded, one at each of the remaining four bonding sites. The IUPAC name for this molecule is tetrafluoroethene.

Example

Draw the structural diagram that represents trichloromethane.

Solution

Trichloromethane, which is also known as chloroform, is a methane molecule that has three hydrogen atoms replaced with chlorine atoms. The structural diagram is shown as follows.

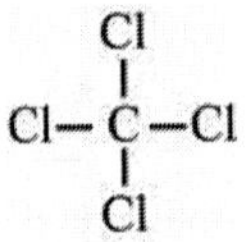

Example

Name the organic compound in the following structural diagram:

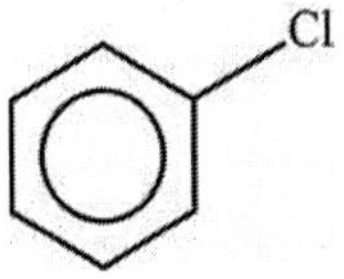

Solution

The addition of a chlorine atom to a benzene ring yields an aryl halide named chlorobenzene.

Example 6

Draw a structural diagram to represent 1-chloro-2-methylbenzene.

Solution

This molecule is constructed using a benzene ring as the parent chain and two branches. One branch will be composed of a chlorine atom, and the adjacent carbon will have a methyl group attached to it. The molecule has the following structural diagram:

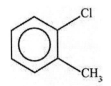

ALCOHOLS

An alcohol is formed from a hydrocarbon that is covalently bonded to a hydroxyl group. The general structure of an alcohol is expressed as R–OH, where R represents a hydrocarbon chain or ring, and OH represents at least one hydroxyl group consisting of an oxygen atom and a hydrogen atom.

Alcohols dissolve in water because they are polar molecules. The polarity exists because of a difference in electronegativities between oxygen and carbon and between oxygen and hydrogen. Alcohols have higher boiling points than alkanes because of the hydrogen bonds resulting from their –OH groups

Fermentation is the process in which ethanol is produced from sugar by the action of yeast or bacteria, in an anaerobic (without oxygen) respiration reaction. Ethanol, C_2H_5OH, is represented by the following diagram:

$$-\overset{\displaystyle |}{\underset{\displaystyle |}{C}}-\overset{\displaystyle |}{\underset{\displaystyle |}{C}}-OH$$

Ethanol is the alcohol found in beer, wine, and spirits.

NOMENCLATURE OF ALCOHOLS

According to IUPAC guidelines, alcohols are named using the following procedure:
1. Find the parent chain. This is the longest continuous carbon chain, and it contains the hydroxyl group (OH).
2. Change the ending of the name to "-ol."
3. The carbon with the OH attached gets the lowest possible number.
4. Name and number the remaining branches.
5. Number the position of the OH.
6. If there is more than one OH, put a prefix in front of "ol" (using the Greek language prefixes). Two OH groups are labelled "-diol."
7. A benzene ring with an attached OH group is known as a phenol, and the suffix is –phenol.

NOTES

Example

Name the organic compound in the following structural diagram.

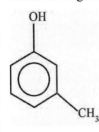

Solution

An OH group attached to a benzene ring is known as a phenol molecule. Number the six carbons around the benzene ring starting with the carbon-hydroxyl bond, and give the methyl branch the lowest possible number, as shown in the following diagram.

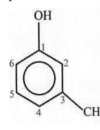

The name of this molecule is therefore 3-methylphenol.

Example

Draw a structural diagram to represent ethane-1,2-diol, also known as ethylene glycol.

Solution

The basic structure of ethane is that of a two-carbon alkane. Replacing one hydrogen on each of the carbons with a hydroxyl group yields a structural diagram like the one in the following diagram:

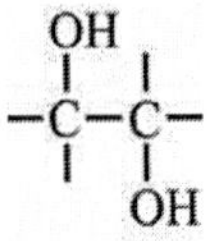

Example

Name the organic compound in the following structural diagram.

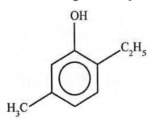

Solution

The benzene ring forms the parent chain of this molecule, so this compound is a phenol. The hydroxyl group is always given the lowest number, so the ethyl group is attached to the number 2 carbon, and the methyl group is attached to the number 5 carbon.

The name of this compound is 2-ethyl-5-methylphenol.

TYPES OF ALCOHOLS

Alcohols are grouped into three types, according to the number of R groups that are attached to the hydroxyl group. The carbon-oxygen bond forms the basis of a C-OH group, and the number of branches that are attached to that carbon dictates the classification of the alcohol. A primary alcohol (1°) has one R group attached to the C-OH, as seen in the following diagram of ethanol. In this case, an ethane alkane group is attached to the hydroxyl group. Notice that the OH group is attached to the end of the carbon chain.

Ethanol
(C_2H_5OH)

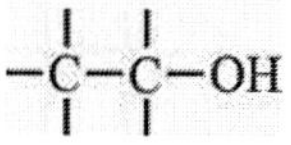

$$-\overset{|}{\underset{|}{C}}-\overset{|}{\underset{|}{C}}-OH$$

A secondary alcohol (2°) has two R groups attached to the C-OH group. Basically, this means that there are two carbon-carbon bonds attached to the C-OH group, as in the case of propan-2-ol, also called isopropyl alcohol.

Propan-2-ol
(C_3H_7OH)

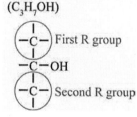

Tertiary alcohols (3°) have three carbon-carbon bonds attached to the C-OH group, as in the case of 2-methylpropan-2-ol.

2-methylpropan-2-ol
(C_4H_9OH)

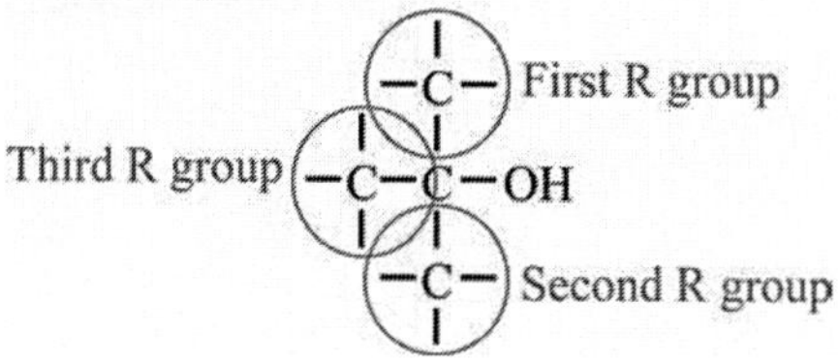

NOTES

Example

Draw 2-methylpentan-2-ol, butan-2-ol, and methanol, and classify them as primary, secondary, or tertiary alcohols.

Solution

In order to classify these three compounds, draw the structural diagrams, identify the C-OH group in each, and then count the number of R groups that are attached to the C-OH group.

The alcohol 2-methylpentan-2-ol has three carbon bonds attached to the C-OH group; therefore, it is a tertiary alcohol (3°).

2-methylpentan-2-ol
($C_6H_{13}OH$)

Butan-2-ol has two carbon bonds attached to the C-OH group; therefore, it is a secondary alcohol (2°).

Butan-2-ol
(C_4H_9OH)

OH
| | | |
−C−C−C−C−
| | | |

OH = hydroxyl group

Carbon double-bonded to oxygen = carbonyl group

Carbon bonded to both a hydroxyl and double-bonded to an oxygen = carboxyl group

Methanol only has one carbon bond with the C-OH group; therefore, it is a primary alcohol (1°).

Methanol
(CH_3OH)

|
−C−OH
|

CARBOXYLIC ACIDS

A carbon-oxygen double bond forms a carbonyl group. A carbon that is bonded to a hydroxyl group and double bonded to an oxygen atom forms what is known as a carboxyl group. The formula for a carboxyl group is (R-COOH). The R group is any hydrocarbon chain or ring that is bonded to a carboxyl group to form a carboxylic acid.

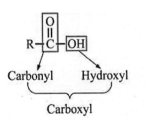
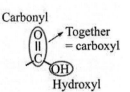

Carboxylic acids are commonly found in nature. For example, vinegar is a carboxylic acid. Carboxylic acids with shorter chains tend to be polar and, therefore, soluble in water. In addition, they tend to have higher melting and boiling points than simpler hydrocarbon molecules with the same number of carbons.

NOMENCLATURE OF CARBOXYLIC ACIDS

Carboxylic acids are named by counting the number of carbons present in the compound and then using the alkane hydrocarbon name ending in "-oic acid."

Carbon Atoms	IUPAC Name	Chemical Formula	Found in
1	Methanoic acid	HCOOH	Insect sting
2	Ethanoic acid	CH_3COOH	Vinegar
3	Propanoic acid	CH_3CH_2COOH	
4	Butanoic acid	$CH_3(CH_2)_2COOH$	Rancid butter
5	Pentanoic acid	$CH_3(CH_2)_3COOH$	
6	Hexanoic acid	$CH_3(CH_2)_4COOH$	
7	Heptanoic acid	$CH_3(CH_2)_5COOH$	
8	Octanoic acid	$CH_3(CH_2)_6COOH$	Coconut
9	Nonanoic acid	$CH_3(CH_2)_7COOH$	
10	Decanoic acid	$CH_3(CH_2)_8COOH$	

Example

Draw the structural diagram of a carboxyl group bonded with a benzene ring to form an aromatic carboxylic acid.

Solution

Adding a -COOH structure to a benzene ring creates benzoic acid, which has the following structural diagram:

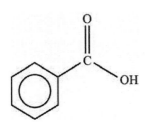

Example

Draw a structural diagram for butanoic acid.

Solution

Butane is a four-carbon alkane, so butanoic acid will have four carbons, the fourth of which forms a carbonyl and a hydroxyl group with an oxygen atom and a hydroxyl group, respectively. Butane has the following structural diagram:

$$-\overset{|}{\underset{|}{C}}-\overset{|}{\underset{|}{C}}-\overset{|}{\underset{|}{C}}-\overset{O}{\overset{\|}{C}}-O-H$$

ALDEHYDES AND KETONES

Hydrocarbons that terminate in a carbonyl group (RCOH) are called aldehydes. If the carbonyl group is found in the middle of a chain (RCOR′), that compound is called a ketone.

It is important to not confuse aldehydes and ketones with carboxylic acids. Consider the differences between the following three structural diagrams of a ketone, an aldehyde, and a carboxylic acid.

Ketone

$$-\overset{|}{\underset{|}{C}}-\overset{O}{\overset{\|}{C}}-\overset{|}{\underset{|}{C}}-$$

(R—CO—R′)

Aldehyde   Carboxylic acid

$$H-\overset{O}{\overset{\|}{C}}-\overset{|}{\underset{|}{C}}-\overset{|}{\underset{|}{C}}- \qquad -\overset{|}{\underset{|}{C}}-\overset{|}{\underset{|}{C}}-\overset{O}{\overset{\|}{C}}-OH$$

(R—CO=H)   (R—COOH)

ESTERS (R-COO-R′)

When a carboxylic acid reacts with an alcohol, a water molecule and a compound known as an ester are formed. Because water is a product of the reaction, this is known as a condensation reaction. The process that creates esters is known as esterification. The general structure of an ester can be expressed in the format R-COO-R′, where R represents the carboxylic acid component of the molecule, and R′ represents the alcohol component. Esters tend to have very characteristic odours and flavours, particularly in fruits, perfumes, and pheromones. Compared with carboxylic acids, esters tend to have higher melting and boiling points.

Example

The ester ethyl butanoate is the result of a reaction between butanoic acid and ethanol. Draw a structural diagram to represent ethyl butanoate.

Solution

Ethyl butanoate
($C_3H_7COOC_2H_5$)

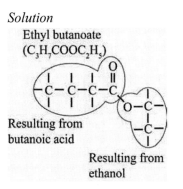

Resulting from butanoic acid

Resulting from ethanol

NOMENCLATURE OF ESTERS

To name an ester, begin with the alcohol component, ending with a "-yl" suffix. Then, name the acid component, ending with a "-oate" suffix. In the case of the condensation reaction between ethanol and butanoic acid, the alcohol component becomes "ethyl," and the acid component is named "butanoate."

Example

Draw and name the ester resulting from the reaction between benzoic acid and methanol.

Solution

The ester that is produced by the condensation reaction of methanol and benzoic acid is named methyl benzoate. The other product of that reaction is water.

Benzoic acid + Methanol ⟶ Methyl benzoate + Water
C_6H_5COOH CH_3OH $C_6H_5COOCH_3$ H_2O

Water condenses out.

THE STRUCTURE AND ODOUR OF SOME ESTERS

Ester Name	Structure	Odour
Methyl ethanoate (commonly called methyl acetate)		Glue
Ethyl ethanoate (commonly called ethyl acetate)		Nail-polish remover
Propyl ethanoate (commonly called propyl acetate)		Pear
Pentyl pentanoate		Apple

PRACTICE EXERCISES

1. Draw the structural diagram for each of the following halides, and indicate if it is an aryl or alkyl halide.

   a) 2,4-dibromohexane

   b) 1,3-dichloro-4-methylcyclohexane

   c) 1-fluoro-2-methylbenzene

2. Draw the structural diagram for each of the following alcohols.

   a) 3,3-dimethylbutan-2-ol

   b) Propan-2ol

   c) 2-chloroethanol

   d) 2,4-dimethylcyclopentanol

3. Draw or name each of the following compounds, as well as the acids and alcohols from which they were made.

   a) Ethyl ethanoate

b) The ester resulting from the reaction between propanol and butanoic acid

c) $CH_3CH_2COOCH_2CH_3$

4. Circle the functional groups in each of the following compounds. Based on these circled functional groups, name the family of organic compounds each compound may be classified as.

a)

b)

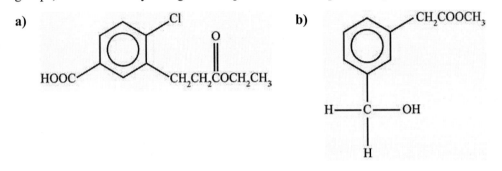

5. For each of the following compounds, name the compound, and identify the types of functional groups it contains.

a)

b)

c)

d)

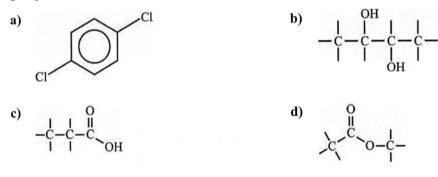

6. Compare the boiling points and solubilities of each of the following pairs of compounds.

a) Propane and butane

b) Ethane and ethanol

c) Ethane-1,2-diol and ethanol

Lesson 6 ORGANIC REACTIONS

There are 10 basic types of reactions that are important to understand in organic chemistry. Some are critical because they represent hydrocarbon decomposition for the purpose of releasing energy. Others are significant because they represent the construction of more complex molecules in the petrochemical industry and biological metabolism.

COMPLETE COMBUSTION

A hydrocarbon that is ignited (burned) in a condition of excess oxygen will combust (oxidize) to form carbon dioxide and energy.

Example

Write the equation that represents the combustion of propane gas. You can always assume complete combustion occurs to form gaseous products unless otherwise indicated.

Solution

The balanced chemical equation of propane combustion follows the following standard hydrocarbon equation:

$$C_xH_y + \left(x+\frac{y}{4}\right)O_2 \to xCO_2 + \left(\frac{y}{2}\right)H_2O$$

In the case of propane, $x = 3$ and $y = 8$. Therefore, the balanced chemical equation is as follows:

$$C_3H_8 + 5O_2 \to 3CO_2 + 4H_2O$$

Combustion is also an exothermic reaction, so the net products of this reaction include a net output of heat energy.

GREENHOUSE GASES

Carbon dioxide gas, which is produced during the combustion of fossil fuels, is a greenhouse gas. A greenhouse gas is a gas that contributes to climate change. Other greenhouse gases are $CH_{4(g)}$, $H_2O_{(g)}$, and $N_2O_{(g)}$. The production of fuel sources and the burning of fossil fuels has had a damaging impact on the environment. Because of the high dependency on the burning of fossil fuels, large amounts of time, technology, and money are being spent to find more environmentally friendly fuel sources.

The following three types of cracking exist:

- Catalytic cracking
- Thermal cracking
- Hydrocracking

INCOMPLETE COMBUSTION

In the absence of any specific evidence to the contrary, chemical combustion reactions are always assumed to be complete. On the other hand, when a reaction involves a stoichiometrically defined quantity of oxygen that limits the combustion, the combustion is said to be incomplete. When incomplete combustion occurs, the products include carbon dioxide, water, carbon monoxide, and elemental carbon. When generated in its elemental form by combustion, carbon is in the form of soot or ash.

HYDROCARBON CRACKING

Given the presence of a catalyst and/or heat and pressure, hydrogen gas can be used to split long chain hydrocarbons into smaller saturated and unsaturated molecules. This process of breaking hydrocarbon chains is used to convert crude oil (a product that is not very useful) into more useful products.

There are three types of hydrocarbon cracking reactions that break down large hydrocarbon molecules into smaller molecules. A chemical material that can facilitate or accelerate a chemical reaction without being affected is known as a catalyst, and cracking reactions that use catalysts to break apart the carbon chains are known as catalytic cracking reactions. Another way of cracking hydrocarbons is by using heat in a thermal cracking reaction. Finally, hydrocarbons can be cracked using heat and hydrogen in a process known as hydrocracking.

Example

Draw a diagram that shows how ethane and butane can be formed by hydrocracking hexane.

Solution

Hydrocracking involves the use hydrogen under heat and pressure to break larger hydrocarbons into smaller hydrocarbons. The heat provides the energy to break both the carbon-carbon bonds and the hydrogen-hydrogen bonds in the reactants. Hydrogen atoms bond to the separated carbons where the larger hydrocarbon splits apart.

The following illustration shows the structural diagram of this reaction:

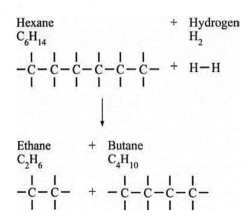

REFORMING

The opposite reaction to hydrocarbon cracking is called reforming. In this type of reaction, heat and/or a catalyst is used to join smaller saturated and unsaturated hydrocarbons together to form larger molecules. Hydrogen gas is also produced as a net result.

Example

Draw the structural diagrams of the components involved in the formation of ethylcyclohexane from cyclohexane and ethane.

Solution

Cyclohexane + Ethane $\longrightarrow$ Ethylcyclohexane + Hydrogen
$C_6H_{12(l)}$ $C_2H_{6(g)}$ $C_8H_{16(g)}$ $H_{2(g)}$

SUBSTITUTION

In a substitution reaction, one or more hydrogen atoms in a hydrocarbon are replaced by another atom or group of atoms. Organic halides are formed during substitution reactions when one halogen atom at a time trades places with one hydrogen atom on an aliphatic or aromatic compound. If a halide has more than one halogen bonded to the structure, then two or more separate substitution reactions must have taken place. The general formula for the halogenation of a hydrocarbon using substitution is shown in the following equation:

hydrocarbon + halogen $\rightarrow$ halocarbon + hydrogen halide

Example

Using structural diagrams, show how 1,2-dichloropropane is formed during a substitution reaction.

Solution

Because 1,2-dichloropropane has two halogens bonded to it, it must be created using two separate substitution reactions.

Step 1

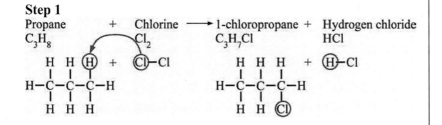

Propane   +   Chlorine $\longrightarrow$ 1-chloropropane + Hydrogen chloride
C_3H_8 Cl_2 C_3H_7Cl HCl

Step 2

1-chloropropane + Chlorine ⟶ 1,2-chloropropane + Hydrogen chloride
C_3H_7Cl Cl_2 $C_2H_4Cl_2$ HCl

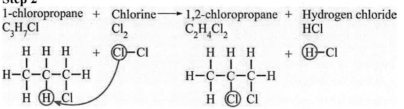

ADDITION

Addition reactions are reactions in which atoms are added to an alkene or alkyne hydrocarbon, resulting in a double bond being replaced by a single bond or a triple bond being replaced by a double or single bond. Addition reactions involve unsaturated hydrocarbons. When a carbon-carbon double or triple bond is broken, there are free valence electrons available with which other atoms and molecules can bond. There are four types of addition reactions, each characterized by a reaction with a different type of molecule.

1. Hydrogenation

During this type of addition reaction, hydrogen atoms are added to an unsaturated compound to make it more saturated. In this way, alkynes may be transformed into alkenes, and alkenes can be transformed into alkanes by the reaction with hydrogen.

Example

Use structural diagrams to show the hydrogenation of ethene that results in the production of ethane.

Solution

Ethene   +   Hydrogen ⟶ Ethane
C_2H_4 H_2 C_2H_6

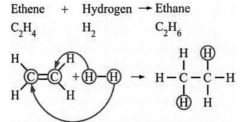

2. Hydration

During this type of addition reaction, water is added to an unsaturated hydrocarbon, resulting in the production of an alcohol.

Example

Use structural diagrams to show the hydration of prop-1-ene that results in the production of propan-1-ol.

Solution

Prop-1-ene   +   Water $\longrightarrow$ Propan-1-ol
C_3H_6 H — OH C_3H_7OH

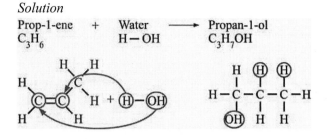

3. Addition of Halogens, Hydrogen Halides, and Acids

During this type of addition reaction, alkenes and alkynes are reacted with substances such as F_2, Cl_2, and HCl.

Example

Use structural diagrams to show the addition of bromine to *trans*-but-2-ene during an addition reaction.

Solution

But-2-ene   +   Bromine $\longrightarrow$ 2,3-dibromobutane
C_4H_8 Br_2 $C_4H_8Br_2$

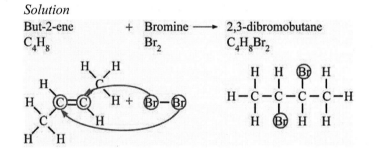

Example

Use structural diagrams to show the addition of hydrogen chloride to but-1-ene to form 2-chlorobutane.

Solution

But-1-ene   +   Hydrogen chloride $\longrightarrow$ 2-chlorobutane
C_4H_8 HCl C_4H_9Cl

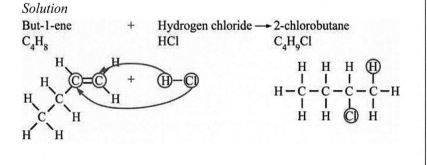

NOTES

Example

Use structural diagrams to show the addition of perchloric acid ($HClO_4$) to cyclohexene to produce cyclohexyl perchlorate.

Solution

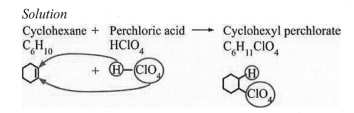

Cyclohexane + Perchloric acid $\longrightarrow$ Cyclohexyl perchlorate
C_6H_{10} $HClO_4$ $C_6H_{11}ClO_4$

4. Multiple Additions

When there are two or more molecules being added to a hydrocarbon, the maximum number of bonds that can be broken in order to add the atoms is two. Most additions of multiple molecular groups are reactions with aromatics or alkynes.

Example

Use structural diagrams to show the addition reaction resulting in the production of 1,1,2,2-tetrafluoropropane by adding two molecules of fluorine gas to propyne.

Solution

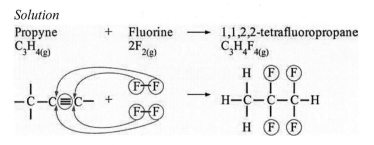

Propyne   +   Fluorine $\longrightarrow$ 1,1,2,2-tetrafluoropropane
$C_3H_{4(g)}$ $2F_{2(g)}$ $C_3H_4F_{4(g)}$

If the amount of $F_{2(g)}$ were limited during the reaction, only 1,2-difluoropropene would be formed.

ELIMINATION

An elimination reaction can be thought of as the opposite of an addition reaction. During most organic elimination reactions, atoms are removed from an organic compound, resulting in the formation of an unsaturated molecule. For example, an alkyl halide reacts with a hydroxide ion to form an alkene, a halide ion, and water. Essentially, the hydroxide ion (OH^-) takes a hydrogen from the hydrocarbon and forms water. The halide then breaks away from the hydrocarbon chain, and the carbons to which the hydrogen and the halide were bonded form a double bond.

Example

Using structural diagrams, show the reaction of 2-chlorobutane with a hydroxide ion that results in the production of but-1-ene, water, and a chloride ion.

Solution

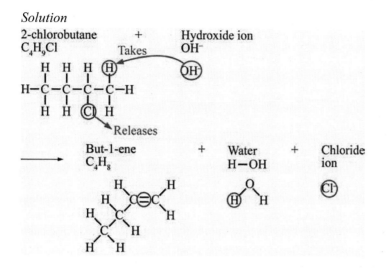

Another example of an elimination reaction is the removal of two hydrogen atoms through a process called dehydrogenation.

DEHYDROGENATION

When a hydrocarbon loses two hydrogen atoms, and those available bonding sites become a double carbon-carbon bond, the process is described as dehydrogenation. Basically, dehydrogenation transforms saturated hydrocarbon compounds into unsaturated ones by removing hydrogen. Dehydrogenation can be accomplished by heating a hydrocarbon or by placing a hydrocarbon in the presence of certain metallic catalysts.

Example

Draw a structural diagram illustrating the dehydrogenation of an ethane molecule.

Solution

Dehydrogenation produces hydrogen gas and an unsaturated hydrocarbon. In the case of ethane, the removal of one molecule of hydrogen gas results in the formation of a carbon-carbon double bond within a molecule of ethene.

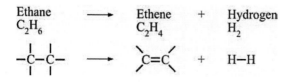

Another example of an elimination reaction is the production of an alkene from an alcohol.

Example

When ethanol is heated with the addition of a strong acid, it undergoes an elimination reaction that results in the production of ethene and water. Use structural diagrams to show the elimination reaction of ethanol.

Solution

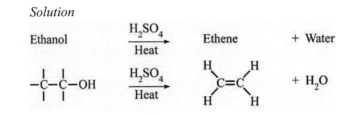

ESTERIFICATION

Esterification is a type of condensation reaction that involves a carboxylic acid and an alcohol and produces an ester and water. It is known as a condensation reaction because the bond between the carboxylic component of the ester and the alcohol component is created by a hydrogen atom leaving the alcohol and a hydroxyl group leaving the carboxylic acid, thereby resulting in the formation of water.

Example

Using structural diagrams, show the esterification reaction between benzoic acid and methanol that produces methyl benzoate and water.

Solution

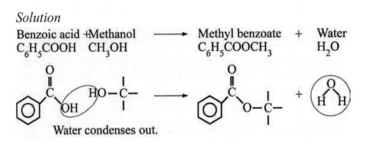

Water condenses out.

POLYMERIZATION

The formation of very large molecules from a number of smaller, repeating molecules is known as polymerization. The smaller units that are chained together are known as monomers, and they can be covalently attached to one another by either addition synthesis or condensation synthesis. The large molecular chains are classified as macromolecules and are known as polymers.

Polymers that are formed from a repeating pattern of the same monomer are known as homopolymers, while polymers that contain more than one kind of monomer are known as copolymers.

The monomers that make up a polymer can greatly affect the properties of the polymer. For example, when ethylene oxide (C_2H_4O) is polymerized, the produced polymer is polar; therefore, it is soluble in water because the monomer is also polar. Styrene is non-polar; therefore, when it is polymerized into polystyrene (a hard, clear plastic), the polymer will also be non-polar and insoluble in water.

The length of the polymer chain also has an impact on the properties of the substance. As the number of monomers making up the polymer increases, strength and toughness generally increase, as do the melting and boiling points of the substance.

Some Synthetic (Man-Made) Polymers	
Name	Common use
Polyethylene	Milk jugs, plastic bags
Kevlar	Bulletproof vests
Polyvinylchloride (PVC)	Household pipes
Teflon	Non-stick pots and pans
Polyester	Clothing
Nylon	Parachutes, clothing

Some Naturally Occurring Polymers	
Name	Common use
DNA	Genetic material
Starch	Metabolic energy storage
Proteins	Biological cellular functions
Natural rubber	Vehicle tires, racquetballs
Cotton	Clothing

Addition Polymerization

Alkenes are polymerized by breaking a double carbon bond and then using the two available bonding sites to attach to two other monomers. A series of alkenes that do this can therefore form a chain, the length of which is limited only by the amount of energy, materials, and catalyst (if required) that are available.

There is a form of macromolecule synthesis called plasma polymerization, but this will not be addressed here.

NOTES

Polyethene is commonly called "polyethylene."

Example

Use structural diagrams to show the polymerization of ethene (the monomer) into polyethene (the polymer).

Solution

Even though the double bonds are broken and the chain contains only single-bonded carbons, polyethene maintains the "-ene" suffix.

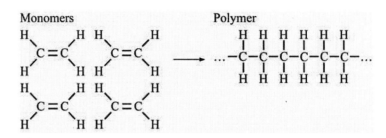

CONDENSATION POLYMERIZATION

Monomers can be joined by taking a hydroxyl group from one molecule and a hydrogen atom from another to create water, and merging the remaining bond sites.

Example

Polyester is created from two alternating monomers and forms a copolymer. One monomer is known as terephthalic acid, but it can be also described as benzene-1,4-dicarboxlic acid. It has a molecular formula of $C_6H_4(COOH)_2$. The other monomer is ethylene glycol, but it could be technically described as ethane-1,2-diol. It has a molecular formula of $C_2H_4(OH)_2$. Use structural diagrams to show the process of synthesizing polyester.

Solution

The hydroxyl groups of each carboxylic acid end of the benzene compound will break away from the terephthalic acid molecule and bond with the hydrogen atoms at the ends of the ethylene glycol molecule to form water molecules. The reaction is drawn in the following diagram:

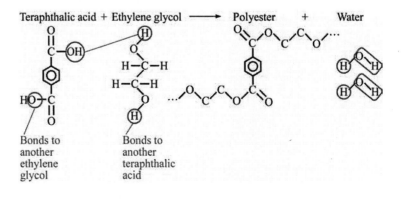

PRACTICE EXERCISES

1. For each of the following reaction equations, classify the reaction type, name the products, and show structural diagrams for all the reactants and products.

   a) 2-methylpent-1-ene + hydrogen →

   b) butane → but-1-ene + hydrogen

   c) cyclohexane + ethane → ethylcyclohexane + hydrogen

   d) chloroethane + chlorine →

   e) ethanol + ethanoic acid →

   f) cyclohexanol $\xrightarrow[\text{heat}]{\text{H}_2\text{SO}_4}$ cyclohexene

2. For each of the following structural diagrams, classify the reaction type, name all the reactants and products, and show structural diagrams for all the products.

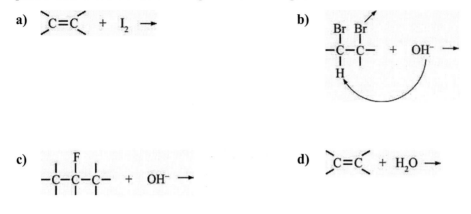

a)

b)

c)

d)

3. Predict the products of each of the following reactions, and classify the type of reaction that occurs.

a) Butane reacts with chlorine.

b) Ethanol burns in an open environment.

c) Hydroxide ions react with 1-chlorobutane.

d) Bromine and ethene react.

e) $CH_3-CH=CH-CH_3 + HOH \rightarrow$

f) but-2-ene + hydrogen $\rightarrow$

g) cyclopentene + hydrogen fluoride $\rightarrow$

h) ethene + water →

i) propanoic acid + ethanol →

4. Classify the polymerization reactions in each of the following reactions:

a)

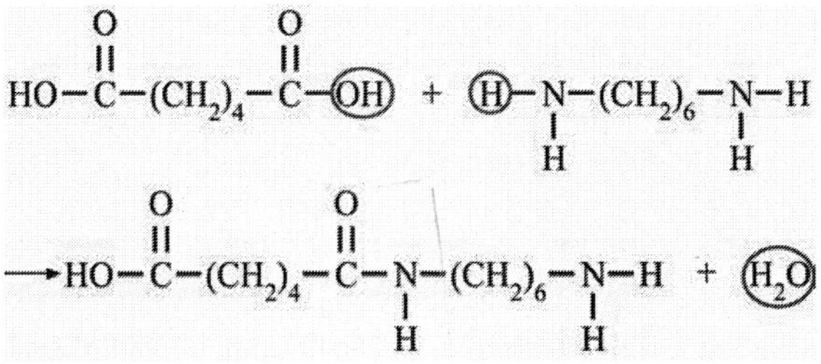

$$HO-\overset{\overset{O}{\|}}{C}-(CH_2)_4-\overset{\overset{O}{\|}}{C}-\boxed{OH} \ + \ \boxed{H}-\underset{H}{\overset{}{N}}-(CH_2)_6-\underset{H}{\overset{}{N}}-H$$

$$\longrightarrow HO-\overset{\overset{O}{\|}}{C}-(CH_2)_4-\overset{\overset{O}{\|}}{C}-\underset{H}{\overset{}{N}}-(CH_2)_6-\underset{H}{\overset{}{N}}-H \ + \ \boxed{H_2O}$$

b) Vinyl chloride   Poly(vinyl chloride) (PVC)

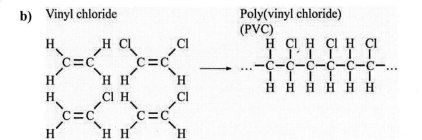

c)

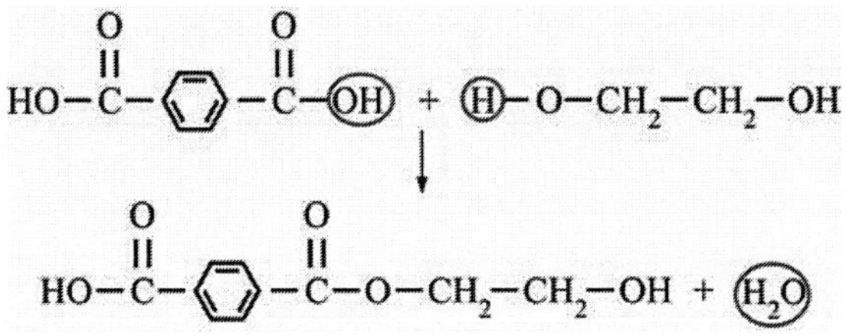

$$HO-\overset{\overset{O}{\|}}{C}-\hexagon-\overset{\overset{O}{\|}}{C}-\boxed{OH} \ + \ \boxed{H}-O-CH_2-CH_2-OH$$

$$\downarrow$$

$$HO-\overset{\overset{O}{\|}}{C}-\hexagon-\overset{\overset{O}{\|}}{C}-O-CH_2-CH_2-OH \ + \ \boxed{H_2O}$$

d)   Propylene   ⟶   Polypropylene

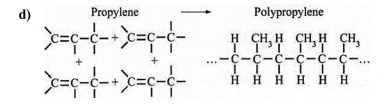

REVIEW SUMMARY

- Carbon is the defining element in all organic compounds because it has a number of important chemical qualities. These include:

    - Four valence electrons that can bond covalently

    - The ability to form chains and rings with carbon-carbon bonds

    - The ability to form single, double, and triple bonds

    - The ability to form isomers (substances with the same molecular formulas but different structures)

- All organic compounds have carbon atoms in them, but not all carbon molecules are organic. The following four major types of carbon compounds are **not** organic:

    - Oxides

    - Carbides

    - Carbonates and bicarbonates

    - Cyanides

- There are three basic types of aliphatic compounds, which are defined by the type of carbon bonding in the molecules: alkanes are saturated and have only single bonds, alkenes have at least one double carbon-carbon bond, and alkynes have at least one triple carbon-carbon bond. Aliphatic molecules can take the form of straight chains or ring structures.

- Aromatic compounds are always found in conjugated ring structures that have electrons that cycle between atoms, such that the carbon-carbon bonds alternate between being single, double, and triple bonds. Benzene is the most common example of an aromatic structure.

- An unsaturated hydrocarbon is one that contains double and triple bonds that can be broken to bond more hydrogen atoms to the carbon chain or ring.

- Organic halides are formed by replacing hydrogen atoms with halogen atoms in hydrocarbons.

- Alcohols contain at least one hydroxyl group.

- Carboxylic acids contain a carbon double bonded to an oxygen (carbonyl) and a hydroxyl group.

- Esterification is the process by which a carboxylic acid reacts with an alcohol to form an ester and water.

- Polymerization is the joining of multiple hydrocarbon units, called monomers, into long-chained macromolecules called polymers.

- There are nine basic types of organic reactions:

    - Complete combustion—a hydrocarbon burns in excess oxygen to produce oxides, water, and energy.

    - Incomplete combustion—a hydrocarbon burns in limited oxygen and produces $CO_{2(g)}$, $CO_{(g)}$, and $C_{(s)}$, in addition to water and energy.

    - Cracking—a large hydrocarbon breaks down into two or more smaller hydrocarbon molecules.

    - Reforming—two or more smaller hydrocarbons join to form a larger one, and hydrogen gas is produced.

    - Substitution—one or more hydrogen atoms are replaced by another atom or group of atoms.

    - Addition—an unsaturated hydrocarbon bonds with hydrogen to form a more saturated hydrocarbon.

    - Elimination—an alkyl halide reacts with a hydroxide ion to form an alkene, a halide ion, and water.

    - Esterification—a carboxylic acid reacts with an alcohol to form an ester and water.

    - Polymerization—repeating units (monomers) form macromolecular chains through addition or condensation reactions.

160

PRACTICE TEST

1. Define what is meant by the term *organic compound*, and provide examples of common compounds that can be classified as organic compounds.

2. Define the term *saturated*, and explain if saturated compounds can undergo addition reactions.

3. Describe, and give an example of an alkyne.

4. Describe, and give an example of an aromatic compound.

Use the following diagram to answer the next question.

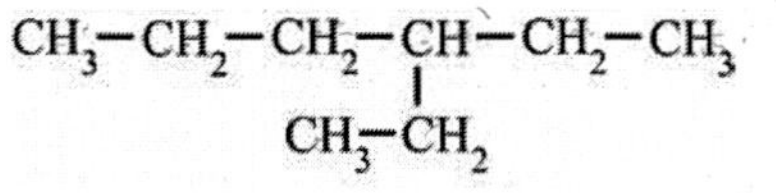

$$CH_3 - CH_2 - CH_2 - CH - CH_2 - CH_3$$
$$CH_3 - CH_2$$

5. Name the given compound, and classify the type of organic compound it is.

Use the following diagram to answer the next question.

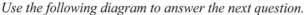

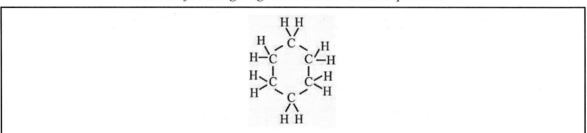

6. Name the given compound, and classify the type of organic compound it is.

Use the following diagram to answer the next question.

$$H-C\equiv C-H$$

7. Name the given compound, and describe its characteristics.

Use the following diagram to answer the next question.

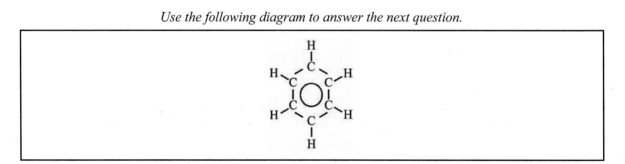

8. Name the given compound.

Use the following diagram to answer the next question.

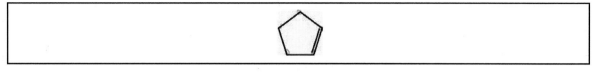

9. Name the given compound, and describe the bonding between the carbons.

10. Explain what "—$CH_2CH_2CH_3$" refers to in an organic compound.

Use the following diagram to answer the next question.

$$CH_3-CH_2-CH_2-CH_2-\overset{\overset{\displaystyle CH_3}{|}}{\underset{\underset{\displaystyle Br}{|}}{C}}-CH_2-\overset{\overset{\displaystyle CH_3}{|}}{\underset{\underset{\displaystyle Br}{|}}{C}}-CH_3$$

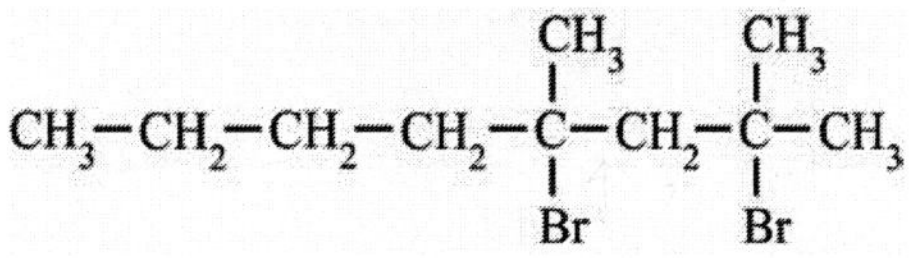

11. Name the given compound.

Use the following diagram to answer the next question.

$$CH_3-CH_2-CH_2-\overset{\overset{\displaystyle CH_3}{|}}{\underset{\underset{\displaystyle F}{|}}{C}}-CH_2-\overset{\overset{\displaystyle CH_3}{|}}{\underset{\underset{\displaystyle CH_3}{|}}{C}}-CH_2-CH_2-CH_2-CH_3$$

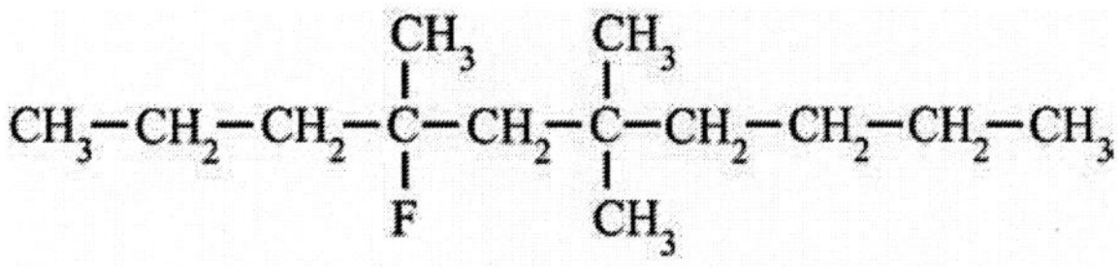

12. Name the given compound.

Use the following diagram to answer the next question.

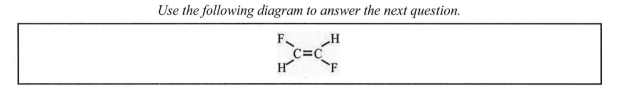

13. Name the given compound, and identify if it is the *-cis* or *-trans* form of the isomer.

Use the following diagram to answer the next question.

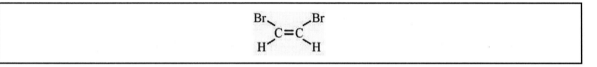

14. Name the given compound, and identify if it is the *-cis* or *-trans* form of the isomer.

Use the following diagram to answer the next question.

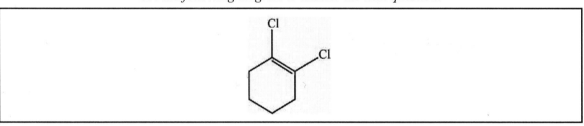

15. Name the given compound.

Use the following diagram to answer the next question.

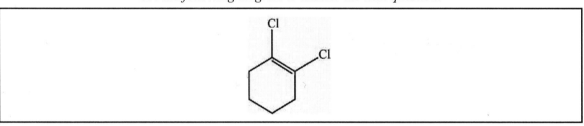

16. Identify the type of organic compound in the given diagram.

Use the following diagram to answer the next question.

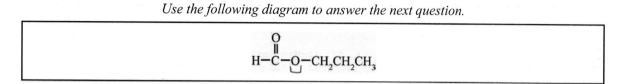

17. Name the given compound, and identify the type of organic compound it is.

18. When coal is burned in an oxygen-limited environment, what type of reaction will occur?

19. Draw and name the nine isomers of heptane.

20. Describe why carbon compounds are so common and why carbon can form long molecular chains.

Use the following information to answer the next question.

Propylene

C_3H_6

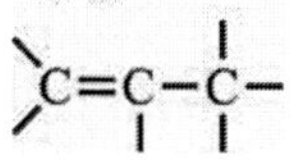

Propene is the systematic name of this compound; propylene is its common name.

21. Draw a polymer of propylene that consists of three monomers, resulting from a polymerization reaction.

22. For each of the following reactions, identify the type of reaction, and name the products of the reaction.

   a) ethane + bromine $\xrightarrow{\text{at } 25°C}$

   b) propene + HCl $\longrightarrow$

   c) propan-2-ol $\xrightarrow[\text{heat}]{H_2SO_4}$

   d) benzoic acid + pentan-1-ol $\longrightarrow$

23. Describe how a mixture of methanol and water can be separated. The boiling point of methanol is approximately 65°C.

Use the following information to answer the next question.

Vinegar (ethanoic, or acetic, acid) is the product in the following reaction:
ethanol + oxygen → ethanoic acid

24. Draw the structural diagrams for the organic compounds in the formation of vinegar reaction.

25. Draw and name four structural isomers of a compound containing two methyl groups and a total of eight carbons.

NOTES

EQUILIBRIUMS OF ACID-BASE SYSTEMS

When you are finished this unit, you will be able to…

• Define equilibrium and state the criteria that apply to a chemical system in equilibrium

• Identify, write and interpret chemical equations for systems at equilibrium

• Write the equilibrium law expression for a given equation

• Predict, qualitatively, using Le Châtelier's principle, shifts in equilibrium caused by changes in temperature, pressure, volume, concentration or the addition of a catalyst and describe how these changes affect the equilibrium constant

• Define K_c, use the value of K_c to predict the extent of a reaction, and write equilibrium-law expressions for given chemical equations, using lowest whole-number coefficients

• Describe Brønsted–Lowry acids as proton donors and bases as proton acceptors

• Write Brønsted–Lowry equations, including indicators, and predict whether reactants or products are favoured for acid-base equilibrium reactions for monoprotic and polyprotic acids and bases

• Identify conjugate pairs and amphiprotic substances

• Define a buffer as a solution containing relatively large amounts of a weak acid or base and its conjugate in equilibrium that maintains a relatively constant pH when small amounts of acid or base are added

• Recall the concepts of pH and hydronium ion concentration and pOH and hydroxide ion concentration, in relation to acids and bases

• Define K_w, K_a, K_b, and use these to determine pH, pOH, $[H_3O^+]$ and $[OH^-]$ of acidic and basic solutions

• Calculate equilibrium constants and concentrations for homogeneous systems and Brønsted–Lowry acids and bases (excluding buffers) when:

  – Concentrations at equilibrium are known

  – Initial concentrations and one equilibrium concentration are known

  – The equilibrium constant and one equilibrium concentration are known

• Interpret, quantitatively, titration curves of monoprotic and polyprotic acids and bases for strong acid-weak base and weak acid–strong base combinations and identify buffering regions.

PREREQUISITE SKILLS AND KNOWLEDGE

Prior to starting this unit, you should be able to…

- Understand concepts of concentration, solubility, saturation point, pressure, density, viscosity, flow rate, and temperature in terms of their effects on chemical reactions
- Understand reactions between strong acids and bases and weak acids and bases
- Describe the concepts of pH and pOH
- Explain the modified Arrhenius theory of acids and bases
- Understand the concepts underlying electrolytes, non-electrolytes, monoprotic acids/bases, polyprotic acids/bases, and indicators
- Solve non-linear equations by either algebraic or graphical means

Lesson 1 EQUILIBRIUM

Most of the reactions you have looked at in thermochemistry and electrochemistry have started out as reactants and ended up as products. Up until this point in chemistry, the common assumption has been that all reactions proceed to completion. This means that all reactants are completely used up in a reaction and completely converted to products as in **quantitative stoichiometric** reactions.

EQUILIBRIUM

Equilibrium is a balance point. It occurs in a closed system, which means that no matter enters or leaves; only energy does. It occurs at a constant temperature and pressure.

Equilibrium is reached under the following conditions:

• The rate of forward reaction is equal to the rate of reverse reaction.

• Concentrations remain constant; this does not necessarily mean equal concentrations of reactants and products.

• All measureable properties are constant, meaning there are no macroscopic changes; concentration, volumes, temperature, pressure, and colour remain constant.

The symbols $\leftrightarrow$, $\rightleftarrows$, and $\rightleftharpoons$ are all symbols for equilibrium.

TYPES OF EQUILIBRIUM

Equilibrium is **static** (fixed and unchanging) when two opposing forces are balanced. This is similar to a tug of war when no motion can occur.

Equilibrium is **dynamic** (constantly changing) when two opposing processes proceed at the same rate. This type of equilibrium takes time to establish.

Dynamic equilibrium is like a border crossing. For example, consider the populations of Canada and the United States. The populations of Canada and the United States stay constant because the large number of people crossing into Canada from the United States is equal to the large number of people making the opposite trip.

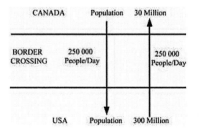

NOTES

Chemical reactions are examples of **dynamic equilibrium**. The opposing processes are the forward and reverse reactions. Assume that all chemical reactions do not go to completion but instead reach a state of equilibrium. Molecules continue to interact, but the rates of forward and reverse reactions are equal, and the end result appears constant.

Systems at equilibrium may have the following qualities:
- More reactants than products (the reaction favours reactants)
- More products than reactants (the reaction favours products)
- Equal quantities of both reactants and products

When systems of equilibrium proceed to such a large extent in one direction, the reverse is not considered. This type of reaction is known as **quantitative**. You can use this type of equilibrium in stoichiometric calculations.

APPROACHING EQUILIBRIUM FROM OPPOSITE DIRECTIONS

It can be demonstrated with two flasks, which end up with a mixture of $NO_{(g)}$, $O_{2(g)}$ and $NO_{2(g)}$, that the reaction will proceed in either a forward or a reverse direction until the rates of forward and reverse reactions are equal, and equilibrium is reached.

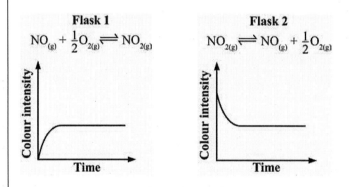

$NO_{(g)}$ and $O_{2(g)}$ are both colourless, whereas $NO_{2(g)}$ is brown.

Both reactions end up at the same point once they reach equilibrium, even though one flask started with both $NO_{(g)}$ and $O_{2(g)}$, and the other started with only $NO_{2(g)}$

EQUILIBRIUM EXPRESSION

Remember [ ] brackets represent molar concentration in mol/L

A general reaction has the following form:
$aA + bB \leftrightarrow cC + dD$

In this equation, A and B are reactants, and C and D are products. All lowercase letters are coefficients.

The equilibrium law expression, which is also referred to as the equilibrium expression, has the following form:

$$K_c = \frac{[\text{products}]}{[\text{reactants}]} \qquad K_c = \frac{[C]^c [D]^d}{[A]^a [B]^b}$$

In this equation, K_c is the equilibrium constant; therefore, units are not necessary. The equation also has the following qualities:

- [C] and [D] are the equilibrium molar concentrations of the products (mol/L).
- [A] and [B] are the equilibrium molar concentrations of the reactants (mol/L).
- Exponents are the coefficients of the balanced equation.

All substances are assumed to be present, or else the concentration would be zero. The K_c value may be very large or very small, but it can never be equal to zero.

The value of K_c depends on temperature, meaning a temperature change will change the value of K_c.

The value of K_c can be used to estimate whether reactants or products are favoured at equilibrium.

CLASSES OF CHEMICAL REACTIONS AT EQUILIBRIUM

The reaction is quantitative if K_c is very large ($K_c > 10$). In this case, the product concentration (numerator) is much larger than the reactant concentration (denominator). The percent reaction is greater than 99%.

The reaction favours the products if K_c is large ($K_c > 1.0$). In this case, the product concentration (numerator) is larger than the reactant concentration (denominator). The percent reaction is greater than 50%.

The reaction favours the reactants if K_c is small ($K_c < 1.0$). In this case, the reactant concentrations (denominator) are larger than the product concentrations (numerator). The percent reaction is less than 50%.

Neither the products nor reactants are favoured if $K_c = 1.0$ ($K_c = 1.0$). In this case, equilibrium contains 50% products. The percent reaction is equal to 50%.

General Rules for the Equilibrium Expression

1. Solids are omitted from the equilibrium expression because their concentrations are unchanging as a result of density (they cannot be significantly compressed).
2. Liquids are omitted from the equilibrium expression if there is only one (as in aqueous solutions).If there is more than one liquid present, the liquid can have its concentration changed by dilution. $H_2O_{(l)}$ is not included, since the dissolved substances do not change the concentration of the water.
3. If there is more than one liquid, include all the liquids in the equilibrium expression. Liquids must be miscible for their proportions to change.

NOTES

4. All other states are included.
5. A complete description of equilibrium state includes the temperature, composition, and concentration of all entities present. The concentration for gases is often expressed as pressure.

ICE TABLE

For many gas reactions, a spectrophotometer (an instrument that measures light intensity) can be used to find the concentrations of the gases involved. You can determine the concentrations at equilibrium of a reactant or product by using an ICE table and the reaction equation. ICE is the abbreviation for the following terms:

I   Initial concentration
C   Change in concentration
E   Equilibrium concentration

At relatively low pressure and high temperature, the reaction between hydrogen gas and iodine gas to form hydrogen iodide is often studied.
$H_{2(g)} + I_{2(g)} \leftrightarrow 2HI_{(g)}$

If small quantities of each gas are injected into a container (closed system), a spectrophotometer can be used to determine the final concentrations of the iodine gas. This allows the K_c for the reaction to be calculated.

When given chemical amounts to work with, consider the volume of the container, and convert the amounts to concentration (mol/L or mmol/L) before entering the data into the ICE table.

An ICE table for this reaction might look like this:

Building an ICE Table

1. Write a balanced chemical equation.

2. Write the equilibrium law expression for the balanced equation.

3. Substitute the concentrations (mol/L or mmol/L) for all reactants and products to calculate the value of K_c.

Concentration (mmol/L)	$[H_{2(g)}]$	$[I_{2(g)}]$	$[HI_{(g)}]$
Initial	5.30	3.52	19.04
Change			
Equilibrium		2.19	

The next step is to calculate the change in $[I_{2(g)}]$, which is also the change in $[H_{2(g)}]$, since $H_{2(g)}$ and $I_{2(g)}$ react in a 1:1 ratio.

The change is calculated as follows:
3.52 mmol/L – 2.19 mmol/L = 1.33 mmol/L

Therefore, the equilibrium $[H_{2(g)}]$ is 3.97 mmol/L.

Concentration (mmol/L)	$[H_{2(g)}]$	$[I_{2(g)}]$	$[HI_{(g)}]$
Initial	5.30	3.52	19.04
Change	**−1.33**	**−1.33**	
Equilibrium	**3.97**	2.19	

Since $H_{2(g)}$ and $I_{2(g)}$ react to form $2HI_{(g)}$ in a 1.00 L container, 1.33 mmol of $H_{2(g)}$ forms 2.66 mmol of $HI_{(g)}$. When added to the initial amount of $HI_{(g)}$, this results in a $HI_{(g)}$ concentration of 19.70 mmol/L at equilibrium.

Concentration (mmol/L)	$[H_{2(g)}]$	$[I_{2(g)}]$	$[HI_{(g)}]$
Initial	5.30	3.52	19.04
Change	−1.33	−1.33	**+2.66**
Equilibrium	3.97	2.19	**19.70**

The K_c can now be calculated by substituting the equilibrium concentrations of products and reactants into the equilibrium law expression for this reaction.

$$K_c = \frac{\left[HI_{(g)}\right]^2}{\left[H_{2(g)}\right]\left[I_{2(g)}\right]} = \frac{19.70^2}{(3.97)(2.19)} = 44.6$$

Remember that equilibrium expressions include only substances that have variable concentrations. This includes gases and substances that are in a dissolved state. This does not include solids or pure liquids because their concentrations do not change noticeably; a change of a few molecules out of billions will not really make much of a difference.

Also, remember the following points:
- K_c will change as the temperature of the system changes.
- K_c is not affected by catalysts.
- K_c is not affected by the rate of reaction; it does not matter if the system reaches equilibrium quickly or slowly. For example, a well-oiled pendulum will reach the same stable position at the bottom of its swing as a similar pendulum with a lot more friction. Only the time taken to reach that position is different.
- Because the units are not the same for all reactions, units are not usually included. The K_c unit for each reaction depends on the ratio of products to reactants.

The units for the reaction $2SO_{3(g)} \leftrightarrow 2SO_{2(g)} + O_{2(g)}$ are as shown:

$$\frac{\dfrac{(mol)^2}{(L)^2} \dfrac{(mol)}{(L)}}{\dfrac{(mol)^2}{(L)^2}} = \frac{mol}{L}$$

The units for the reverse reaction $2SO_{2(g)} + O_{2(g)} \leftrightarrow 2SO_{3(g)}$ are as shown:

$$\frac{\dfrac{(mol)^2}{(L)^2}}{\dfrac{(mol)^2}{(L)^2} \dfrac{(mol)}{(L)}} = \frac{L}{mol}$$

PRACTICE EXERCISES

Use the following information to answer the next question.

Equilibrium is a term that is applied to systems that do not appear to be changing with time. Both static and dynamic systems can achieve equilibrium, but the nature of equilibrium is different.

1. Explain the differences between static and dynamic systems at equilibrium, and describe an example of each.

2. At equilibrium, how do the rates of the forward and reverse reactions compare? How does this relate to the amount of products and reactants at any given time?

3. Define a closed system, and explain why it is necessary in achieving equilibrium.

4. Write the equation and equilibrium law expression that represents each of the following reactions:

   a) Nitrogen gas reacts with hydrogen gas to form ammonia gas.

   b) Combustion of methane gas

   c) Solid copper metal reacts with aqueous silver nitrate.

   d) Hydrogen chloride gas reacts with water to produce aqueous hydronium ions and aqueous chloride ions.

5. Interpret the following K_c values:

a) $K_c = 4.00$ favours _____

b) $K_c = 0.040$ favours _____

c) $K_c = 40$ favours _____

d) $K_c = 1.0$ favours _____

e) Rank reactions **a)** to **d)** from the one that most highly favours the reactants to the one that most highly favours the products.

_____ _____ _____ _____

Use the following information to answer the next question.

Aqueous solutions consist of a solvent (water) and a dissolved solute. However, there is a maximum amount of each solute that can be dissolved in water. This property is called the solubility limit. When this limit is reached and exceeded, the solution can still achieve a state of equilibrium between the solution and the undissolved solute. The following equation represents the dissolution of silver chloride:

$$AgCl_{(s)} \rightleftharpoons Ag^+_{(aq)} + Cl^-_{(aq)}$$

6. Describe what is happening in the given silver chloride reaction at equilibrium.

7. Write the balanced equation and the equilibrium law expression for the dissolution of solid silver nitrate in water.

8. Write the equilibrium law expression for both the forward and reverse reactions for the equation $H_{2(g)} + I_{2(g)} \rightleftharpoons 2HI_{(g)}$. Explain the relationship between the K_c for the forward reaction and the K_c for the reverse reaction.

Lesson 2   LE CHÂTELIER'S PRINCIPLE

When a closed system at equilibrium is exposed to a stress (or change), Le Châtelier's principle states that the equilibrium shifts to oppose and counteract that stress (or change). A stress can be anything that disturbs the reaction; for example, a change in temperature, pressure, or the concentration of one of the chemical species. The only stress that changes the numerical value of the K_c is the temperature.

The following factors affect the rate of reaction:
• Nature of reactants (the chemical properties)
• Concentration
• Temperature
• Pressure and volume (for gases)
• Catalyst

PRESSURE AND VOLUME

Pressure affects only gases. When volume of a fixed amount of gase decreases, the pressure increases. When volume increases, the pressure decreases. Le Châtelier's principle states that when you change the pressure of a closed system at equilibrium, the reaction will counteract the imposed pressure change by shifting to the side with more or fewer molecules of gas.. For example, if you decrease the pressure, the reaction will counteract the shift and increase the pressure because the opposing reaction will create more molecules. The reaction will shift to the side where there are more molecules of gas.

Example

The Haber–Bosch process produces ammonia from nitrogen and hydrogen gases. It is an important process for adding nitrates to fertilizers and was used in the manufacture of explosives during the Second World War. The following table illustrates the effects of manipulating certain stressors on this system at equilibrium.

Given the equilibrium $N_{2(g)} + 3H_{2(g)} \rightleftharpoons 2NH_{3(g)} + heat$, describe and graph the effect the following stresses will have on the concentration of $N_{2(g)}$ when imposed:
• The concentration of $N_{2(g)}$ is increased
• The temperature is decreased, the concentration of $NH_{3(g)}$ is decreased
• A catalyst is added, the pressure of the reaction vessel is increased
• The volume of the reaction vessel is decreased.

Solution

Stress	Reaction Response	Direction of Equilibrium Shift	Rate Change	Graph (• = Point at which stress is applied)
Increase $[N_{2(g)}]$	Decrease $[N_{2(g)}]$	→Right To produce more products	Forward reaction rate increases to get rid of reactants and make more products.	
Cool reaction (temperature decreased)	Increase temperature	→Right To produce more heat	Forward reaction rate increases.	
Decrease $[NH_{3(g)}]$ (i.e., remove ammonia as it is produced)	Increase $[NH_{3(g)}]$	→ Right To produce more ammonia	Forward reaction rate increases.	
Add catalyst	Does not change the position of equilibrium Will not affect the yield	No shift	Forward reaction rate and reverse reaction rate increase by the same amount. This increases the speed of a chemical reaction.	
Decrease pressure	Increase pressure	←Left Shifts to produce more molecules of gas in the same volume to increase the pressure. (Four moles of reactants and two moles of products)	Reverse reaction rate increases.	
Decrease the volume	Decreasing the volume increases the pressure. Reaction opposes stress and shifts to decrease the pressure.	→ Right Fewer molecules of gas in the same volume decreases the pressure. (Two moles of products and four moles of reactants)	Increases forward rate of reaction.	

PRACTICE EXERCISES

1. Use Le Châtelier's principle to describe and explain the shift in direction that occurs when the following changes are applied to the system at equilibrium. (Use left, right, or no change to describe the shift in each case.)

   a) Increased volume of $N_{2(g)} + O_{2(g)} \rightleftharpoons 2NO_{(g)}$

   b) Decreased volume of $CH_{4(g)} + H_2O_{(g)} \rightleftharpoons 3H_{2(g)} + CO_{(g)}$

   c) Inert gas added to $CO_{(g)} + H_2O_{(g)} \rightleftharpoons H_{2(g)} + CO_{2(g)}$ in a fixed-volume container

   d) Catalyst introduced to $CO_{(g)} + H_2O_{(g)} \rightleftharpoons H_{2(g)} + CO_{2(g)}$

   e) Reaction heated: $2NO_{2(g)} \rightleftharpoons N_2O_{4(g)} +$ heat

   f) Reaction is cooled: $H_2SO_{3(aq)} + H_2O_{(aq)} \rightleftharpoons HSO_3^-{}_{(aq)} + H_3O^+{}_{(aq)} +$ heat

   g) $NaOH_{(aq)}$ is added to $HA_{(aq)} + H_2O_{(l)} \rightleftharpoons A^-{}_{(aq)} + H_3O^+{}_{(aq)}$

   h) $HCl_{(aq)}$ is added to $A^-{}_{(aq)} + H_2O_{(l)} \rightleftharpoons HA_{(aq)} + OH^-{}_{(aq)}$

   i) NaSCN is added to $Fe^{3+}{}_{(aq)} + SCN^-{}_{(aq)} \rightleftharpoons FeSCN^{2+}{}_{(aq)}$

   j) $SO_{2(g)}$ is removed from $2SO_{2(g)} + O_{2(g)} \rightleftharpoons 2SO_{3(g)}$

2. What effect does the addition of a catalyst have on a system at equilibrium? Does the catalyst affect the equilibrium position? Explain your answer.

3. How does Le Châtelier's principle help scientists get the maximum amount of products from a reaction?

Use the following information to answer the next question.

Consider the following equilibrium system:
$$N_2O_{4(g)} + \text{ energy } \rightleftharpoons 2NO_{2(g)}$$
colourless   brown gas

gas

4. What direction will the equilibrium shift when each of the following changes are made to the system at equilibrium? Describe the colour of the system after each change takes place.

a) Add $NO_{2(g)}$

b) Remove $N_2O_{4(g)}$

c) Increase the pressure

d) Increase the volume

e) Decrease the temperature

f) Increase the temperature

Use the following information to answer the next question.

> Consider the following equilibrium system:
> $$NaClO_{(aq)} + HCl_{(aq)} \rightleftharpoons NaCl_{(aq)} + H_2O_{(l)} + Cl_{2(g)}$$

5. When the given system is cooled, gas bubbles are produced. Is this reaction endothermic or exothermic?

Use the following information to answer the next question.

> When the reaction represented by the equation $C_{(g)} + O_{2(g)} \rightleftharpoons CO_{2(g)}$ reaches equilibrium, the following equilibrium concentrations were measured:
> $$\left[C_{(g)}\right] = 0.50 \text{ mol/L}$$
> $$\left[O_{2(g)}\right] = 0.80 \text{ mol/L}$$
> $$\left[CO_{2(g)}\right] = 0.30 \text{ mol/L}$$

6. Determine the equilibrium constant for the given reaction.

Lesson 3   ACIDS, BASES, AND CONJUGATE PAIRS

DEFINITIONS OF ACIDS AND BASES

Brønsted–Lowry Acids and Bases

Brønsted and Lowry thought of acid and base behaviour in terms of proton transfers. When a hydrogen atom loses its only electron, it will consist of a single proton with a positive charge. Thus, an H_+ ion is the same as a proton. Because a proton is so small, its positive charge is concentrated in a very small volume.

Arrhenius's definition of an acid was revised to explain this proton and its attraction to the negative end of the polar water molecule or molecules that make up a very high percentage of any aqueous solution.

Brønsted and Lowry then made the following suggestions:

• An acid could be any entity that loses a proton to another entity in a solution.

• A base could be the entity that receives the proton in a reaction.

Chemists call acids, or the entity that loses a proton, the proton donor. It is assumed that the acid does not release free protons directly to the solution; rather that they are taken from them by the base.

The base pulls the proton away and is referred to as the proton acceptor. The following equation represents a Brønsted–Lowry reaction:

$$HF_{(aq)} + HCO_3^-{}_{(aq)} \rightleftharpoons H_2CO_{3(aq)} + F^-{}_{(aq)}$$

H^+ (proton) H^+ (proton)
transfer   transfer
                      (reverse reaction)

In the forward reaction, a proton is transferred from $HF_{(aq)}$ to $HCO_3^-{}_{(aq)}$. In the reverse reaction, a proton is transferred from the $H_2CO_{3(aq)}$ to $F^-{}_{(aq)}$. The acids in the reaction are $HF_{(aq)}$ and $H_2CO_{3(aq)}$; they donate the proton. The bases in the reaction are $HCO_3^-{}_{(aq)}$ and $F^-{}_{(aq)}$; they accept the proton. $HF_{(aq)}$ is a stronger acid than $H_2CO_{3(aq)}$ because it is higher up on the relative strengths of acids and bases chart. As you can see on the table, the K_a of $HF_{(aq)}$ (6.3×10^{-4}) is greater than the K_a of $H_2CO_{3(aq)}$ (4.5×10^{-7}).. In this reaction, the products are favoured because in a Brønsted–Lowry reaction, the side of the equilibrium that has the weaker acid is favoured.

Strong acids lose H^+ ions easily because the bond with the H^+ is weaker. Weak acids do not lose their H^+ ions as easily because the bond with the H^+ is stronger. In a weak acid, a much smaller number of H^+ ions are in the solution and available to react.

Amphiprotic (or **amphoteric**) substances can act as acids in some reactions and as bases in others. They can either accept or donate protons.

An H^+ ion is a proton.

Examples of amphiprotic species include $H_2O_{(l)}$, $HCO_3^-{}_{(aq)}$, $HOOCCOO^-{}_{(aq)}$, and $H_2PO_4^-{}_{(aq)}$.

The following two Brønsted–Lowry reactions show how the amphiprotic species $HSO_3^-{}_{(aq)}$ can act as either an acid or a base, depending on the reaction.

$$HSO_3^-{}_{(aq)} + NH_{3(aq)} \rightleftharpoons NH_4^+{}_{(aq)} + SO_3^{2-}{}_{(aq)}$$
Acid

H^+ transfer

$$HSO_3^-{}_{(aq)} + H_2CO_{3(aq)} \rightleftharpoons H_2SO_{3(aq)} + HCO_3^-{}_{(aq)}$$
Base

H^+ transfer

A **polyprotic acid** is an acid with more than one proton to donate. For example, $H_2CO_{3(aq)}$ can donate two protons, and $H_3PO_{4(aq)}$ can donate three protons.

A **polybasic base** is a base that can accept more than one proton. For example, $PO_4^{3-}{}_{(aq)}$ can accept three protons, and $SO_4^{2-}{}_{(aq)}$ can accept two protons.

REVIEW OF pH AND pOH

You should be able to determine whether a solution is acidic, basic, or neutral from the names or formulas given, from the effect of the solution on litmus or other pH paper, or from the reading of a pH meter. The following equations are needed for calculations involving $[H^+{}_{(aq)}]$, $[OH^-{}_{(aq)}]$, pH, or pOH. The term $[H_3O^+]$ can be used in place of the term $[H^+]$ in these equations.

- $pH = -\log [H^+{}_{(aq)}]$
- $pOH = -\log [OH^-{}_{(aq)}]$
- $[H^+{}_{(aq)}] = 10^{-pH}$
- $[OH^-{}_{(aq)}] = 10^{-pOH}$
- $pH + pOH = 14.00$ at SATP

An acid is a substance that donates protons.

A base is a substance that accepts protons.

An amphiprotic substance can donate or accept protons.

NOTES

CONJUGATING ACID-BASE PAIRS

According to the Brønsted–Lowry theory, an acid donates a proton, and a base accepts a proton. If you consult your acid-base table, you can see that the loss of one hydrogen ion (a proton) is the only difference between an acid and the base listed next to it.

These two entities—the acid and the conjugate base—differ by one proton, $H^+_{(aq)}$, and are known as a conjugate acid–base pair.

Example

$$HCl_{(aq)} \quad + \quad H_2O_{(l)} \quad \leftrightarrow \quad Cl^-_{(aq)} \quad + \quad H_3O^+_{(aq)}$$

| Acid | Base | Conjugate base of HCL | Conjugate acid of H_2O |

From this equation, two conjugate acid–base pairs result. The following acid-base pair results from the forward reaction:

$HCl_{(aq)}/Cl^-_{(aq)}$
acid–conjugate base

For the reverse reaction, the following acid-base pair results:

$H_3O^+_{(aq)}/H_2O_{(l)}$
conjugate acid–base

A stronger acid will have a weaker conjugate base. A strong acid, such as HCl, loses its proton very easily. Its conjugate base, the Cl^- ion, is not very attractive to that proton.

A weaker acid will have a stronger conjugate base for the opposite reason. A weak acid does not donate protons very readily because the conjugate base has a relatively strong attraction for the proton.

PRACTICE EXERCISES

1. Explain how the Brønsted–Lowry theory classifies species as acids or bases. Is it possible to classify a species as an acid or a base without knowing the specific reaction that occurs?

2. Is it possible to measure the pH of every reaction in which protons are being transferred? Explain your answer.

3. Write the equation that represents the ionization of $HNO_{3(aq)}$. Use the Brønsted–Lowry theory to identify the acid, base, and proton transfer.

4. Write the equation that represents the Brønsted–Lowry reaction between ammonia and hypochlorous acid. Use the Brønsted–Lowry theory to identify the acid, base, and proton transfer in the forward reaction.

5. Write the equation that represents the Brønsted–Lowry reaction of sodium carbonate with hydrocyanic acid and the equation that represents the reaction of sodium hydrogen carbonate with hydrocyanic acid. What is the relationship between the carbonate ion and the hydrogen carbonate ion?

Use the following information to answer the next question.

> The hydrogen sulfate ion, the hydrogen phosphate ion, and the hydrogen sulfite ion are all considered to be amphiprotic species according to the Brønsted–Lowry theory.

6. For each of the given amphiprotic acids, list its conjugate acid and its conjugate base. Is the conjugate acid of each of these amphiprotic species a polyprotic or monoprotic acid?

Use the following information to answer the next question.

> An ammonium ion reacts with a sulfite ion to form a hydrogen sulfite ion and ammonia.

7. a) Write the equation that represents the given reaction. Identify the Brønsted–Lowry acids and the Brønsted–Lowry bases in the reaction, and identify all conjugate acid–base pairs.

b) Identify the species present in the reaction that are amphiprotic.

8. Identify the Brønsted–Lowry acids, the Brønsted–Lowry bases, and the conjugate acid–base pairs in the reaction represented by the following equation:

$$HCO_3^-{}_{(aq)} + HF_{(aq)} \rightleftharpoons H_2CO_{3(aq)} + F^-{}_{(aq)}$$

Lesson 4 SPECIAL EQUILIBRIUM CONSTANTS (K_w, K_a, K_b)

WATER EQUILIBRIUM (K_W)

Fewer than two in every billion molecules of water dissociate.

The water dissociation equation is shown in the following equation:
$$H_2O_{(l)} \rightleftharpoons H^+_{(aq)} + OH^-_{(aq)}$$

K_w is the equilibrium, or dissociation, constant for water.

The equilibrium expression is as follows:

$$K_a = \frac{\left[H^+_{(aq)}\right] \times \left[OH^-_{(aq)}\right]}{\left[H_2O_{(l)}\right]} = \left[H^+_{(aq)}\right]\left[OH^-_{(aq)}\right]$$

Water is omitted because it is the only liquid. Its concentration does not really change.

$$K_w = \left[H^+_{(aq)}\right] \times \left[OH^-_{(aq)}\right]$$

This water dissociation equation can also be written as follows:
$$H_2O_{(l)} + H_2O_{(l)} \rightleftharpoons H_3O^+_{(aq)} + OH^-_{(aq)}$$

The equilibrium expression can be established as follows:

$$K_a = \frac{\left[H_3O^+_{(aq)}\right] \times \left[OH^-_{(aq)}\right]}{\left[H_2O_{(l)}\right] \times \left[H_2O_{(l)}\right]} = \left[H_3O^+_{(aq)}\right]\left[OH^-_{(aq)}\right]$$

Omit water as the only liquid.

$$K_w = \left[H_3O^+_{(aq)}\right] \times \left[OH^-_{(aq)}\right]$$

The following statements are true at SATP:

- In all aqueous solutions, $K_w = \left[H_3O^+_{(aq)}\right] \times \left[OH^-_{(aq)}\right] = 1.00 \times 10^{-14}$.

- In a neutral solution, $\left[H_3O^+_{(aq)}\right] = \left[OH^-_{(aq)}\right] = 1.00 \times 10^{-7}$ mol/L.

- In an acid, $\left[H_3O^+_{(aq)}\right] > 10^{-7}$ mol/L, and $\left[OH^-_{(aq)}\right] < 10^{-7}$ mol/L.

- In a base, $\left[H_3O^+_{(aq)}\right] < 10^{-7}$ mol/L, and $\left[OH^-_{(aq)}\right] > 10^{-7}$ mol/L.

As long as there is water present (any aqueous solution), the K_w applies. No matter how strongly acidic or basic a solution is, there will always be some of each type of ion, $H_3O^+_{(aq)}$ and $OH^-_{(aq)}$.

CONCENTRATION VERSUS STRENGTH OF ACIDS

Concentration refers to the number of moles dissolved per litre of solution. The more moles dissolved per litre, the more concentrated the solution is. The fewer moles dissolved per litre, the more dilute the solution is.

Strength is the extent to which an acid ionizes.

NOTES

Strong Acids

Strong acids ionize completely in a quantitative reaction and have a very large K_a.

There are six strong acids listed in the acid-base table:
- Hydrobromic acid (HBr)
- Hydrochloric acid (HCl)
- Hydroiodic acid (HI)
- Nitric acid (HNO_3)
- Perchloric acid ($HClO_4$)
- Sulfuric acid (H_2SO_4)

The general ionization expression for a strong acid is as follows:

$$HA_{(aq)} \xrightarrow{>99\%} H^+_{(aq)} + A^-_{(aq)}$$

Strong acids yield almost 100% products. Because of this, the concentration of hydrogen ions in a strong acid is equal to the acid concentration.

$[H+_{(aq)}] = [HA_{(aq)}]$ (where A is the acid anion)

For example, if you start with 100 molecules of hydrochloric acid and they all ionize, 100 hydrogen ions and 100 chloride ions will be formed.

$$HCl_{(aq)} \xrightarrow{>99\%} H^+_{(aq)} + Cl^-_{(aq)}$$

100 molecules   100 molecules   100 molecules

The only exception to this rule is sulfuric acid. For example, if you start with 100 molecules of sulfuric acid and they all ionize, 100 hydrogen ions and 100 hydrogen sulfate ions will be formed. In H_2O, H_2SO_4 will lose its first H^+ completely, but the second H^+ transfer will not be complete. Sulfuric acid is a strong acid but hydrogen sulfate is not. In a reaction with a strong base, the second H^+ will also be completely donated.

$$H_2SO_{4(aq)} \xrightarrow{>99\%} H^+_{(aq)} + HSO_4{}^-_{(aq)}$$

100 molecules   100 molecules   100 molecules

Weak Acids

Weak acids only partially ionize (less than 99%). They also have small K_a values ($K_a < 1$).

$$HA_{(aq)} \rightleftharpoons H^+_{(aq)} + A^-_{(aq)}$$

For example, if you start with 100 molecules of acetic acid and it ionizes 1.3%, approximately one acetate ion and one hydrogen ion will be produced.

$$CH_3COOH_{(aq)} \rightleftharpoons H^+_{(aq)} + CH_3COO^-_{(aq)}$$

100 molecules   1 molecule   1 molecule

ACID IONIZATION

To calculate the equilibrium constant, you must compare the concentration of the products with the concentration of the reactants.

$$K_c = \frac{[\text{products}]}{[\text{reactants}]} \qquad K_c = \frac{[C]^c [D]^d}{[A]^a [B]^b}$$

Acids react with water to produce positive hydrogen ions, $H^+_{(aq)}$ or $H_3O^+_{(aq)}$, and a variety of acid anions.

The equilibrium constant, K_c, is written as K_a when it is describing the ionization of an acid.

Acid ionization can be expressed two ways:

1. $HA_{(aq)} + H_2O_{(l)} \rightleftharpoons H_3O^+_{(aq)} + A^-_{(aq)}$

The equilibrium constant for this expression is as follows:

$$K_a = \frac{\left[H_3O^+_{(aq)}\right] \times \left[A^-_{(aq)}\right]}{\left[HA_{(aq)}\right]}$$

Omit $H_2O_{(l)}$, as the concentration of water does not change.

2. $HA_{(aq)} \rightleftharpoons H^+_{(aq)} + A^-_{(aq)}$ (where A^- is any acid anion)

The equilibrium constant for this expression is as follows:

$$K_a = \frac{\left[H^+_{(aq)}\right] \times \left[A^-_{(aq)}\right]}{\left[HA_{(aq)}\right]}$$

The strength of an acid depends on the amount of hydrogen ions present (the degree of ionization).

K_a VALUES

The larger the K_a, the stronger the acid. Usually, K_a values are used to find the concentration of hydrogen ions in a weak acid.

- Strong acids ionize completely (quantitative reaction).
  $[H^+_{(aq)}] = [HA_{(aq)}]$

- Weak acids do not ionize completely; equilibrium is established with less than 99% of the reactants forming products.

CALCULATING THE PH OF WEAK ACIDS

The calculation of the pH of a weak acid involves the use of the appropriate equilibrium constant and some simple algebra. When the weak acid $CH_3COOH_{(aq)}$ ionizes, a small amount of $CH_3COOH_{(aq)}$ reacts to produce $H_3O^+_{(aq)}$ and $CH_3COO^-_{(aq)}$, as represented by the following equation:

$$CH_3COOH_{(aq)} + H_2O_{(l)} \rightleftharpoons H_3O^+_{(aq)} + CH_3COO^-_{(aq)} \quad K_a = 1.8 \times 10^{-5}$$

If the initial concentration of $CH_3COOH_{(aq)}$ is 0.50 mol/L, then the concentration of each species at equilibrium can be expressed in the following ICE table, where x represents the amount that ionizes.

Concentration (mol/L)	$CH_3COOH_{(aq)}$	$H_3O^+_{(aq)}$	$CH_3COO^-_{(aq)}$
Initial	0.50	0	0
Change	$-x$	$+x$	$+x$
Equilibrium	$0.50 - x$	x	x

You can determine the pH of the 0.50 mol/L $CH_3COOH_{(aq)}$ solution by substituting into the equilibrium constant.

$$K_a = \frac{\left[H_3O^+_{(aq)}\right] \times \left[CH_3COO^-_{(aq)}\right]}{\left[CH_3COOH_{(aq)}\right]} \quad \text{where} \quad \left[H_3O^+_{(aq)}\right] = \left[CH_3COO^-_{(aq)}\right]$$

$$K_a = \frac{x^2}{(0.50 - x)} \quad K_a = 1.8 \times 10^{-5} \; \therefore$$

$$1.8 \times 10^{-5} \approx \frac{x^2}{(0.50)} \quad (\text{approximation})$$

$$x = \sqrt{(1.8 \times 10^{-5})(0.50)}$$

$$= 0.0030 \text{ mol/L}$$

$$pH = -\log\left(H_3O^+_{(aq)}\right)$$

$$\therefore pH = -\log(0.0030 \text{ mol/L}) = 2.52$$

The amount that ionizes is generally not significant compared to the initial concentration of acid. Therefore, an approximation can usually be used instead of using the quadratic equation to solve for x. A general rule of thumb to use is if $\dfrac{[HA]}{K_a} > 1\,000$, then the approximation method can be used.

Example

Write the reaction representing the ionization of lactic acid ($C_2H_5OCOOH_{(aq)}$), and determine the pH of a 50.0 mL sample of 0.50 mol/L lactic acid.

Solution

Lactic acid is a weak acid; therefore, the ionization of lactic acid can be represented by the following equation:

$$C_2H_5OCOOH_{(aq)} + H_2O_{(l)} \rightleftarrows C_2H_5OCOO^-_{(aq)} + H_3O^+_{(aq)}$$

$$K_a = \frac{\left[C_2H_5OCOO^-_{(aq)}\right] \times \left[H_3O^+_{(aq)}\right]}{\left[C_2H_5OCOOH_{(aq)}\right]} \text{ where}$$

$$\left[C_2H_5OCOO^-_{(aq)}\right] = \left[H_3O^+_{(aq)}\right]$$

If $x = \left[H_3O^+_{(aq)}\right]$, the equilibrium equation can be simplified by using the following assumption.

$$K_a = 1.4 \times 10^{-4} \approx \frac{x^2}{(0.50 \text{ mol/L})} \qquad \left(\begin{array}{l} \frac{[0.50 \text{ mol/L}]}{1.4 \times 10^{-4}} \text{ is} > 1\,000 \\ \text{Therefore, the approximation} \\ \text{method can be used.} \end{array} \right)$$

$$x = \sqrt{(1.4 \times 10^{-4})(0.50 \text{ mol/L})}$$

$$= 0.008\,37 \text{ mol/L}$$

$$pH = -\log\left(H_3O^+_{(aq)}\right)$$

$$\therefore pH = -\log(0.008\,37 \text{ mol/L})$$

$$= 2.08 \text{ (reduced to two significant digits)}$$

The pH of a 0.50 mol/L solution of lactic acid is 2.08.

STRONG BASES

When an ionic compound that contains a metal ion and a hydroxide ion is dissolved in water, it becomes a **strong base**. Strong bases dissociate completely (quantitative reaction).

$$KOH_{(aq)} \xrightarrow{>99\%} K^+_{(aq)} + OH^-_{(aq)}$$

100 molecules 100 molecules 100 molecules

Barium hydroxide is a strong base. When it dissociates, it releases two hydroxide ions for every $Ba(OH)_2$.

$$Ba(OH)_{2(aq)} \xrightarrow{>99\%} Ba^{2+}_{(aq)} + 2OH^-_{(aq)}$$

100 molecules 100 molecules 200 molecules

WEAK BASES

Weak bases dissociate only partially in water (less than 99%). A weak base is a substance that reacts with water to produce hydroxide ions.

For example, if there are initially 100 molecules of ammonia, a weak base, only a few molecules of hydroxide are formed when it dissociates.

$$NH_{3(aq)} + H_2O_{(l)} \rightleftharpoons OH^-_{(aq)} + NH_4^+{}_{(aq)}$$

If even just a few molecules form hydroxide, it becomes a basic solution.

BASE DISSOCIATION

For a dissociating base that occurs as a singly charged anion, use the following equation:

$$A^-{}_{(aq)} + H_2O_{(l)} \rightleftharpoons HA_{(aq)} + OH^-_{(aq)}$$

Where $A^-{}_{(aq)}$ is the base, the equilibrium expression is as follows:

$$K_b = \frac{\left[HA_{(aq)}\right]\left[OH^-_{(aq)}\right]}{\left[A^-{}_{(aq)}\right]}$$

K_b is the dissociation constant for a base.

Again, $H_2O_{(l)}$ is ignored since its concentration does not change.

CALCULATING THE pH OF A WEAK BASE

The calculation of the pH of a weak base is done in the same manner as that for a weak acid. It involves the use of the appropriate equilibrium constant and some simple algebra. When a 1.00 mol/L solution of $CH_3NH_{2(aq)}$ (a weak base) dissociates, a small amount reacts to produce

$OH^-{}_{(aq)}$ and $CH_3NH_3^+{}_{(aq)}$, as represented by the following equation:

$$CH_3NH_{2(aq)} + H_2O_{(l)} \rightleftharpoons CH_3NH_3^+{}_{(aq)} + OH^-_{(aq)}$$

The K_b for $CH_3NH_{2(aq)}$ is 4.6×10^{-4}.

The pH (or pOH) of the solution can be calculated using the same method used for weak acids.

Concentration (mol/L)	$CH_3NH_{2(aq)}$	$CH_3NH_3^+{}_{(aq)}$	$OH^-_{(aq)}$
Initial	1.00	0	0
Change	$-x$	$+x$	$+x$
Equilibrium	$1.00 - x$	x	x

$$K_b = \frac{\left[CH_3NH_3^+{}_{(aq)}\right] \times \left[OH^-_{(aq)}\right]}{\left[CH_3NH_{2(aq)}\right]}$$

$$\left(\begin{array}{l} \frac{\left[1.00 \text{ mol/L}\right]}{4.6 \times 10^{-4}} > 1\,000 \\ \text{Therefore, the approximation} \\ \text{method can be used.} \end{array} \right)$$

$$4.6 \times 10^{-4} \doteq \frac{x^2}{(1.00 \text{ mol/L})}$$

$$x = \sqrt{(4.6 \times 10^{-4}) \times (1.00 \text{ mol/L})}$$

$$x = 0.021 \text{ mol/L}$$

$$\therefore \left[OH^-_{(aq)}\right] = 0.021 \text{ mol/L}$$

Recall that pH + pOH = 14.00. Therefore, pH = 14.00–pOH.

$$pOH = -\log(0.021 \text{ mol/L})$$
$$= 1.68$$
$$pH = 14.00 - 1.68$$
$$= 12.32$$

The pH of a 1.00 mol/L $CH_3NH_{2(aq)}$ solution is 11.32.

THE RELATIONSHIP BETWEEN K_A AND K_B

K_a values can be used to find K_b values. The acid–conjugate base chart in the data book only lists the K_a values, but you can still use the chart to find the K_b.

*Since $K_a = \dfrac{\left[H_3O^+_{(aq)}\right]\left[A^-_{(aq)}\right]}{\left[HA_{(aq)}\right]}$ and $K_b = \dfrac{\left[HA_{(aq)}\right]\left[OH^-_{(aq)}\right]}{\left[A^-_{(aq)}\right]}$,

then $K_a \times K_b = \dfrac{\left[H_3O^+_{(aq)}\right]\left[A^-_{(aq)}\right]}{\left[HA_{(aq)}\right]} \times \dfrac{\left[HA_{(aq)}\right]\left[OH^-_{(aq)}\right]}{\left[A^-_{(aq)}\right]}$.

Reduce mathematically.

$$K_a \times K_b = \left[H_3O^+_{(aq)}\right] \times \left[OH^-_{(aq)}\right]$$

Since $\left[H_3O^+_{(aq)}\right] \times \left[OH^-_{(aq)}\right]$ also equals K_w, $K_a \times K_b = K_w$.

This means that you can find the K_b from the table by rearranging the formula as follows:

$$K_{b \text{ (base)}} = \frac{K_w}{K_{a \text{ (conjugate acid)}}}$$

$$K_a \times K_b = K_w$$

$$K_b = \frac{K_w}{K_a}$$

Example

Using the values for the weak acid NH_4^+, determine the K_b for its conjugate base, NH_3.

Solution

Since $K_a = \dfrac{\left[H_3O^+\right]\left[NH_3\right]}{\left[NH_4^+\right]}$ and $K_b = \dfrac{\left[NH_4^+\right]\left[OH^-\right]}{\left[NH_3\right]}$,

then $K_a \times K_b = \dfrac{\left[H_3O^+\right]\left[NH_3\right]}{\left[NH_4^+\right]} \times \dfrac{\left[NH_4^+\right]\left[OH^-\right]}{\left[NH_3\right]}$.

When reduced mathematically, $K_a \times K_b$ becomes $\left[H_3O^+ \right] \times \left[OH^- \right]$.

Since this equals K_w, the K_b for the reaction of ammonia with water to form a base is the K_w divided by the K_a for the reaction of ammonium ions to form an acid in water:

$$K_{b\,(NH_3)} = \frac{K_w}{K_{a\,(NH_4^+)}} = \frac{1.00 \times 10^{-14}}{5.6 \times 10^{-10}} = 1.8 \times 10^{-5}$$

PREDICTING ACID-BASE EQUILIBRIUM EQUATIONS

Use the following steps to predict acid-base equilibriums equations:

1. Identify all the species that are present in the solution: molecules, ions, and atoms.
2. Assume that ionic compounds and bases dissociate into ions in the solution; for example, $Mg(OH)_{2(aq)}$ can be written to show that $Mg^{2+}_{\,(aq)}$ and $OH^-_{\,(aq)}$ are present.
3. Weak acids are written as complete molecules because they do not ionize very much. Assume that the majority of the acid molecules have not separated into $H^+_{\,(aq)}$ and the conjugate base; for example, $H_2CO_{3(aq)}$ is written as $H_2CO_{3(aq)}$ rather than as $H^+_{\,(aq)}$ and $HCO_3^-_{\,(aq)}$.
4. Strong acids ionize more than 99% to form $H_3O^+_{\,(aq)}$ and an anion. (Make sure you do this automatically for all strong acids). For example, $H_2SO_{4(aq)}$ is written as $H_3O^+_{\,(aq)}$ and $HSO_4^-_{\,(aq)}$, which shows that just the first proton transferred from H_2SO_4. Another example is $HBr_{(aq)}$, which is written as $H_3O^+_{\,(aq)}$ and $Br^-_{\,(aq)}$.
5. Label each species as an acid, a base, or a spectator ion. Suggestions:

   • Write "A" above any species that can act as an acid according to the acid-base data table.

   • Write "B" below any species that can act as a base according to the acid-base data table. Include both labels for those amphiprotic substances (for example, $H_2O_{(l)}$) that appear on both sides of the table.

Ignore all other species that cannot be identified as either an acid, a base, or both. These are merely spectators and do not need to be considered in the reaction.

For example, $H_2CO_{3(aq)}$ reacts with $NaCN_{(aq)}$.

A   A
H_2CO_3 ~~Na^+~~ CN^- H_2O
                        B   B

In this reaction, Na^+ is a spectator ion and is ignored.

From the acid-base data table, identify the strongest acid and the strongest base present.

SA   A
H_2CO_3 ~~Na^+~~ CN^- H_2O
                       SB   B

6. Write the reaction that shows proton transfer from the strongest acid present to the strongest base present.

$$H_2CO_{3(aq)} + CN^-_{(aq)} \rightleftharpoons HCO_3^-{}_{(aq)} + HCN_{(aq)}$$

7. Include the extent of the reaction above the equilibrium arrow, if known. There are four possibilities:

- More than 50% of the possible products are formed.

- Less than 50% of the possible products are formed.

- More than 99% of the possible products are formed (this is usually written as a single forward arrow, $\Rightarrow$, which indicates that there is practically no reverse reaction when it reaches equilibrium). This is generally the case when a strong acid reacts with a strong base.

Reaction Spontaneity Rule

Use the reaction spontaneity rule to decide whether a reaction will proceed at more than or less than 50% in the forward direction.

$H_2O_{(l)}$ is amphiprotic.

Acid

Base   Reaction yields more than 50% products (favours products).

Base

Acid   Reaction yields less than 50% products (favours reactants).

Therefore, because H_2CO_3 is above the CN^- on the acid–base table, the prediction is as follows:

$$H_2CO_{3(aq)} + CN^-_{(aq)} \xrightarrow{>50\%} HCO_3^-{}_{(aq)} + HCN_{(aq)}$$

Quantitative reactions are reactions that go to completion. They are marked by an endpoint or sharp increase on the pH curve or a dramatic colour change.

Titrations give a sharp endpoint under the following conditions:
- A strong acid reacts with a strong base.
- A strong acid reacts with a weak base.
- A strong base reacts with a weak acid.

PRACTICE EXERCISES

1. Write the net equation that represents each of the following reactions, and identify whether products or reactants are favoured.

   a) Aqueous sodium bicarbonate and aqueous ammonium chloride are mixed.

   b) Aqueous potassium hydrogen sulfate and aqueous sodium acetate are mixed.

   c) Hypochlorous acid and aqueous sodium bicarbonate are mixed. Is the acid completely neutralized? Explain

   d) Hydrochloric acid is titrated with aqueous sodium hydroxide.

   e) Aqueous calcium carbonate that is dissolved in some Alberta lakes reacts to neutralize acid pollution in the lake. (Assume the polluting acid is sulfuric acid.)

   f) During a volcano demonstration, baking soda ($NaHCO_{3(s)}$) reacts with vinegar to produce a gas. Is baking soda capable of completely neutralizing vinegar?

2. Write the chemical equation and the K_a expression for the ionization of acetic acid.

3. Given the following chemical equation, write an equilibrium expression, and explain what it represents in terms of acid-base chemistry:

$$ClO^-_{(aq)} + H_2O_{(l)} \rightleftharpoons OH^-_{(aq)} + HClO_{(aq)}$$

4. If $K_w = \left[H_3O^+_{(aq)}\right]\left[OH^-_{(aq)}\right]$, show that $K_w = K_a K_b$ for one conjugate acid–base pair.

Use the following information to answer the next question.

The acid 2,4,6-trichlorophenol ($HOC_6H_2Cl_{3(aq)}$) is a common hospital disinfectant and a weak acid.

5. **a)** Write an appropriate equation to describe the ionization of 2,4,6-trichlorophenol.

   b) A 0.10 mol/L aqueous solution of 2,4,6-trichlorophenol has a pH of 3.55. Calculate the value of the acid ionization constant, K_a, of this weak acid.

c) Use the K_a to calculate the value of the base ionization constant, K_b, for the conjugate base of 2,4,6-trichlorophenol, $OC_6H_2Cl_3^-{}_{(aq)}$.

d) Write the appropriate ionization equation and the equilibrium constant expression for the conjugate base of 2,4,6-trichlorophenol.

6. Compare the pH of a 0.50 mol/L $H_2SO_4{}_{(aq)}$ solution with the pH of a 0.50 mol/L $H_2SO_3{}_{(aq)}$ solution. Which solution contains the higher concentration of $H_3O^+{}_{(aq)}$ ions? Explain your answer.

7. a) Determine the K_b for the conjugate base of $H_2CO_3{}_{(aq)}$.

b) Determine the pH of 0.10 mol/L solution of $HCO_3^-{}_{(aq)}$.

Lesson 5   *TITRATION*

TITRATION CURVES

Titration is a laboratory procedure by which the concentrations of acidic or basic solutions can be examined and determined. In the case of a strong acidic solution, a carefully measured amount of a strong basic solution of known concentration is added until the solution is neutralized. More complicated types of titration involve using strong bases to titrate weak acids and strong acids to titrate weak bases. In these cases and in cases involving polyprotic acids and bases, the endpoint may not be a pH of 7, or neutralization. Using a balanced chemical equation and the ratio of moles involved in the reaction, the number of moles and the concentration of the sample solution being titrated can be determined. Titration is therefore a volumetric analysis of solutions.

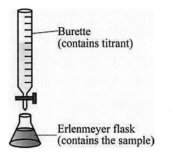

Burette
(contains titrant)

Erlenmeyer flask
(contains the sample)

Recall the following information about titrations:

• The sample is in the flask below the burette.

• The burette contains the titrant.

• The titrant is added to the sample; for example, when NaOH is titrated with HCl, this means that HCl from the burette is added to the NaOH sample in the flask.

TITRATION CURVES (pH CURVES)

Graphs that show changes in pH as the titrant is added to the sample depict the pH curve of the titration. The curve is drawn with the amount of titrant added as the *x*-axis and the pH as the *y*-axis. The midpoint of a nearly vertical portion of the line is known as the equivalence point. The number of equivalence points in a pH graph indicate the molar ratio between the acid and the base involved in the titration. There will be one equivalence point for each complete proton transfer that occurs.

The following terms are important to remember when assessing the information from an acid-base titration experiment:

• Buffering region

• Endpoint

• Equivalence point

• Titrant

• Excess acid

• Excess base

NOTES

Example

Sketch the titration curve of HNO_3 (a strong acid) titrated with NaOH (a strong base).

Solution

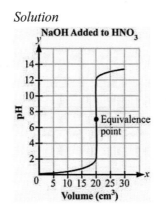

At the equivalence point, the number of moles of acid titrant added is enough to completely react with the number of moles of base available in the sample in a 1:1 ratio.

Example

Sketch the titration curve of NaOH (a strong base) titrated with HNO_3 (a strong acid).

Solution

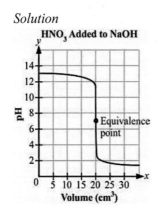

At the equivalence point, the number of moles of base titrant added is enough to completely react with the number of moles of acid available in the sample in a 1:1 ratio. The following formula equation represents this titration:

$$NaOH_{(aq)} + HNO_{3(aq)} \rightarrow H_2O_{(l)} + NaNO_{3(aq)}$$

The net ionic equation for this titration is

$$OH^-_{(aq)} + H_3O^+_{(aq)} \rightarrow H_2O_{(l)}$$

The pH is greater than 7 at the equivalence point for the titration of a weak acid with a strong base.

Example

Sketch the titration curve of CH_3COOH (a weak acid) titrated with NaOH (a strong base).

Solution

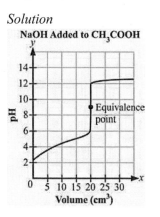

Unlike strong acid–strong base curves, the equivalence point in this titration is at a pH higher than 7. The CH_3COOH has reacted with NaOH, but some of the CH_3COO^- that is produced has reacted with the H_2O molecules to form OH^- ions. Because the CH_3COOH is a weak acid, it does not give up the H^+ very easily. It needs to be surrounded by more OH^- (a basic solution) before the H^+ is finally transferred.

The pH might be at 8 or 9 when the equivalence point is reached. The following net equation represents this titration:

$$CH_3COOH_{(aq)} + NaOH_{(aq)} \rightleftharpoons H_2O_{(l)} + NaCH_3COO_{(aq)}$$

Example

Sketch the titration curve that represents ammonia (NH_3, a weak base) titrated with nitric acid (HNO_3, a strong acid).

Solution

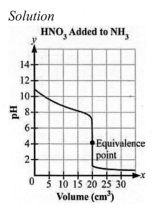

The pH is equal to 7 at the equivalence point for the titration of a strong acid with a strong base.

In this titration, NH_3 has reacted with HNO_3, but some of the NH_4^+ that is produced has reacted with the H_2O molecules to form H_3O^+ ions. This makes the solution more acidic. The pH might be at 5 or 6 when the equivalence point is reached.

NH$_3$ would not be recognized as a base by Arrhenius because it does not contain OH⁻. However, it is recognized as a base by the Brønsted–Lowry theory because it accepts a proton from the HCl.

Titration curves of acids depend on the K_a (because of the different strengths of the acids). This means the pH at the endpoint will depend on the acid concentration.

The pH is less than 7 at the equivalence point for a titration of a weak base with a strong acid.

Example

Compare the pH at the equivalence points of strong and weak acids.

Solution

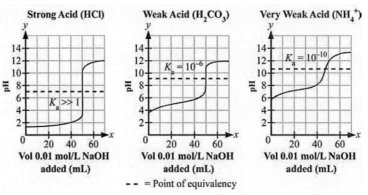

= Point of equivalency

The same number of moles of titrant are needed to reach the equivalence point, but the pH is different at that equivalence point. Because a strong acid and a strong base react to form water and a neutral salt, the pH at the equivalence point of a strong acid-strong base titration is always 7.

SELECTING INDICATORS FROM TITRATION CURVE DATA

To select an indicator from titration curve data, use the following steps:
1. Look at the curve, and decide on the equivalence point (find the midpoint of the nearly vertical section of a titration curve).
2. From the indicator list in the data tables, select an indicator that changes colour (it has a visible endpoint) at a pH close to the actual equivalence point. Think about the colour change that you expect—will it be a quick, obvious change, or will it be gradual? Some changes are much easier to see than others. Instead of using an indicator, you could also use a pH meter to signal when the equivalence point is reached.

Example

Sketch the titration curve of a polyprotic base, Na_2CO_3, titrated with a strong acid, HCl. Use 25 mL of 0.20 mol/L Na_2CO_3 titrated with 0.20 mol/L HCl for your data.

Solution

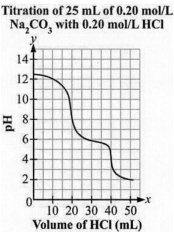

Titration of 25 mL of 0.20 mol/L Na_2CO_3 with 0.20 mol/L HCl

Note that there is a second equivalence point, which could be identified by the use of methyl orange indicator. The presence of two equivalence points indicates that Na_2CO_3 is diprotic and can accept two protons from the hydrochloric acid.

Example

Sketch the titration curve of the titration of a polyprotic acid, H_3PO_4, titrated with a strong base, NaOH. In terms of experimental data, use 25 mL of 0.12 mol/L H_3PO_4 titrated with 0.12 mol/L NaOH.

Solution

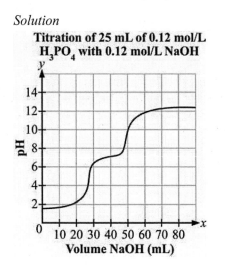

Titration of 25 mL of 0.12 mol/L H_3PO_4 with 0.12 mol/L NaOH

H_3PO_4 is triprotic, which means that it is capable of losing three protons:

By the first equivalence point, one proton (H^+ ion) has been pulled away from each H_3PO_4 molecule by OH^- ions.

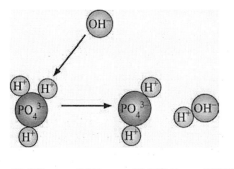

$$H_3PO_{4(aq)} + OH^-_{(aq)} \rightarrow H_2PO_4^-_{(aq)} + HOH_{(l)}$$

By the second equivalence point, one more proton has been pulled away from each $H_2PO_4^-$ ion by the OH^- ions.

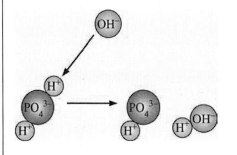

$$H_2PO_4^-_{(aq)} + OH^-_{(aq)} \rightarrow HPO_4^{2-}_{(aq)} + HOH_{(l)}$$

Since H_3PO_4 has three protons attached to the PO_4^{3-} ion, you might expect a third equivalence point:

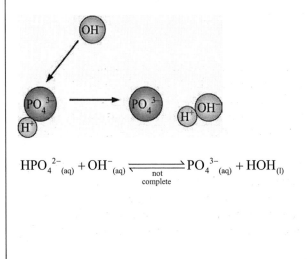

$$HPO_4^{2-}_{(aq)} + OH^-_{(aq)} \underset{\substack{not \\ complete}}{\rightleftharpoons} PO_4^{3-}_{(aq)} + HOH_{(l)}$$

However, at this point the HPO_4^{2-} ion has a large negative charge to use to hold onto the last hydrogen ion. The OH^- ions cannot pull all of the remaining H^+ ions from all of the HPO_4^{2-} ions, leaving many HPO_4^{2-} ions intact. Therefore, the titration does not reach a third equivalence point (it does not go to completion).

Adding more OH^- ions to the solution continues to slowly raise the pH, but the third step in the reaction does not reach an equivalence point.

The following analogy may be useful:

Imagine that you are carrying three basketballs in a crowded hallway. You represent the PO_4^{3-} ion, and the basketballs are the three H^+ ions. People bumping into you in the hallway knock one basketball away from you very easily. You now find it easier to hang on to the remaining two basketballs. However, the right bump (collision) can quite easily remove the second basketball. The last ball is much more difficult to get away from you because you will be able to wrap both arms around it. It might even take more than one person to get the ball away from you. They might act like the OH^- ions surrounding the HPO_4^{2-} ion, trying to pull away the last H^+ ion.

INDICATORS

To determine the equivalence point, titrations most often use indicators or pH meters. An **indicator** is a solution that changes colour to signal that the equivalence point has been reached. Recall that the point at which an indicator changes colour is called its transition point (endpoint). Ideally, an indicator is chosen so that the pH at its transition point is as close as possible to the pH at the equivalence point in a particular titration.

Acid-base indicators are conjugate weak acid–weak base pairs that have distinctly different colours when dissolved in water, as represented by the following equation:

$HIn_{(aq)} + H_2O_{(l)} \rightleftharpoons H_3O^+_{(aq)} + In^-_{(aq)}$
Colour 1   Colour 2

The acid form of the indicator (often abbreviated as HIn) has a characteristic colour, and the conjugate base form of the indicator (In^-) has a different colour. This is because a change in pH affects its shape. When surrounded by H^+, it assumes one form. When it is surrounded by a more basic solution, its bonds are affected, so it changes shape slightly.

The shape of an indicator molecule affects the wavelength of the light that reaches your eyes, so you perceive a different colour. Because each indicator molecule can be in either form, depending on its surroundings, a gradual change from one colour to the other occurs in many indicators. For example, the indicator methyl red can be represented by the following equilibrium equation:

$HMr_{(aq)} + H_2O_{(l)} \rightleftharpoons H_3O^+_{(aq)} + Mr^-_{(aq)}$
Red   Yellow

Refer to the acid-base indicator chart for a list of common indicators. For example, the pH range of methyl red is 4.8 to 6.0.

NOTES

If methyl red is added to a basic solution, most of the indicator molecules will be in their yellow form, $Mr^-_{(aq)}$, when surrounded by $OH^-_{(aq)}$ ions, and the solution will appear yellow in colour.

When acid is gradually added to the solution, the $H_3O^+_{(aq)}$ ions increase, and the indicator's equilibrium is shifted to the left, producing more of the $HMr_{(aq)}$ form of the indicator.

As the pH of the solution drops below 6.0, the red (HMr) form mixes with those molecules that are still yellow (Mr^-). The resulting mixture produces a peach-coloured solution.

As more H^+ ions are added, the colour will become less yellow and more red as the yellow molecules are converted to the red form of the indicator.

By the time the pH reaches 4.8, there will be few yellow molecules left, and the solution will appear red.

Chemical indicators used in titration procedures are generally compounds that do not change the pH of a solution but express different colours at different pH ranges. During titration, the pH will be constantly altering with the addition of the titrate, and the indicator changes colour near the endpoint of the titration. In the case of polyprotic acids or bases, more than one indicator can be used in order to locate different equivalence points within the same solution. Multiple indicators can also be used with different samples of the same solution in order to more precisely determine the point or points of equivalence.

Recall that a strong acid being titrated by a strong base should have an equivalence point near a pH of 7. A good indicator to use in a titration of a strong acid by a strong base or vice versa would be one that has a transition point on or near the point of neutrality. The following diagram illustrates a pH graph of hydrochloric acid being titrated by sodium hydroxide:

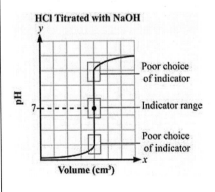

Appropriate choices for titration indicators in a strong acid–strong base titration include bromothymol blue and phenol red. The transition points of these are shown in the following diagrams. In phenol red, the transition point occurs when the first drop of titrant changes the yellow form to a peach colour.

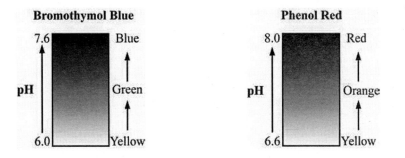

A weak acid that is titrated with a strong base will have a point of equivalence when the pH is above 7. When performing this type of titration, an indicator with a transition point slightly higher than pH 7 should be selected.

In the following diagram, acetic acid is titrated with sodium hydroxide.

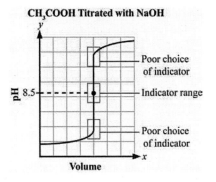

A useful choice for a titration indicator might be phenolphthalein, which should reach its endpoint when one drop of titrant changes all of the sample solution to a light pink (not just the point where the drop lands in the flask).

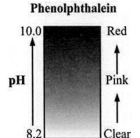

NOTES

Example

A student finds that an unknown solution is colourless when mixed with phenolphthalein, red when mixed with chlorophenol red, and blue when in the presence of bromocresol green. The student hypothesizes that the pH of the solution is 7.5. Do the indicators provide evidence to support this hypothesis?

Solution

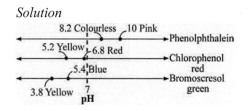

Given the colour states of the indicators, you can deduce the following:

• Colourless phenolphthalein means that the pH is less than 8.2.

• Red chlorophenol red means that the pH is greater then 6.8.

• Blue bromocresol green indicates that the pH is greater than 5.4.

• Therefore, the pH is greater than 6.8 and less than 8.2.

The student's hypothesis is supported by the evidence, since pH 7.5 fits within the pH range suggested by the indicators.

PRACTICE EXERCISES

The indicator bromothymol blue can be used to determine the endpoint of a titration with an equivalence point equal to 7.

1. **a)** Write the equilibrium equation that represents the indicator bromothymol blue.

   b) What colour will the solution containing the indictor be when a solution has the following pH values during titration:

   i) 4

   ii) 7

   iii) 10

2. Sketch a titration curve for each of the following titrations, indicate if the equivalence point would be equal to, greater than, or less than 7, and identify the type of titration the curve represents.

   a) $NH_{3(aq)}$ titrated with $HCl_{(aq)}$

   b) $HNO_{3(aq)}$ titrated with $NaOH_{(aq)}$

Lesson 6 BUFFERS

EQUILIBRIUMS IN BUFFER SOLUTIONS

A buffer can be described as a solution of a weak acid or base and its conjugate pair in equilibrium. The buffer has the ability to maintain a relatively constant pH when small amounts of acid or base are added.

In order to explain how buffers work, you must have a good understanding of the equilibriums present in buffer solutions.

Equilibriums in Acidic Buffer Solutions

An acidic buffer solution consists of a weak acid and its conjugate base, which are both in reasonably high concentrations. To write the equilibrium equation for an acidic buffer, simply write the equation for the ionization of the weak acid in water.

For example, consider a buffer solution that is prepared that contains 1.0 mol/L CH_3COOH and 1.0 mol/L $NaCH_3COO$. This buffer has the following equilibrium equation:

$$CH_3COOH_{(aq)} + H_2O_{(l)} \rightleftharpoons H_3O^+_{(aq)} + CH_3COO^-_{(aq)}$$
$$\text{1.0 mol/L} \qquad\qquad\qquad\qquad\qquad \text{1.0 mol/L}$$

> Focus on $[H_3O^+]$ when something is added to an acidic buffer solution.

When a small amount of acid or base is added to a buffer solution, the $[H_3O^+]$ is immediately changed. The equilibrium will then shift either left or right in order to counteract the change in the $[H_3O^+]$.

- If the $[H_3O^+]$ is increased, the equilibrium will shift to the left to decrease it.

- If $[H_3O^+]$ is decreased, the equilibrium will shift to the right to increase it.

Example

A small amount of hydrochloric acid (HCl) is added to an unbuffered solution, and the pH changes from 7.0 to 5.0. If the same amount of hydrochloric acid is added to a buffer solution with the same volume as the unbuffered solution, how would this affect the pH of the buffer solution?

Solution
The pH would change only slightly, such as from 7.0 to 6.9.

NOTES

Remember that 1 M = 1 mol/L.

Because pH = –log $[H_3O^+]$, as the $[H_3O^+]$ increases, the pH decreases.

The equilibrium can continue to shift left only as long as there is enough CH_3COO^- to react with the excess H_3O^+.

A buffer solution does not completely prevent a change in pH; it just minimizes the change.

212

Equilibriums in Basic Buffer Solutions

A basic buffer solution consists of a weak base and the salt of its conjugate acid. To write the equation for the equilibrium existing in a basic buffer solution, write the equation for the ionization of the weak base in water.

For example, a buffer solution is prepared containing 1.0 mol/L NH_3 and 1.0 mol/L NH_4Cl. The following equation describes the equilibrium present:

$$NH_{3(aq)} + H_2O_{(l)} \rightleftharpoons NH^+_{4\ (aq)} + OH^-_{(l)}$$

1.0 mol/L   1.0 mol/L

Focus on [OH^-] when something is added to a basic buffer solution.

If the [OH^-] is increased, this equilibrium will shift to the left to counteract the increase. If [OH^-] is decreased, the equilibrium will shift to the right. The Cl^- from NH_4Cl is a spectator ion, so it is left out of the equilibrium equation for this buffer.

Example

A small amount of sodium hydroxide (NaOH) is added to an unbuffered solution, and the pH changes from 7.0 to 9.0. If the same amount of sodium hydroxide is added to a buffer solution with the same volume as the unbuffered solution, how would this affect the pH of the buffer solution?

Solution

The pH would change only slightly, such as from 7.0 to 7.1.

COMPOSITION AND TYPES OF BUFFER SOLUTIONS

There are two types of buffer solutions: acidic buffers and basic buffers.

Type	Composition	pH Range of Operation
Acidic buffer	A weak acid and the salt of its conjugate base	pH of 7 or below
Basic buffer	A weak base and the salt of its conjugate acid	pH of 7 or above

Neither a strong acid nor a strong base can be used to prepare a buffer solution.

In any buffer solution, the concentrations of both components should be moderately high.

For example, a solution consisting of 1.0 mol/L HCOOH and 1.0 mol/L NaHCOO would be an effective buffer solution, whereas a solution consisting of 1.0×10^{-4} mol/L HCOOH and 1.0×10^{-4} mol/L NaHCOO would not be very useful as a buffer.

NOTES

Weak acids that are ions (like HSO_3^-) often come in the form of salts (like $NaHSO_3$). For example, a combination of the two salts $NaHSO_3$ and Na_2SO_3 will produce an acidic buffer solution.

Some Examples of Acidic Buffers

Weak Acid	Conjugate Base	Salt of the Conjugate Base
CH_3COOH	CH_3COO^-	$NaCH_3COO$
HNO_2	NO_2^-	KNO_2
HSO_3^-	SO_3^{2-}	Na_2SO_3
$H_2PO_4^-$	HPO_4^{2-}	Li_2HPO_4
HF	F^-	KF

ADDING AN ACID TO AN ACIDIC BUFFER SOLUTION

A small amount of HCl is added to a buffer solution containing 1.0 mol/L acetic acid (CH_3COOH) and 1.0 mol/L sodium acetate ($NaCH_3COO$). The buffer solution has the following equilibrium equation:

$$CH_3COOH_{(aq)} + H_2O_{(l)} \rightleftarrows H_3O^+ + CH_3COO^-_{(aq)}$$
$$1.0 \text{ mol/L} \qquad\qquad\qquad 1.0 \text{ mol/L}$$

The following sequence of events takes place:
1. The addition of HCl (strong acid) immediately increases the $[H_3O^+]$.
2. In order to counteract the increase in the $[H_3O^+]$, the equilibrium shifts to the left.
3. As the equilibrium shifts to the left, CH_3COO^- reacts with H_3O^+.
4. The $[H_3O^+]$ decreases close to—but not quite as low as—its original concentration.
5. In the overall process, the final $[H_3O^+]$ is slightly higher (and the pH is slightly lower) than it was before the acid was added.

A graph of $[H_3O^+]$ versus time shows what happens in the given process.

Study this graph, and make sure you understand what is happening during each time interval

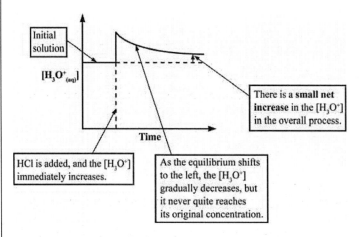

Example

Describe the effect of adding a strong acid to a solution of carbonic acid ($H_2CO_{3(aq)}$) and its conjugate base, hydrogen carbonate ion ($HCO_3^-{}_{(aq)}$).

Solution

When a strong acid is added, the concentration of H_3O^+ ions increases. The buffer decreases the concentration of hydronium ions by reacting them with the hydrogen carbonate ion.

Entities: $H_2CO_{3(aq)}$ $HCO_3^-{}_{(aq)}$ $H_3O^+{}_{(aq)}$ $H_2O_{(l)}$

            A   A/B   A   A/B

                    Strongest B   Strongest A

Reaction: $H_3O^+{}_{(aq)}$ + $HCO_3^-{}_{(aq)}$ $\rightleftarrows$ $H_2O_{(l)}$ + $H_2CO_{3(aq)}$

            A   A/B   CB   CA

The final $[H_3O^+]$ is slightly higher (and pH is slightly lower) than it was before the acid is added.

The following abbreviations are used when referring to buffers:

A = Acid

B = Base

CB = Conjugate base

CA = Conjugate acid

BASIC BUFFERS

Some examples of basic buffers and their composition are given in the following table:

Some Examples of Basic Buffers

Weak Base	Conjugate Acid	Salt of the Conjugate Acid
NH_3	NH_4^+	NH_4Cl
NH_3	NH_4^+	NH_4NO_3
N_2H_4	$N_2H_5^+$	N_2H_5Br

ADDING A BASE TO A BASIC BUFFER SOLUTION

A small amount of NaOH solution is added to a buffer solution consisting of 1.0 mol/L NH_3 and 1.0 mol/L NH_4Cl.

The buffer solution has the following equilibrium equation:

$$NH_{3(aq)} + H_2O_{(l)} \rightleftarrows NH_4^+{}_{(aq)} + OH^-{}_{(aq)}$$

The following sequence of events takes place:

1. The addition of $NaOH_{(aq)}$ (strong base) immediately increases the $[OH^-{}_{(aq)}]$.
2. In order to counteract the increase in the $[OH^-{}_{(aq)}]$, the equilibrium shifts to the left.
3. As the equilibrium shifts to the left, $NH_4^+{}_{(aq)}$ reacts with $OH^-{}_{(aq)}$.
4. The $[OH^-{}_{(aq)}]$ decreases close to—but not quite as low as—its original concentration.
5. In the overall process, the final $[OH^-{}_{(aq)}]$ is slightly higher (and the pH is slightly higher) than it was before the base was added.

The effectiveness of the basic buffer with the equilibrium shown by

$$NH_3 + H_2O \rightleftarrows NH_4^+ + OH^-$$

is limited by the initial $[NH_3]$ and $[NH_4^+]$.

If there were no buffer present, the addition of a base would result in a large net increase in the $[OH^-]$ and a large net increase in pH.

A graph of $[OH^-_{(aq)}]$ versus time shows what happens in the given process.

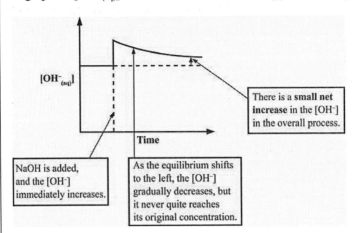

There is a **small net increase** in the $[OH^-]$ in the overall process.

NaOH is added, and the $[OH^-]$ immediately increases.

As the equilibrium shifts to the left, the $[OH^-]$ gradually decreases, but it never quite reaches its original concentration.

Example

Describe the effect of adding a strong base to a solution containing relatively equal amounts of carbonic acid ($H_2CO_{3(aq)}$) and its conjugate base, hydrogen carbonate ion ($HCO_3^-{}_{(aq)}$).

Solution

When a strong base is added, the buffer removes the hydroxide by reacting it with the carbonic acid.

Entities: $H_2CO_{3(aq)}$ $HCO_3^-{}_{(aq)}$ $OH^-_{(aq)}$ $H_2O_{(l)}$

            A   A/B   B   A/B

    Strongest A   Strongest B

Reaction: $H_2CO_{3(aq)}$ $+$ $OH^-_{(aq)}$ $\rightleftarrows$ $HCO_3^-{}_{(aq)}$ $+$ $H_2O_{(l)}$

           A   B   CB   CA

The final $[OH^-_{(aq)}]$ is slightly higher (and the pH is slightly higher) than it was before the base was added.

LIMITATIONS OF BUFFER SOLUTIONS

Consider a buffer solution consisting of 1.0 mol/L $HNO_{2(aq)}$ and 1.0 mol/L $NaNO_{2(aq)}$.

One litre of this solution contains 1 mol of $HNO_{2(aq)}$ and 1 mol of $NO^-{}_{2(aq)}$ (from $NaNO_{2(aq)}$).

The following equilibrium equation may be written for this buffer:

$HNO_{2(aq)} + H_2O_{(l)} \rightleftarrows H_3O^+{}_{(aq)} + NO_2^-{}_{(aq)}$
   1 mol   1 mol

1 mol of NO_2^- would react with 1 mol of H_3O^+. There would still be 0.5 mol of H_3O^+ left over.

A student adds 1.5 mol of $HCl_{(aq)}$ to 1 L of this buffer solution. The $[H_3O^+_{(aq)}]$ increases by 1.5 mol/L, and the equilibrium shifts to the left to counteract this increase. The reverse reaction predominates for a time:

$$H_3O^+_{(aq)} + NO_2^-_{(aq)} \rightleftarrows HNO_{2(aq)} + H_2O_{(l)}$$

1.5 mol   1 mol

Notice that there is not enough $NO_2^-_{(aq)}$ to react with all the added $H_3O^+_{(aq)}$.

After 1 mol of the NO_2^- has been used up, there is no longer any left to react with excess H_3O^+. The $[H_3O^+]$ has now increased significantly, and the pH has decreased significantly.

The action of a buffer solution is limited by the original concentrations of the weak acid and the weak base it contains.

BUFFERING REGIONS ON TITRATION CURVES

Whenever a weak acid (or base) is titrated with a strong base (or acid), a buffer region or regions will occur. The buffer region is the flatter portion of the titration curve that occurs before the equivalence point. This is the point of the titration where a buffer solution is present as a result of a weak acid (or base) being in solution with its conjugate base (or acid) pair. This flat region on the graph is caused when this buffer solution momentarily resists a change in pH. Eventually the continued addition of a strong base (or acid) exceeds the buffer's capacity.

Consider the titration curve for a strong base added to a weak acid.

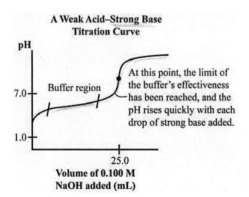

When all the weak acid in the buffer solution has been used up by the strong base added, there is no more buffering, and the pH goes up rapidly.

The buffer solution is present when there is some weak acid left over and some weak base produced by the neutralization reaction. At a certain point (shown on the graph), the amount of base added overcomes the buffer's ability to control it, and the pH goes up rapidly.

A WEAK BASE–STRONG ACID TITRATION CURVE

The behaviour of buffers can be used to explain the observations made during a titration of a weak base with a strong acid in a similar manner.

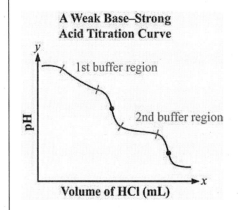

In the titration of $Na_2CO_{3(aq)}$ with $HCl_{(aq)}$, two buffer regions appear on the titration curve. The first buffer region occurs when both $CO_3^{2-}_{(aq)}$ and $HCO_3^-_{(aq)}$ are present in the solution. The second buffer region occurs when both $HCO_3^-_{(aq)}$ and $H_2CO_{3(aq)}$ are present in the solution.

SOME USES OF BUFFER SOLUTIONS

Buffer solutions are widely used today. Some uses include the following:

• Stabilizing pH in hot tubs and swimming pools

• Maintaining optimum pH for production of pharmaceuticals and other chemicals

• Controlling the pH in wines and foods

• Providing solutions with accurate pHs for calibrating pH meters

Living things contain many naturally occurring buffer solutions, which maintain optimum pH levels for biological processes.

The optimum pH of human blood is 7.35. If the pH of the blood goes below 7.20 or above 7.50, serious conditions can result. Recall how the shape of the indicator molecule is altered by the pH of its environment. Enzymes in the body have definite shapes at different pH levels. They cannot work if they are not the correct shape.

Fortunately, carbon dioxide, a product of human metabolism, and other substances present in the body produce a naturally occurring buffer solution that stabilizes the pH of the blood.

A Buffer Solution in Human Blood

Carbon dioxide (CO_2) is a product of metabolism in human cells. The CO_2 produced in cells dissolves in blood plasma. Think of CO_2 dissolving in water to form a solution of the weak acid H_2CO_3.

$$CO_{2(g)} + H_2O_{(l)} \rightleftarrows H_2CO_{3(aq)}$$

H_2CO_3 ionizes to form H_3O^+ and HCO_3^-.

$$H_2CO_{3(aq)} + H_2O_{(l)} \rightleftarrows H_3O^+{}_{(aq)} + HCO_3^-{}_{(aq)}$$

Because there is no actual evidence of H_2CO_3 molecules in the aqueous solution, the given process is usually summarized as follows:

$$CO_{2(g)} + 2H_2O_{(l)} \rightleftarrows H_3O^+{}_{(aq)} + HCO_3^-{}_{(aq)}$$

In this case, $CO_{2(g)}$ is the weak acid, and $HCO_3^-{}_{(aq)}$ is the conjugate base. This buffer helps keep the blood pH level close to 7.35.

During periods of high physical exertion, the level of CO_2 is controlled by an automatic increase in breathing rate, and the concentration of HCO_3^- is controlled by the kidneys.

A Buffer Solution in Cells

The following buffer system stabilizes the pH within the cells:

$$H_2PO_4^- + H_2O \rightleftarrows H_3O^+ + HPO_4^{2-}$$

$H_2PO_4^-$ is the weak acid, and HPO_4^{2-} is its conjugate base.

PRACTICE EXERCISES

Use the following information to answer the next question.

Buffering regions on a titration curve are the result of a buffering solution forming during a titration.

1. Describe what a buffering region on a titration curve is and what a buffering solution is.

Use the following information to answer the next question.

Maintaining blood pH at around 7.2 is extremely important, as most biological molecules only function well in a narrow range of pH. However, extreme exercise can result in the favouring of anaerobic respiration in muscles, which produces an excess of protons and acts to lower pH. Also, hyperventilation reduces the amount of carbon dioxide in the blood (stored as carbonic acid) and can cause an increase in pH. Humans can survive both conditions by maintaining a steady blood pH.

2. Explain how blood can resist these pressures toward a change in pH.

Use the following information to answer the next two questions.

$$K_a = \frac{[A^-][H_3O^+]}{[HA]} \quad \text{so} \quad [H_3O^+] = K_a \times \frac{[HA]}{[A^-]}$$

3. Describe how the values of [HA], [A$^-$], [H$_3$O$^+$], and pH for a buffer solution might change when a small amount of HCl$_{(aq)}$ is added to the buffer solution.

4. Describe how the values of [HA], [A$^-$], [H$_3$O$^+$], and pH for a buffer solution might change when a small amount of NaOH$_{(aq)}$ is added to the buffer solution.

Use the following information to answer the next question.

A buffer solution is prepared by mixing relatively equal amounts of CH$_3$COOH$_{(aq)}$ and CH$_3$COO$^-$$_{(aq)}$. It is determined that in the buffer solution the [CH$_3$COOH$_{(aq)}$] is 0.15 mol/L, and the [CH$_3$COO$^-$$_{(aq)}$] is 0.10 mol/L.

5. a) Write the equilibrium reaction equation for this buffer system.

b) Write the equilibrium constant expression for this buffer system.

c) Use the given concentrations of the buffer components and the K_a of ethanoic acid to determine the [H$_3$O$^+$] and the pH of this buffer.

d) A very small lump of NaOH$_{(s)}$ is dissolved in this buffer solution. Write the net equation that represents the reaction that takes place.

e) Describe any predicted changes that might occur to the pH of the buffer solution when the NaOH$_{(s)}$ is added. Explain your prediction.

REVIEW SUMMARY

- Equilibrium refers to a balance point. It occurs in a closed system at a constant temperature.

- Equilibrium is reached when the rate of the forward reaction is equal to the rate of the reverse reaction, concentrations remain constant, and all measurable properties are constant.

- A general reaction can be written as $aA + bB = cC + dD$, where A and B are reactants, C and D are products, and lowercase letters are coefficients.

- K_c is the equilibrium constant at a specific temperature.

- The equilibrium expression can be written $K_c = [\text{products}] \div [\text{reactants}]$ or $K_c = [C]^c [D]^d \div [A]^a [B]^b$

- [C] and [D] are equilibrium molar concentrations of products (mol/L); [A] and [B] are equilibrium molar concentrations of reactants (mol/L); exponents are coefficients of the balanced equation.

- K_c can be used to predict the extent of reactions and whether products or reactants are favoured. If $K_c > 1$, products are favoured; if $K_c < 1$, reactants are favoured; if $K_c = 1$, neither products nor reactants are favoured.

- Shifts in equilibrium can be caused by changes in temperature, pressure, volume, concentration, or the addition of a catalyst. Le Châtelier's principle predicts the reaction's response to oppose the change. For example, if the temperature is decreased, the reaction response is to increase temperature. For example, if the temperature of an exothermic reaction is decreased, the equilibrium shifts right to produce more heat, and the forward reaction rate increases.

- Adding a catalyst does not change the position of equilibrium; it only increases the speed of the chemical reaction.

- A Brønsted–Lowry acid is any entity that loses a proton to something else in a solution, while a Brønsted–Lowry base is what receives the proton in a reaction. The acid is a proton donor, and the base is a proton acceptor.

- Amphiprotic or amphoteric substances can act as acids in some reactions and bases in others. They are both proton donors and proton acceptors.

- A polyprotic substance is an acid with more than one proton to donate.

- K_w is the equilibrium, or dissociation, constant for water; K_a is the dissociation constant for acids; and K_b is the equilibrium dissociation constant for bases.

- The equilibrium constant for water can be calculated using the formula $K_w = K_a \times K_b$

- A conjugate acid–base pair consists of an acid and a base that differ by one proton, $H^+_{(aq)}$.

- Titration (or pH) curves are graphic representations of a titration. The volume of titrant added is recorded on the x-axis, and the pH is recorded on the y-axis.

- Indicators used in titration are compounds that do not change the pH of a solution but express different colours at different pH ranges.

- An acidic buffer solution consists of a weak acid and the salt of its conjugate base. A basic buffer solution consists of a weak base and the salt of its conjugate acid.

- When a small amount of acid or base is added to a buffer solution, the equilibrium shifts to counteract the change.

- The action of a buffer is limited by the original concentration of the weak acid and the weak base it contains. At a certain point, the addition of any more strong acid or base overcomes the ability of the buffer to control it, and the pH changes rapidly.

PRACTICE TEST

1. Predict whether the reactants or products are favoured for each of the following reaction equilibriums.

    A. $2H_{2(g)} + O_{2(g)} \rightleftharpoons 2H_2O_{(g)}; K_c = 1.4 \times 10^{17}$

    B. $N_2O_{(g)} + NO_{2(g)} \rightleftharpoons 3NO_{(g)}; K_c = 4.2 \times 10^{-4}$

    C. $N_2O_{4(g)} \rightleftharpoons 2NO_{2(g)}; K_c = 5.7 \times 10^{-3}$

    D. $H_{2(g)} + I_{2(g)} \rightleftharpoons 2HI_{(g)}; K_c = 2.67 \times 10^{-2}$

2. Write the net ionic equation for the hydrolysis of KCN.

Use the following information to answer the next question.

> A saturated solution of calcium phosphate is a system at equilibrium, as represented by the following equation:
>
> $$Ca_3(PO_4)_{2(s)} \rightleftharpoons 3Ca^{2+}_{(aq)} + 2PO_4^{3-}_{(aq)}$$

3. Write three statements that describe this system at equilibrium.

Use the following information to answer the next question.

> $$2CO_{(g)} + O_{2(g)} \rightleftharpoons 2CO_{2(g)} + heat$$

4. Indicate the direction of the equilibrium shift when each of the following changes is imposed on the given reaction.

    a) The pressure of the system is decreased.

    b) The temperature of the system is decreased.

Use the following information to answer the next question.

$$H_{2(g)} + I_{2(g)} \rightleftharpoons 2HI_{(g)}; \Delta H = 270.2 \text{ kJ/mol}$$

5. Indicate how each of the following changes will affect the system at equilibrium.

   A. Increase in $[HI]$

   B. Decrease in $[I_2]$

   C. Decrease in pressure

   D. Increase in temperature

Use the following information to answer the next question.

The following equation represents the oxidation of sulfur dioxide into sulfur trioxide:
$$2SO_{2(g)} + O_{2(g)} \rightleftharpoons 2SO_{3(g)} + 193.2 \text{ kJ}$$

6. What changes can be made to temperature and pressure of the system to produce the highest yield of $SO_{3(g)}$?

Use the following information to answer the next question.

In the reaction between hydrogen and iodine, which yields hydrogen iodide, the value of K_c at 458°C is 49.7. The reaction is represented by the following equation:
$$H_{2(g)} + I_{2(g)} \rightleftharpoons 2HI_{(g)}$$

7. Describe what happens to the system at equilibrium and the value of K_c when the concentration of hydrogen gas is reduced.

Use the following information to answer the next question.

The following equilibrium is obtained when $BaSO_{4(s)}$ is added to water:
$$BaSO_{4(s)} \rightleftharpoons Ba^{2+}_{(aq)} + SO_4^{2-}_{(aq)}$$

8. What effect does an increase or decrease in pressure have on the given equilibrium system? Explain your answer.

Use the following information to answer the next question.

The equilibrium system representing phenolphthalein, a pH indicator, can be represented by the following equilibrium equation:

$$HIn + H_2O \rightleftharpoons H_3O^+ + In^-$$
colourless $\qquad\qquad\qquad$ pink

9. Describe what happens to the colour of the equilibrium system when $NaOH_{(aq)}$ is added. Explain your answer.

Use the following information to answer the next question.

Quick lime is prepared by heating a source of calcium carbonate such as limestone.
$$CaCO_{3(s)} \rightleftharpoons CaO_{(s)} + CO_{2(g)}$$

10. Write the equilibrium law expression for the forward reaction.

Use the following information to answer the next question.

Gaseous ammonia is prepared from nitrogen gas and hydrogen gas by the following reaction.
$$N_{2(g)} + 3H_{2(g)} \rightleftharpoons 2NH_{3(g)} + heat$$

At a certain temperature, a 50.0 L vessel with an equilibrium mixture of nitrogen, hydrogen and ammonia was analyzed and found to contain 1.0 mol of $N_{2(g)}$, 3.0 mol of $H_{2(g)}$, and 0.50 mol of $NH_{3(g)}$.

11. a) Determine the value of the equilibrium constant for this reaction.

b) The temperature of this system was changed to 400°C, and the value of equilibrium constant was found to be 1.6×10^{-4}. Which direction will the reaction have to proceed to re-establish the calculated equilibrium position?

Use the following information to answer the next question.

In a system, 0.1908 mol of $CO_{2(g)}$, 0.0908 mol of $H_{2(g)}$, 0.0092 mol of $CO_{(g)}$, and 0.0092 mol of $H_2O_{(g)}$ are present in a 2.0 L vessel at equilibrium.

$$CO_{2(g)} + H_{2(g)} \rightleftharpoons CO_{(g)} + H_2O_{(g)}$$

12. Determine the value of this reaction's equilibrium constant (K_c).

Use the following information to answer the next question.

For the following gaseous reaction, ethene and hydrogen were added to a reaction chamber so that the initial concentrations of ethene and hydrogen were 0.335 mol/L and 0.526 mol/L, respectively.

$$C_2H_4 + H_2 \rightleftharpoons C_2H_6; K_c = 0.99$$

13. The concentration of $C_2H_{2(g)}$ at equilibrium was found to be 0.235 mol/L. Determine the equilibrium concentrations of the other species in the reaction.

Use the following information to answer the next question.

K_{c1} and K_{c2} are the equilibrium constants of the following two reactions.

Reaction 1: $CH_3COOH_{(aq)} + C_2H_5OH_{(aq)} \rightleftharpoons CH_3COOC_2H_{5(aq)} + H_2O_{(l)}$

Reaction 2: $CH_3COOC_2H_{5(aq)} + H_2O_{(l)} \rightleftharpoons CH_3COOH_{(aq)} + C_2H_5OH_{(aq)}$

14. What is the relation between K_{c1} and K_{c2}?

15. For each of the following salts, describe the solution (in terms of acidity) that results when the salt is dissolved in water.

A. $NaCl_{(s)}$

B. $K_2SO_{4(s)}$

C. $NH_4Cl_{(s)}$

D. $CH_3COONa_{(s)}$

Use the following information to answer the next question.

Sodium hydroxide ($NaOH_{(aq)}$) reacts with hydrochloric acid ($HCl_{(aq)}$) to produce sodium chloride ($NaCl_{(aq)}$) and water ($H_2O_{(l)}$).

16. Write the net ionic equation that represents the given reaction.

17. Write the net ionic equation that represents the dissociation of $KCl_{(s)}$ in water.

Use the following information to answer the next question.

A solution of CH_3COOH, a weak acid, is titrated with $NaOH$, a strong base.

18. Write the net ionic equation for the given reaction.

Use the following information to answer the next question.

The equilibrium reaction represented by the following equation favours the formation of products.

$$HCO_3^-{}_{(aq)} + HCl_{(aq)} \rightleftharpoons H_2CO_{3(aq)} + Cl^-{}_{(aq)}$$

19. Identify the strongest base in the given equilibrium reaction. Explain your answer.

20. Define the term *amphiprotic*, and explain why $NaHCO_3$ forms an amphiprotic species when in solution.

21. Define the term *conjugate base*, and identify the conjugate base of $H_2SO_{4(aq)}$.

22. For each of the following pairs of substances, explain whether or not they could be used as a buffer solution when mixed together.

A. $HCl_{(aq)}$ and $NaCl_{(aq)}$

B. $H_2S_{(aq)}$ and $NaHS_{(aq)}$

C. $NH_4OH_{(aq)}$ and $NH_4Cl_{(aq)}$

D. $CH_3COOH_{(aq)}$ and $CH_3COONa_{(aq)}$

Use the following information to answer the next question.

The following equilibrium reaction represents a solution of acetic acid, CH_3COOH, at equilibrium.

$$CH_3COOH_{(aq)} + H_2O_{(l)} \rightleftarrows H_3O^+_{(aq)} + CH_3COO^-_{(aq)}$$
$$2.0 \text{ mol/L} \qquad 1.0 \times 10^{-4} \text{ mol/L} \quad 1.0 \times 10^{-4} \text{ mol/L}$$

23. Would a solution of acetic acid as represented by the given equilibrium reaction be a good buffer solution? Explain your answer.

24. Rainwater contains dissolved $CO_{2(g)}$. Explain why the pH of normal rainwater is 5.6 and not 7.0.

25. Write the equation that represents the reaction of water with a proton, $H^+_{(aq)}$.

26. When comparing a 0.050 mol/L solution of $HNO_{3(aq)}$ with a 0.050 mol/L solution of $HF_{(aq)}$, which solution will have the highest concentration of $H_3O^+_{(aq)}$? Explain your answer.

27. The self-ionization constant of water K_w, is related to the pH and pOH of the solution. Write the equation that represents the relationship among pH, pOH, and pK_w.

28. Write the balanced equation representing the reaction of $NH_{3(aq)}$, a weak base, and water, and the equilibrium expression for the K_b of $NH_{3(aq)}$.

29. Determine the pH of a 1.0 mol/L solution of acetic acid, $CH_3COOH_{(aq)}$.

Use the following information to answer the next question.

The self-ionization of water is an endothermic reaction, as represented by the following equation:
$$2H_2O_{(l)} + heat \rightleftharpoons H_3O^+_{(aq)} + OH^-_{(aq)}$$

30. If the temperature of the water is increased, what will happen to the system at equilibrium and the value of the equilibrium constant, K_w?

31. Determine the value of K_b for $CH_3COO^-_{(aq)}$.

32. A sample of $KCN_{(s)}$ is dissolved in water. Write a balanced net ionic equation that represents the reaction between water and $KCN_{(s)}$, and describe the acidity of the solution that is formed.

Use the following information to answer the next question.

The conjugate base of the weak acid $HF_{(aq)}$ hydrolyzes in water as represented by the following equation:

$$F^-_{(aq)} + H_2O_{(l)} \rightleftharpoons HF_{(aq)} + OH^-_{(aq)}$$

33. Determine the $[OH^-_{(aq)}]$ present in a 1.00 mol/L solution of $F^-_{(aq)}$.

Use the following information to answer the next question.

A reaction reaches equilibrium in a 5.0 L container. The reaction is represented by the following equation:

$$PCl_{5(g)} \rightleftharpoons PCl_{3(g)} + Cl_{2(g)}$$

At equilibrium, the container contained 1.5 mol of $PCl_{5(g)}$, 0.525 mol of $PCl_{3(g)}$, and 0.525 mol of $Cl_{2(g)}$.

34. Determine the value of K_c for the given reaction.

Use the following information to answer the next question.

The following graph represents a titration reaction.

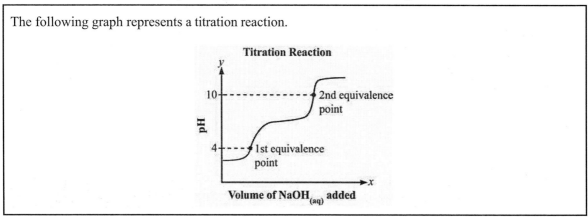

35. a) Describe the sample being titrated.

b) Identify the buffer region or regions that occur during the titration on the graph.

230

Student Notes and Problems

ANSWERS AND SOLUTIONS

CASTLE ROCK
RESEARCH CORP

THERMOCHEMICAL CHANGES

Lesson 1—Analyzing Heat Transfer

PRACTICE EXERCISES
ANSWERS AND SOLUTIONS

1. $Q = mc\Delta T$
   $Q = (300 \text{ g})(0.385 \text{ J/g} \cdot °\text{C})(280°\text{C})$
   $Q = 3.23 \times 10^4 \text{ J} = 32.3 \text{ kJ}$

3. $Q = mc\Delta T$
   $Q = (1.00 \times 10^6 \text{ g})(1.23 \text{ J/g} \cdot °\text{C})(500°\text{C})$
   $Q = 6.15 \times 10^8 \text{ J} = 615 \text{ MJ}$

5. At any given time, Q, t, and m would be constant,

   so $\dfrac{\Delta T}{t} = \dfrac{k}{c}$ or $\dfrac{\Delta T}{t} \mu \dfrac{1}{c}$, so the smaller the value

   of c, the greater the value of $\dfrac{\Delta T}{t}$.

   $$\frac{Q}{t} = \frac{mc\Delta T}{t} \Rightarrow \frac{\Delta T}{t} = \frac{\dfrac{Q}{t}}{mc}$$

   Since $c_{Pt} < c_{Cu} < c_{Al}$, the following inequalities must be true:

   $$\left(\frac{\Delta T}{t}\right)_{Pt} > \left(\frac{\Delta T}{t}\right)_{Cu} > \left(\frac{\Delta T}{t}\right)_{Al}$$

   In other words, platinum will heat up the most quickly and therefore reach 300°C first.

   or

   If the specific heat capacity of a substance is given, the amount of energy that is required to increase the temperature of one gram of that substance by one degree is known.

   If several different substances absorb the same amount of energy per minute, then the one with the lowest specific heat capacity will display the greatest temperature change per minute. In other words, the substance with the lowest specific heat capacity will heat up the fastest. In this case, that substance is platinum.

Lesson 2—Photosynthesis, Cellular Respiration, and Hydrocarbon Combustion

PRACTICE EXERCISES
ANSWERS AND SOLUTIONS

1. During photosynthesis, glucose is produced from carbon dioxide and water. This takes place in chloroplasts found in plant material. Sunlight provides the energy for the reaction to take place. The net reaction for this endothermic process is represented as follows:

   $$6CO_{2(g)} + 6H_2O_{(l)} + \text{energy} \rightarrow C_6H_{12}O_{6(s)} + 6O_{2(g)}$$

   Therefore, during photosynthesis, light energy is converted into chemical energy in the form of glucose (sugar).

   During cellular respiration, glucose is consumed, and carbon dioxide, water, and energy are produced.

   The net reaction for this process is represented as follows:
   $$C_6H_{12}O_{6(s)} + 6O_{2(g)} \rightarrow 6CO_{2(g)} + 6H_2O_{(l)} + \text{energy}$$
   Photosynthesis and cellular respiration have the following differences:

   - Photosynthesis traps and uses solar energy and stores it in the form of glucose. During cellular respiration, the stored energy in glucose is released. Photosynthesis is an endothermic reaction (it requires energy), and cellular respiration is an exothermic reaction (it releases energy).

   - Photosynthesis takes place in plants, algae, and some bacteria. In contrast, cellular respiration occurs in the mitochondria of all living cells.

   - Carbon dioxide gas and liquid water are reactants in photosynthesis, but they are products of cellular respiration.

   - In photosynthesis, oxygen gas is a product; in cellular respiration, oxygen gas is a reactant.

   - Respiration can occur day or night, whereas photosynthesis is a light-dependent reaction; therefore, it requires sunlight.

Despite the differences, the two processes are similar in many ways:

- Photosynthesis and cellular respiration are responsible for maintaining the carbon dioxide levels in the atmosphere. Carbon is cycled between the atmosphere and living systems by the activity of these two processes. Both are parts of the carbon cycle.

- Electron transport plays an important role in both processes, as they are both redox reactions.

- Cellular respiration is the reverse reaction of photosynthesis.

Lesson 3—Defining and Communication Reaction Enthalpies

PRACTICE EXERCISES
ANSWERS AND SOLUTIONS

1. The balanced chemical equation for the combustion of gasoline can be represented as follows:

   $2C_8H_{18(l)} + 25O_{2(g)}$
   $\rightarrow 16CO_{2(g)} + 18H_2O_{(g)} + 10\ 148.2\ kJ$

   Since the reaction is exothermic, the energy term is included as a product because energy is produced by the reaction. The balanced reaction represents the combustion of 2 mol of $C_8H_{18(l)}$, so the energy released is $2 \times (5\ 074.1\ kJ)$.

3. The decomposition of ammonia is the reverse reaction of its formation. The decomposition of ammonia releases hydrogen and nitrogen gas and can be represented as follows:

   $NH_{3(g)} + 45.9\ kJ \rightarrow \frac{1}{2}N_{2(g)} + \frac{3}{2}H_{2(g)}$

   The molar enthalpy of formation for ammonia is –45.9 kJ/mol. Therefore, during the decomposition of 1.0 mol of ammonia, 45.9 kJ of energy is absorbed from the surroundings.

   The balanced chemical equation for the decomposition of ammonia in terms of whole number coefficients (with energy on the reactant or product side) can be represented as follows:

   $2NH_{3(g)} \rightarrow N_{2(g)} + 3H_{2(g)} - 91.8\ kJ$
   or $2NH_{3(g)} + 91.8\ kJ \rightarrow N_{2(g)} + 3H_{2(g)}$

5. • The standard molar enthalpy of formation of ammonium nitrate is $\Delta_f H_m° = -365.6\ kJ/mol$.

   Therefore, the value of $\Delta_r H°$ for the decomposition of 1.0 mol of $NH_4NO_{3(s)}$ is +365.6 kJ.

   • The balanced equation for the simple decomposition of 1 mol of ammonium nitrate can be represented as follows:

   $NH_4NO_{3(s)} + 365.6\ kJ \rightarrow N_{2(g)} + 2H_{2(g)} + \frac{3}{2}O_{2(g)}$

   • The decomposition of ammonium nitrate is an endothermic process. Therefore, the enthalpy graph for the decomposition of ammonium nitrate can be represented as follows:

Potential Energy Diagram for the Decomposition of Ammonium Nitrate

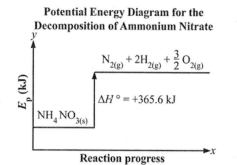

Lesson 4—Calculating Enthalpy Changes

PRACTICE EXERCISES
ANSWERS AND SOLUTIONS

1. The combustion reaction for methane gas is represented by the following equation:
   $CH_{4(g)} + 2O_{2(g)} \rightarrow CO_{2(g)} + 2H_2O_{(l)}$

   This reaction can be interpreted as follows:
   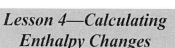
   $$\frac{802.5\ kJ\ released}{1\ mol\ of\ CH_{4(g)}\ burned}$$

Therefore, the energy released when 20.0 kg of methane gas is burned is calculated as follows:

$$\Delta H = \left\{ 20.0 \times 10^3\, g \times \frac{mol\ CH_{4(g)}}{16.05\ g} \right\}$$

$$\times \left\{ \frac{802.5\ kJ}{1\ mol\ of\ CH_{4(g)}\ burned} \right\}$$

$$\Delta H = 1\ 000\ 000.0\ kJ$$

$$\therefore \Delta H = 1.00\ GJ$$

Therefore, 1.00 GJ of energy is released when 20.0 kg of methane is burned.

3. **a)** The energy-to-mole ratios are as follows:

$$\frac{1\ 328.3\ kJ\ released}{1\ mol\ of\ CH_3OCH_{3(g)}\ consumed}$$

$$= 1\ 328.3\ kJ/mol\ CH_3OCH_{3(g)}\ consumed$$

$$\frac{1\ 328.3\ kJ\ released}{3\ mol\ of\ O_{2(g)}\ consumed}$$

$$= 442.8\ kJ/mol\ O_{2(g)}\ consumed$$

$$\frac{1\ 328.3\ kJ\ released}{2\ mol\ of\ CO_{2(g)}\ produced}$$

$$= 664.2\ kJ/mol\ CO_{2(g)}\ produced$$

$$\frac{1\ 328.3\ kJ\ released}{3\ mol\ of\ H_2O_{(g)}\ produced}$$

$$= 442.8\ kJ/mol\ H_2O_{(g)}\ produced$$

b) The energy released upon burning 1.00 kg of dimethyl ether can be calculated as follows:

$$\Delta H = \left(1.00 \times 10^3\ g \right) \left\{ \frac{mol\ of\ CH_3OCH_{3(g)}}{46.08\ g} \right\}$$

$$\times \left\{ \frac{1\ 328.3\ kJ}{mol\ of\ CH_3OCH_{3(g)}} \right\}$$

$$= 28\ 825.95\ kJ$$

$$\therefore \Delta H = 28.8\ MJ$$

Therefore, 28.8 MJ of energy is released when 1.00 kg of dimethyl ether is burned.

5. The burning of biodiesel can be interpreted as follows:

$$\frac{11\ 887\ kJ\ given\ off}{1\ mol\ of\ C_{19}H_{36}O_{2(l)}\ consumed}$$

The energy released per kilogram of biodiesel is calculated as follows:

$$\Delta H = \left(1.00 \times 10^3\ g \right) \left\{ \frac{mol\ of\ C_{19}H_{36}O_{2(l)}}{296.55\ g} \right\}$$

$$\times \left\{ \frac{11\ 887\ kJ}{mol\ of\ C_{19}H_{36}O_{2(l)}} \right\}$$

$$= 40\ 084.3\ kJ$$

$$\therefore \Delta H = 40.1\ MJ$$

Therefore, 40.1 MJ of energy is produced when 1.00 kg of biodiesel is burned. On the other hand, 45.8 MJ of energy is produced from 1.0 kg of petrodiesel. Therefore, petrodiesel is a better fuel than biodiesel in terms of energy produced.

7. Use the equality $\Delta H = n\Delta_c H$.

$$\Delta H = \left(\frac{1.00\ g}{885.61\ g/mol} \right) (35\ 099.6\ kJ/mol)$$

$$\therefore \Delta H = 39.6\ kJ$$

Therefore, 39.6 kJ of energy is produced per gram of triolein burned.

Lesson 5—Predicting Enthalpy Changes

PRACTICE EXERCISES
ANSWERS AND SOLUTIONS

1. The enthalpy change for a reaction $\left(\Delta_r H^\circ \right)$ is written as follows:

$$\Delta_r H^\circ = \sum_{products} \left(n\Delta_f H_m^{\ \circ} \right) - \sum_{reactants} \left(n\Delta_f H_m^{\ \circ} \right)$$

- n = number of moles of a substance present in the balanced chemical equation

- $\Delta_f H_m^{\ \circ}$ = standard molar enthalpy of formation of the reactants or products in kJ/mol.

The balanced chemical equation for the complete combustion of methane is as follows:

$CH_{4(g)}$	+	$O_{2(g)}$	$\rightarrow$	$CO_{2(g)}$	+	$2H_2O_{(g)}$
−74.6 kJ/mol		0 kJ/mol		−393.5 kJ/mol		−241.8 kJ/mol

Therefore, the enthalpy change can be calculated as follows:

$$\Delta_r H° = \sum_{products} \left(n\Delta_f H_m°\right) - \sum_{reactants} \left(n\Delta_f H_m°\right)$$

$$= \begin{Bmatrix} 1\ mol \times (-393.5\ kJ/mol) \\ +2\ mol \times (-241.8\ kJ/mol) \end{Bmatrix}$$
$$-\begin{Bmatrix} 1\ mol \times (-74.6\ kJ/mol) \\ +1\ mol \times (0\ kJ/mol) \end{Bmatrix}$$

$$= -393.5\ kJ - 483.6\ kJ + 74.6\ kJ$$
$$\therefore \Delta_r H° = -802.5\ kJ$$

The enthalpy change for the combustion of natural gas is –802.5 kJ.

3. The equation is given as follows:

$$\begin{array}{ccccccc} C_6H_{12}O_{6(s)} & + & 6O_{2(g)} & \rightarrow & 6CO_{2(g)} & + & 6H_2O_{(l)} \\ -1\ 273.3\ kJ/mol & & 0\ kJ/mol & & -393.5\ kJ/mol & & -285.8\ kJ/mol \end{array}$$

The enthalpy change can be calculated as follows:

$$\Delta_r H° = \sum_{products} \left(n\Delta_f H_m°\right) - \sum_{reactants} \left(n\Delta_f H_m°\right)$$

$$\Delta_r H° = \begin{Bmatrix} 6\ mol \times (-393.5\ kJ/mol) \\ +6\ mol \times (-285.8\ kJ/mol) \end{Bmatrix}$$
$$-\begin{Bmatrix} 1\ mol \times (-1\ 273.3\ kJ/mol) \\ +6\ mol \times (0\ kJ/mol) \end{Bmatrix}$$

$$\Delta_r H° = -4\ 075.8\ kJ + 1\ 273.3\ kJ$$
$$\Delta_r H° = -2\ 802.5\ kJ$$

The enthalpy change for cellular respiration is –2802.5 kJ. During this reaction, 1.0 mol of glucose is consumed. Since 1 mol of glucose is burned, it can be said that the molar enthalpy of combustion of glucose is –2 802.5 kJ/mol.

5. The balanced chemical equation for roasting 1 mol of copper(II) sulfide can be represented as follows:

$$\begin{array}{ccccccc} CuS_{(s)} & + & \frac{3}{2}O_{2(g)} & \rightarrow & CuO_{(s)} & + & SO_{2(g)} \\ -53.1\ kJ/mol & & 0\ kJ/mol & & -157.3\ kJ/mol & & -296.8\ kJ/mol \end{array}$$

$$\Delta_r H° = \sum_{products} \left(n\Delta_f H_m°\right) - \sum_{reactants} \left(n\Delta_f H_m°\right)$$

$$\Delta_r H° = \begin{Bmatrix} 1\ mol \times (-157.3\ kJ/mol) \\ +1\ mol \times (-296.8\ kJ/mol) \end{Bmatrix}$$
$$-\begin{Bmatrix} 1\ mol \times (-53.1\ kJ/mol) \\ +\frac{3}{2}\ mol \times (0\ kJ/mol) \end{Bmatrix}$$

$$= -157.3\ kJ - 296.8\ kJ + 53.1\ kJ$$
$$\Delta_r H° = -401.0\ kJ$$

Therefore, the enthalpy change to roast 1 mol of copper(II) sulfide is –401.0 kJ.

7. The balanced chemical equation for the complete combustion of 1 mol of ethyne can be represented as follows:

$$\begin{array}{ccccccc} C_2H_{2(g)} & + & \frac{5}{2}O_{2(g)} & \rightarrow & 2CO_{2(g)} & + & H_2O_{(g)} \\ +227.4\ kJ/mol & & 0\ kJ/mol & & -393.5\ kJ/mol & & -241.8\ kJ/mol \end{array}$$

$$\Delta_r H° = \sum_{products} \left(n\Delta_f H_m°\right) - \sum_{reactants} \left(n\Delta_f H_m°\right)$$

$$\Delta_r H° = \begin{Bmatrix} 2\ mol \times (-393.5\ kJ/mol) \\ +1\ mol \times (-241.8\ kJ/mol) \\ 1\ mol \times (-227.4\ kJ/mol) \\ +\frac{5}{2}\ mol \times (0\ kJ/mol) \end{Bmatrix}$$

$$= -787.0\ kJ - 541.8\ kJ - 227.4\ kJ$$
$$\Delta_r H° = -1\ 256.2\ kJ$$

The enthalpy change for the reaction is $\Delta_r H° = -1\ 256.2\ kJ$. During this reaction, 1.0 mol of ethyne is combusted (consumed). Therefore the molar enthalpy of combustion for ethyne is –1 256.2 kJ/mol.

Lesson 6—Hess's Law

PRACTICE EXERCISES
ANSWERS AND SOLUTIONS

1. Rewrite the given equations:

I. $\quad C_{(s)} + 2H_{2(g)} \rightarrow CH_{4(g)} \qquad \Delta_1 H^\circ = -74.6 \text{ kJ}$

II. $\qquad\quad C_{(g)} \rightarrow C_{(s)} \qquad\quad \Delta_2 H^\circ = -715.0 \text{ kJ}$

III. $\qquad 4H_{(g)} \rightarrow 2H_{2(g)} \qquad \Delta_3 H^\circ = -2 \times 436.0 \text{ kJ}$

$\overline{\quad C_{(g)} + 4H_{(g)} \rightarrow CH_{4(g)} \quad \Delta_{net} H^\circ = -872.0 \text{ kJ}}$

Apply Hess's law:
Equation I does not need to be manipulated.
Equation II is reversed.
Equation III is reversed and multiplied by 2.

$$\Delta_{net} H^\circ = \Delta_1 H^\circ + \Delta_2 H^\circ + \Delta_3 H^\circ$$
$$= -74.6 \text{ kJ} - 715.0 \text{ kJ} - 872 \text{ kJ}$$
$$= -1\,661.6 \text{ kJ}$$

Therefore, the enthalpy change for the reaction that forms methane gas is –1 661.6 kJ.

3. Rewrite the equations, and add them to get the net equation and enthalpy change:

I. $\quad \left[2H_{2(g)} + O_{2(g)} \rightarrow 2H_2O_{(g)}\right] \times \dfrac{3}{2} \qquad \Delta_r H^\circ = \dfrac{3}{2} \times \left(-483.6 \text{ kJ}\right)$

II. $\qquad\quad \left[2O_{3(g)} \rightarrow 3O_{2(g)}\right] \times \dfrac{1}{2} \qquad \Delta_r H^\circ = \dfrac{1}{2} \times \left(-248.6 \text{ kJ}\right)$

$\overline{\quad 3H_{2(g)} + O_{3(g)} \rightarrow 3H_2O_{(g)} \qquad \Delta_r H^\circ \left(net\right) = -849.7 \text{ kJ}}$

Therefore, the enthalpy change for the reaction that forms water is –849.7 kJ.

5. a) The balanced chemical equation for the formation of calcium carbide can be represented as follows:

$$2C_{(s)} + Ca_{(s)} \rightarrow CaC_{2(s)}$$

b) To determine the enthalpy change for the formation of $CaC_{2(s)}$, the equations are manipulated and combined.

$$CaO_{(s)} + 3C_{(s)} \rightarrow CaC_{2(s)} + CO_{(g)} \quad \Delta_r H^\circ = +464.8 \text{ kJ}$$

$$CO_{(g)} \rightarrow C_{(s)} + \dfrac{1}{2}O_{2(g)} \quad \Delta_f H^\circ = +110.5 \text{ kJ}$$

$$Ca + \dfrac{1}{2}O_{2(g)} \rightarrow CaO_{(s)} \qquad\qquad \Delta_f H^\circ = -634.9 \text{ kJ}$$

$\overline{\quad 2C_{(s)} + Ca_{(s)} \rightarrow CaC_{2(s)} \qquad\qquad\qquad \Delta_r H^\circ = -59.6 \text{ kJ}}$

Therefore, the molar enthalpy of formation of calcium carbide is –59.6 kJ/mol.

c) In part **b)**, it was determined that the $\Delta_f H_m^\circ$ for calcium carbide is –59.6 kJ/mol.

$$CaC_{2(s)} + 2\,H_2O_{(l)} \rightarrow Ca(OH)_{2(s)} + C_2H_{2(g)}$$
$$-59.6 \text{ kJ/mol} \quad -285.8 \text{ kJ/mol} \quad -985.2 \text{ kJ/mol} \quad 227.4 \text{ kJ/mol}$$

The enthalpy of the reaction $\left(\Delta_r H^\circ\right)$ can be written as follows:

$$\Delta_r H^\circ = \sum_{products} \left(n\Delta_f H_m^\circ\right) - \sum_{reactants} \left(n\Delta_f H_m^\circ\right)$$

In this equation, n is the number of moles of the chemicals in the chemical reaction.

$$\left(\Delta_r H^\circ\right) = \begin{cases} 1\ \text{mol} \times \left(-985.2\ \text{kJ/mol}\right) + 1\ \text{mol} \\ \times \left(227.4\ \text{kJ/mol}\right)\{-\}1\ \text{mol} \\ \times \left(-59.6\ \text{kJ/mol}\right) + 2\ \text{mol} \\ \times \left(-285.8\ \text{kJ/mol}\right) \end{cases}$$

$$= -985.2\ \text{kJ} + 227.4\ \text{kJ} + 59.6\ \text{kJ} + 571.6\ \text{kJ} = -126.6\ \text{kJ}$$

Therefore, the enthalpy of the reaction for producing ethyne is $\Delta_r H^\circ = 126.6\ \text{kJ}$.

Lesson 7—Predicting the Enthalpy Change of a Reaction Component

PRACTICE EXERCISES
ANSWERS AND SOLUTIONS

1. The balanced chemical equation for the combustion of 1 mol of decane can be represented as follows:

$$C_{10}H_{22(l)} + \frac{31}{2}O_{2(g)} \rightarrow 10CO_{2(g)} + 11H_2O_{(l)} + 6\ 777.9\ \text{kJ}$$

$$\quad ? \qquad 0\ \text{kJ/mol} \quad -393.5\ \text{kJ/mol} \quad -285.8\ \text{kJ/mol}$$

Note that the enthalpy of reaction, $\Delta_r H^\circ$, is $-6\ 777.9\ \text{kJ}$. The enthalpy of reaction can be represented as follows:

$$\Delta_r H^\circ = \sum_{\text{products}} \left(n\Delta_f H_m^\circ\right) - \sum_{\text{reactants}} \left(n\Delta_f H_m^\circ\right)$$

$$\Rightarrow \sum_{\text{reactants}} \left(n_f H_m^\circ\right) = \sum_{\text{products}} \left(n_f H_m^\circ\right) - \Delta_r H^\circ$$

$$= 10\ \text{mol} \times \left(-393.5\ \text{kJ/mol}\right) + 11\ \text{mol} \times \left(-285.8\ \text{kJ/mol}\right) - \left(-6\ 777.9\ \text{kJ/mol}\right)$$

$$\Delta_f H_m{}^\circ{}_{C_{10}H_{22}} = -3\ 935.0\ \text{J} - 3\ 143.8\ \text{kJ} + 6\ 777.9\ \text{kJ}$$

$$\therefore \Delta_f H_m{}^\circ{}_{C_{10}H_{22}} = -300.9\ \text{kJ/mol}$$

Therefore, the enthalpy of formation of decane is $-300.9\ \text{kJ/mol}$.

3. a) Molar mass of urea = 60.06 g/mol.

It is given that 6.00 g of urea burns to produce 63.3 kJ of energy. Therefore, 1.00 mol of urea burns to produce the following amount of energy:

$$\frac{63.3\ \text{kJ}}{6.00\ \text{g}} \times 60.06\ \text{g} = 633.6\ \text{kJ}$$

Therefore, the enthalpy of combustion of urea is $-633.6\ \text{kJ/mol}$.

The balanced chemical equation for the burning of 1 mol of urea can be represented as follows:

$$\left(NH_2\right)_2 CO_{(s)} + \frac{3}{2}O_{2(g)} \rightarrow N_{2(g)} + CO_{2(g)} + 2\ H_2O_{(l)} + 633.6\ \text{kJ}$$

$$\quad ? \qquad\quad 0\ \text{kJ/mol} \quad 0\ \text{kJ/mol} \quad -393.5\ \text{kJ/mol} \quad -285.8\ \text{kJ/mol}$$

The enthalpy of the given combustion reaction is $\Delta_r H^\circ = -633.6\ \text{kJ/mol}$.

The enthalpy of the reaction can be represented as follows:

$$\Delta_r H^\circ = \sum_{products} \left(n\Delta_f H_m^\circ \right) - \sum_{reactants} \left(n\Delta_f H_m^\circ \right)$$

$$\Rightarrow \sum_{reactants} \left(n_f H_m^\circ \right) = \sum_{products} \left(n_f H_m^\circ \right) - \Delta_r H^\circ$$

$$(1 \text{ mol})\left(\Delta_f H^\circ_{urea} \right) + \left(\frac{3}{2} \text{ mol} \right)(0 \text{ kJ/mol}) = \left\{ \begin{array}{l} (1 \text{ mol})(0 \text{ kJ/mol}) + (1 \text{ mol})(-393.5 \text{ kJ/mol}) \\ +(2 \text{ mol})(-285.8 \text{ kJ/mol}) - (-633.6 \text{ kJ}) \end{array} \right\}$$

$$\therefore \quad n\Delta_f H^\circ_{urea} = -393.5 \text{ kJ} - 571.6 \text{ kJ/mol} + 633.6 \text{ kJ}$$
$$= -331.5 \text{ kJ}$$

Therefore, the molar enthalpy of formation of urea is $\Delta_f H^\circ = -331.5$ kJ/mol .

5. The given reaction is as follows:

$$C_2H_5Cl_{(g)} \rightarrow \quad C_2H_{4(g)} \quad + \quad HCl_{(g)}$$
$$? \qquad\quad +52.4 \text{ kJ/mol} \quad -92.3 \text{ kJ/mol}$$

The enthalpy of the reaction is $\Delta_r H^\circ = +72.2$ kJ .

Enthalpy of reaction can be represented as follows:

$$\Delta_r H^\circ = \sum_{products} \left(n\Delta_f H_m^\circ \right) - \sum_{reactants} \left(n\Delta_f H_m^\circ \right)$$

$$\Rightarrow \sum_{reactants} \left(n_f H_m^\circ \right) = \sum_{products} \left(n_f H_m^\circ \right) - \Delta_r H^\circ$$

or,

$$n\Delta_f H^\circ_{C_2H_5Cl} = 1 \text{ mol}(52.4 \text{ kJ/mol}) + 1 \text{ mol}(-92.3 \text{ kJ/mol}) - (72.2 \text{ kJ})$$
$$= -52.4 \text{ kJ} - 92.3 \text{ kJ} - 72.2 \text{ kJ}$$
$$\therefore \Delta_f H^\circ_{C_2H_5Cl} = -112.1 \text{ kJ/mol}$$

Therefore, the molar enthalpy of formation of chloroethane is −112.1 kJ/mol.

Lesson 8—Using Simple and Bomb Calorimeter Data to Determine $\Delta_r H°$

PRACTICE EXERCISES
ANSWERS AND SOLUTIONS

1. The molar enthalpy of the solution of sodium nitrate is calculated as follows:

$$\Delta H = -\left(mc\Delta T\right)_{cal}$$
and $\Delta H = n\Delta_s H$
$$\therefore n\Delta_s H = -\left(mc\Delta T\right)_{cal}$$

This equation uses the following variables:
- n = number of moles of sodium nitrate dissolved in water
- m = mass of water taken
- c = specific heat capacity of water
- ΔT = temperature difference
- $\Delta_s H$ = molar enthalpy of the solution

$$\Delta_s H = \frac{-\left(mc\Delta T\right)_{cal}}{n}$$

$$\Delta_s H = \frac{-(104.52 \text{ g})(4.19 \text{ J/g}\cdot°\text{C})(-4.4°\text{C})}{\left(\dfrac{8.95 \text{ g}}{85.0 \text{ g/mol}}\right)}$$

$$= 18\ 300 \text{ J/mol}$$
$$\Delta_s H = +18.3 \text{ kJ/mol}$$

Therefore, the molar enthalpy of the solution of sodium nitrate is 18.3 kJ/mol.

Substitute the values in the given equation as follows:

$$\Delta T = -\frac{(0.1022 \text{ mol})(-75 \text{ kJ/mol})}{0.100 \text{ kg} \times 4.19 \text{ kJ/kg}\cdot°\text{C}}$$

$$\Delta T = 18.3°\text{C}$$

The final temperature is calculated as follows:
$$\Delta T = T_f - T_i$$
$$T_f = T_i + \Delta T$$
$$T_f = 22.0°\text{C} + 18.3°\text{C} = 40.3°\text{C}$$

The final temperature is 40.3°C.

3. The expression of molar enthalpy of solution gives the following equation:

$$n\Delta_r H = -\left(mc\Delta T\right)_{cal}$$

$$\Delta T = -\frac{n\Delta_r H}{\left(mc\right)_{cal}}$$

This equation uses the following variables:
- ΔT = temperature difference
- n = number of moles of salt $= \dfrac{8.30 \text{ g}}{166 \text{ g/mol}}$
- n = 0.0500 mol
- $\Delta_s H$ = molar enthalpy of solution = +21.4 kJ/mol
- m = mass of water present in calorimeter = 0.0500 kg (50.0 mL of solution contains 50.0 g of water)
- c = specific heat capacity of water = 4.19 kJ/kg·°C

Substitute the values in the given equation as follows:

$$\Delta T = -\frac{(0.0500 \text{ mol})(21.4 \text{ kJ/mol})}{(0.0500 \text{ kg})(4.19 \text{ kJ/kg}\cdot°\text{C})}$$

$$\Delta T = -5.11°\text{C}$$

The molar enthalpy of the solution is positive. This indicates that the reaction is endothermic. Therefore, a temperature drop of 5.11°C is expected, as indicated by the negative sign of ΔT.

Lesson 9—Common Applications of Thermodynamic Principles

PRACTICE EXERCISES
ANSWERS AND SOLUTIONS

1. **a)** The amount of heat generated when 60.0 g of butane is burned can be represented by the following chemical equation:

$$C_4H_{10} + \frac{13}{2}O_{2(g)} \rightarrow 4CO_{2(g)} + 5H_2O_{(g)}$$

Heat produced during the combustion of 60 g of butane is calculated as follows:

$$60.0 \text{ g} \times \frac{1 \text{ mol of } C_4H_{10}}{58.14 \text{ g}} \times 2\ 657.4 \text{ kJ/mol}$$

$$= 2\ 742.4 \text{ kJ}$$

Since all the heat goes into the water, the

amount of water that can be heated from it can be calculated as follows:

$$m = \frac{2\,742.4 \text{ kJ}}{c_{H_2O}\Delta T}$$

$$m = \frac{2\,749.0 \times 10^3 \text{ J}}{(4.19 \text{ J/g} \cdot {}^\circ\text{C})(100 - 20.0){}^\circ\text{C}}$$

$$m = 8\,181.4 \text{ g}$$

$$m = 8.18 \text{ kg}$$

Therefore, 8.18 kg of water can be heated.

b) The following three factors can be considered:
   i) Efficiency of the stove
   ii) Loss of water by evaporation
   iii) Heat loss to the surroundings

The efficiency of a stove is never 100%. Some loss of heat takes place as loss to the surroundings. The maximum amount of heat that can be transferred is approximately 70%. In part a, 100% transference of heat produced by combustion to water is assumed.

During the temperature change from 20°C to 100°C, there must be some amount of water that is lost as a result of evaporation. This evaporative loss is not considered here.

Therefore, these three factors make the calculated mass of water unrealistic.

3. a) The burning of natural gas can be represented by the following chemical equation:
$$CH_{4(g)} + 2O_{2(g)} \rightarrow CO_{2(g)} + 2H_2O_{(l)}$$

The amount of heat produced by burning 1.00 kg of natural gas can be calculated as follows:

$$\Delta H_{CH_4} = \left\{ \begin{array}{l} \left(1.00 \times 10^3 \text{ g}\right)\left(\dfrac{1 \text{ mol of } CH_4}{16.05 \text{ g}}\right) \\ \times \left(\dfrac{-802.5 \text{ kJ}}{1 \text{ mol of } CH_4}\right) \end{array} \right\}$$

$$= -50\,000 \text{ kJ}$$

$$\Delta H_{CH_4} = -50.0 \text{ MJ}$$

Therefore, 50.0 MJ of heat energy will be released by burning 1.00 kg of natural gas.

Similarly, the burning of propane can be represented by the following chemical equation:
$$C_3H_{8(g)} + 5O_{2(g)} \rightarrow 3CO_{2(g)} + 4H_2O_{(l)}$$

The amount of heat produced by burning 1.00 kg of propane can be calculated as follows:

$$\Delta H_{C_3H_8} = \left\{ \begin{array}{l} \left(1.00 \times 10^3 \text{ g}\right)\left(\dfrac{1 \text{ mol of } C_3H_8}{44.11 \text{ g}}\right) \\ \times \left(\dfrac{-2\,043.9 \text{ kJ}}{1 \text{ mol of } C_3H_8}\right) \end{array} \right\}$$

$$\therefore \Delta H_{C_3H_8} = -46\,336 \text{ kJ}$$

$$= -46.3 \text{ MJ}$$

Therefore, 46.3 MJ of energy will be produced by burning 1.00 kg of propane. Therefore, natural gas releases more energy per kilogram than propane.

b) The burning of natural gas can be represented by the following reaction equation:
$$CH_{4(g)} + 2O_{2(g)} \rightarrow CO_{2(g)} + 2H_2O_{(l)}$$

This equation can be interpreted as follows:
$$\frac{802.5 \text{ kJ given off}}{1 \text{ mol of } CH_{4(g)} \text{ consumed}}$$
$$= \frac{802.5 \text{ kJ given off}}{2 \text{ mol of } O_{2(g)} \text{ consumed}}$$
$$= \frac{802.5 \text{ kJ given off}}{1 \text{ mol of } CO_{2(g)} \text{ produced}}$$
$$= \frac{802.5 \text{ kJ given off}}{2 \text{ mol of } H_2O_{(l)} \text{ produced}}$$

The amount of heat that will be produced per kilogram of CO_2 can be calculated as follows:

$$\Delta H_{CH_4} = n\Delta_c H^\circ$$

$$= \left\{ \begin{array}{l} \left(1.00 \times 10^3 \text{ g}\right)\left(\dfrac{1 \text{ mol of } CO_2}{44.01 \text{ g}}\right) \\ \times \left(-802.5 \text{ kJ/mol}\right) \end{array} \right\}$$

$$= -18\,234.5 \text{ kJ}$$

$$\Delta H_{CH_4} = -18.2 \text{ MJ}$$

Therefore, burning natural gas releases 18.2 MJ of energy per kilogram of CO_2 produced.

Similarly, for propane, the amount of heat that will be produced can be calculated as follows:
$$C_3H_{8(g)} + 5O_{2(g)} \rightarrow 3CO_{2(g)} + 4H_2O_{(l)}$$

$$\Delta H_{C_3H_8} = \left\{ \begin{array}{l} \left(1.00 \times 10^3 \text{ g}\right)\left(\dfrac{1 \text{ mol of } CO_2}{44.01 \text{ g}}\right) \\ \times \left(\dfrac{-2\,043.9 \text{ kJ}}{3 \text{ mol of } CO_2}\right) \end{array} \right\}$$

$$\Delta H_{C_3H_8} = -15\,480.6 \text{ kJ} = -15.5 \text{ MJ}$$

Therefore, burning propane releases 15.5 MJ of energy per kilogram of CO_2 produced.

Therefore, natural gas produces more energy per kilogram of CO_2 produced.

c) Compare the calculations from parts **a)** and **b)**.
$\Delta H_{CH_4} = -50.0$ MJ per kilogram of CH_4

$\Delta H_{C_3H_8} = -46.3$ MJ per kilogram of C_3H_8

Therefore, natural gas (CH_4) is a better fuel than propane (C_3H_8) in terms of energy produced.

Lesson 10—*Energy Exchanges in Chemical Reactions*

PRACTICE EXERCISES
ANSWERS AND SOLUTIONS

1. Since the bond in A-B is stronger than the bond in A_2 and B_2, the product A-B is more stable than A_2 and B_2. Therefore, the energy of A-B should be less than A_2 and B_2. The energy diagram can be represented as follows:

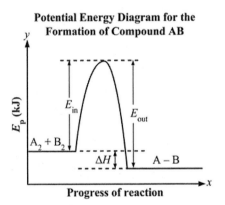

Potential Energy Diagram for the Formation of Compound AB

3. The process of dissolving an ionic compound such as potassium hydroxide (KOH) involves three steps:
I. Breaking of ionic bonds of the compound: energy is absorbed (E_I).
II. Breaking of hydrogen bonds present in water: energy is absorbed (E_{II}).
III. Formation of ion-dipole bonds (that is, when the bonds between the dissociated ions and the water molecules that surround them are formed): energy is released (E_{III}).

When the energy absorbed in the first two steps ($E_I + E_{II}$) is less than the energy released in the last step (that is, $E_I + E_{II} < E_{III}$), the process is exothermic on the whole.

Since potassium hydroxide (KOH) dissolves exothermically, the sum of the first two energies ($E_I + E_{II}$) is less than the energy that is released during the formation of the ion-dipole bonds (E_{III}).

5. Catalysts are substances that speed up the rate of a reaction without being consumed in it. A catalyst remains as it is when the reaction is over. Catalysts speed up the reaction rate by lowering the activation energy, as shown in the following graph:

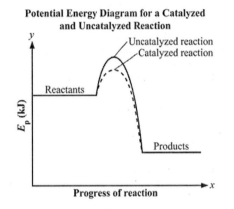

Potential Energy Diagram for a Catalyzed and Uncatalyzed Reaction

The damage to the ozone layer is more extensive when chlorine atoms act as catalysts. Chlorine atoms are not consumed during the reaction. Each chlorine atom can destroy 1000 molecules of ozone.

Practice Test

ANSWERS AND SOLUTIONS

1.
$$6CO_{2(g)} + 6H_2O_{(l)} \rightarrow C_6H_{12}O_{6(s)} + 6O_{2(g)}$$
$$-393.5 \text{ kJ/mol} \quad -285.8 \text{ kJ/mol} \quad -1\,273.3 \text{ kJ/mol} \quad 0 \text{ kJ/mol}$$

$$\Delta_r H^\circ = \sum_{products} \left(n\Delta_f H_m^\circ\right) - \sum_{reactants} \left(n\Delta_f H_m^\circ\right)$$
$$\Delta_r H^\circ = 1 \text{ mol}\left(-1\,273.3 \text{ kJ/mol}\right)$$
$$- \left\{ \begin{array}{l} 6 \text{ mol}\left(-393.5 \text{ kJ/mol}\right) \\ +6 \text{ mol}\left(-285.8 \text{ kJ/mol}\right) \end{array} \right\}$$
$$= \left(-1\,273.3 \text{ kJ}\right) - \left(-4\,075.8 \text{ kJ}\right)$$
$$\Delta_r H^\circ = +2\,802.5 \text{ kJ}$$

The reaction is endothermic.

3. $C_2H_{4(g)} + 3O_{2(g)} \rightarrow 2CO_{2(g)} + 2H_2O_{(g)}$

$\Delta_r H° = \sum\limits_{products} \left(n\Delta_f H_m°\right) - \sum\limits_{reactants} \left(n\Delta_f H_m°\right)$

$\Delta_r H° = \left[2\Delta_f H°\left(CO_2\right) + 2\Delta_f H°\left(H_2O\right)\right]$
$\qquad - \left[\Delta_f H°\left(C_2H_4\right) + 3\Delta_f H°\left(O_2\right)\right]$

$\Delta_r H° = \left[2\left(-393.5\right) + 2\left(-241.8\right)\right]$
$\qquad - \left[52.4 + 3\left(0\right)\right]$

$\Delta_r H° = -787.0 - 483.6 - 52.4 \text{ kJ}$

$\Delta_r H° = -1\,323.0 \text{ kJ}$

During the given combustion reaction, 1.00 mol of $C_2H_{4(g)}$ is consumed. Therefore, the molar enthalpy of combustion for $C_2H_{4(g)}$ is $-1\,323.0$ kJ/mol.

5. The reaction is exothermic since $\Delta H = -92.4$ kJ.

Therefore, the energy of products is less than the energy of reactants. Since the products have less energy than the reactants, the reactants released the extra energy when they changed into products.

7.
$\qquad H_{2(g)} + I_{2(g)} \rightarrow \qquad 2HI_{(g)}$
$\Delta_f H_m° \quad 0 \qquad 0 \qquad +26.5 \text{ kJ/mol}$

$\Delta_r H° = \sum\limits_{products} \left(n\Delta_f H_m°\right) - \sum\limits_{reactants} \left(n\Delta_f H_m°\right)$

$\Delta_r H° = 2 \text{ mol} \times 26.5 \text{ kJ/mol}$

$\Delta_r H° = 53.0 \text{ kJ}$

Adding a catalyst to the reaction will speed up the rate of reaction, but will have no effect on $\Delta_r H°$.

The $\Delta_r H°$ will remain the same.

9. $n\Delta_r H = n\Delta_r H_m$ $\Delta_r H$ for the reaction = 124.0 kJ

The energy-to-mole ratio for $Cl_{(g)}$ is $\dfrac{124.0 \text{ kJ}}{1 \text{ mol}}$.

$n_{Cl_{2(g)}} = \dfrac{5.00 \text{ g}}{70.9 \text{ g/mol}} = 0.0705 \text{ mol of } Cl_{2(g)}$

The energy absorbed is calculated as follows:

$0.0705 \text{ mol} \times \left(\dfrac{124.0 \text{ kJ}}{1 \text{ mol}}\right) = 8.74 \text{ kJ}$

11. $n\Delta_c H = -C\Delta T$

$C = 9.624 \text{ kJ/°C}$

$\Delta T = 25.75°C - 93.90°C$
$\quad = 1.85°C$

$n = (1.173 \text{ g})\left(\dfrac{\text{mol}}{90.09 \text{ g}}\right) = 0.0130 \text{ mol } C_3H_6O_3$

$0.0130 \text{ mol}\left(\Delta_c H\right) = -\left(9.624 \text{ kJ/°C}\right) \times 1.85°C$

$\Delta_c H = -1\,369.5 \text{ kJ/mol}$
$\quad = -1.37 \text{ MJ/mol}$

$n_{C_3H_6O_3} \text{ in } 1.00 \text{ g} = \dfrac{1.00 \text{ g}}{90.09 \text{ g/mol}}$
$\qquad = 0.0111 \text{ mol in } 1.00 \text{ g}$
$\qquad \text{ of } C_3H_6O_{3(s)}$

Therefore, the enthalpy change per gram can be calculated as follows:

$= -1.37 \text{ MJ/mol} \times \dfrac{0.0111 \text{ mol}}{1.00 \text{ g}}$

$= -15.2 \text{ kJ/g}$

13. The mathematical expression of Hess's law is as follows:

$\Delta_{net} H = \Delta_1 H + \Delta_2 H + \Delta_3 H + ...$

Manipulate the equations before combining.

The first equation is multiplied by 2.

$2S_{(s)} + 2O_{2(g)} \rightarrow 2SO_{2(g)} \quad \Delta H = 2 \times \left(-297 \text{ kJ}\right)$

The second equation is reversed.

$2SO_{2(g)} + O_{2(g)} \rightarrow 2SO_{3(g)} \quad \Delta H = -198 \text{ kJ}$

The manipulated equations are combined as follows:

$2S_{(s)} + 3O_{2(g)} \rightarrow 2SO_{3(g)}$

$\Delta_r H = 2 \times \left(-297 \text{ kJ}\right) + \left(-198 \text{ kJ}\right)$

$\Delta_r H = -792 \text{ kJ}$

15. The potential energy diagram for the endothermic reaction can be represented as follows:

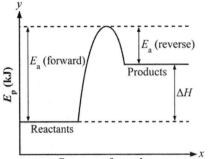

Progress of reaction

The following equivalency can be observed from the diagram:

$$E_{a(reverse)} = E_{a(forward)} - (\Delta H)$$

17. Catalysts provide an alternate pathway for a reaction to take place by decreasing the activation energy. Therefore, the addition of a catalyst to a reaction leads to a decrease in the activation energy of the reaction. Only the addition of a catalyst can alter the activation energy of a reaction.

ELECTROCHEMICAL CHANGES

Lesson 1—Oxiation and Reduction

PRACTICE EXERCISES
ANSWERS AND SOLUTIONS

1. Metals in the oxidized state are not in their atomic form; they are positive ions. In Fe_2O_3, each oxygen atom has extracted two electrons from the iron atoms, leaving them with a +3 charge. In order to return iron to the neutral state of Fe, 6 electrons are necessary for the reduction of the iron(III) ions into iron metal (3 for each iron(III) ion).

3. The oxidizing agent is the substance that gets reduced in the reaction. Silver goes from a +1 state to a neutral state, which represents a one-electron reduction for each silver atom. The half-reaction is as follows: $Ag^+_{(aq)} + e^- \rightarrow Ag_{(s)}$

The reducing agent is the atom that gets oxidized in the reaction. Copper goes from a neutral state to a +2 state, which represents a two-electron oxidation for each copper atom. The half-reaction is as follows: $Cu_{(s)} \rightarrow Cu^{2+}_{(aq)} + 2e^-$

5. The oxidation numbers for the reaction are as follows:

$$\overset{0}{4S_{(s)}} + 4\overset{+1\ -2}{H_2O_{(l)}} \rightarrow \overset{+6\ -2}{SO_4}{}^{2-}_{(aq)} + 3\overset{+1\ -2}{HS}{}^-_{(aq)} + 5\overset{+1}{H}{}^+_{(aq)}$$

Oxygen and hydrogen most often have oxidation numbers of –2 and +1, respectively. Sulfur, in its elemental form, has an oxidation number of 0. In $SO_4{}^{2-}$, each oxygen contributes –2 for a total of –8, leaving the sulfur to have a +6 oxidation number to equal the –2 overall charge of the compound. In HS^-, hydrogen has a +1 oxidation number, which means that sulfur has a –2 oxidation number to equal the –1 overall charge. Elemental sulfur has been both oxidized (to +6) and reduced (to –2). Therefore, the reaction is a redox disproportionation reaction.

7. A redox table ranks half-reactions according to the relative strength of the substance as an oxidizing and reducing agent, with the best oxidizing agents on top. Since the reaction in which A^+ goes to A (a reduction) does not occur with any reducing agent, it is safe to assume it is lowest on the table. The reduction of B^+ to B occurs with every other reducing agent, which means it is highest on the table. D^+ (the oxidizing agent) reacts with C (the reducing agent), which means D is higher than C on the table. The completed table is as follows:

strongest oxidizing agent

$$B^+_{(aq)} + e^- \leftrightarrow B_{(s)}$$
$$D^+_{(aq)} + e^- \leftrightarrow D_{(s)}$$
$$C^+_{(aq)} + e^- \leftrightarrow C_{(s)}$$
$$A^+_{(aq)} + e^- \leftrightarrow A_{(s)}$$

strongest reducing agent

9. Copper(II) sulfate becomes $Cu^{2+}_{(aq)}$ and $SO_4{}^{2-}_{(aq)}$ in an aqueous solution. The entities present are $Fe_{(s)}$, $Cu^{2+}_{(aq)}$, and $SO_4{}^{2-}_{(aq)}$. Since $Cu^{2+}_{(aq)}$ is the oxidizing agent and its half-reaction has a higher reduction potential then the iron, the reaction is spontaneous, and $Fe_{(s)}$ will react with $Cu^{2+}_{(aq)}$.

11. LEO stand for Loss of Electrons occurs in Oxidation. GER stands for Gain of Electrons occurs in Reduction.

13. Cellular respiration:
$C_6H_{12}O_6 + 6O_2 \rightarrow 6CO_2 + 6H_2O +$ energy

Glucose ($C_6H_{12}O_6$) is oxidized, and oxygen is reduced.

Photosynthesis:
$6CO_2 + 6H_2O +$ energy $\rightarrow C_6H_{12}O_6 + 6O_2$

CO_2 is reduced, and H_2O is oxidized.

15. I. Identify the oxidizing agent and the reducing agent in the reaction.

II. Locate both the oxidizing agent (on the left-hand side of the table) and the reducing agent (on the right-hand side).

III. If the oxidizing agent is above the reducing agent on the table, the reaction will be spontaneous.

Lesson 2—Redox Reactions in Solution

PRACTICE EXERCISES
ANSWERS AND SOLUTIONS

1. The entities present are $Al_{(s)}$, $Ag^+_{(aq)}$, and $NO_3^-{}_{(aq)}$.

$Al_{(s)}$ is the strongest reducing agent, and $Ag^+_{(aq)}$ is the strongest oxidizing agent.
The half-reactions for this reaction are as follows:

$Al_{(s)} \rightarrow Al^{3+}_{(aq)} + 3e^-$

$Ag^+_{(aq)} + e^- \rightarrow Ag_{(s)}$

Since the aluminum half-reaction involves three electrons and the silver only one electron, the silver half-reaction must be multiplied by 3 to balance the electrons:

$Al_{(s)} \rightarrow Al^{3+}_{(aq)} + 3e^-$

$3\left(Ag^+_{(aq)} + e^- \rightarrow Ag_{(s)}\right)$

When combined, the following balanced redox equation results:

$Al_{(s)} + 3Ag^+_{(aq)} \rightarrow Al^{3+}_{(aq)} + 3Ag_{(s)}$

3. $\overset{0}{Cu}_{(s)} + \overset{+1\ +5\ -2}{H\,N\,O_{3(aq)}}$

$\rightarrow \overset{+2}{Cu}\left(\overset{+5\ -2}{NO_3}\right)_{2(aq)} + 2\overset{+2\ -2}{NO}_{(g)} + \overset{+1\ -2}{H_2\,O}_{(l)}$

The oxidation number of Cu changes from 0 to +2 (it increases by 2). The oxidation number of N changes from +5 to +2 (it decreases by 3).

The net change in oxidation number is +2 for copper and –3 for nitrogen. It should be noted that only some of the nitrogen goes through this change. Ignore the NO_3^- on each side. Multiply the Cu reactant by 3 and the N product by 2 to obtain a net transfer of six electrons.

$3\,Cu_{(s)} + HNO_{3(aq)}$

$\rightarrow Cu\left(NO_3\right)_{2(aq)} + 2\,NO_{(g)} + H_2O_{(l)}$

Next, balance copper.

$3\,Cu_{(s)} + HNO_{3(aq)}$

$\rightarrow 3Cu\left(NO_3\right)_{2(aq)} + 2\,NO_{(g)} + H_2O_{(l)}$

Then, balance nitrogen.

$3\,Cu_{(s)} + 8HNO_{3(aq)}$

$\rightarrow 3Cu\left(NO_3\right)_{2(aq)} + 2\,NO_{(g)} + H_2O_{(l)}$

Then balance oxygen.

$3\,Cu_{(s)} + 8HNO_{3(aq)}$

$\rightarrow 3Cu\left(NO_3\right)_{2(aq)} + 2\,NO_{(g)} + 4H_2O_{(l)}$

This also balances the hydrogen.

5. Balance the following reaction:
$UO^{2+}_{(aq)} + Cr_2O_7^{2-}{}_{(aq)} \rightarrow UO_2^{2+}{}_{(aq)} + Cr^{3+}_{(aq)}$

Step 1
Write the skeleton half-reactions.

$UO^{2+}_{(aq)} \rightarrow UO_2^{2+}{}_{(aq)}$

$Cr_2O_7^{2-}{}_{(aq)} \rightarrow Cr^{3+}_{(aq)}$

Step 2
Balance the half-reactions for the following atoms:

• Atoms other than H and O

• O atoms. Balance O by adding H_2O with the needed coefficient.

• H atoms. Balance H by adding H^+ with the needed coefficient.

$UO^{2+}_{(aq)} + H_2O_{(l)} \rightarrow UO_2^{2+}{}_{(aq)} + 2H^+_{(aq)}$

$Cr_2O_7^{2-}{}_{(aq)} + 14H^+_{(aq)} \rightarrow 2Cr^{3+}_{(aq)} + 7H_2O_{(l)}$

Step 3
Balance the half-reactions for electric charge by adding electrons.

$UO^{2+}_{(aq)} + H_2O_{(l)} \rightarrow UO_2^{3+}{}_{(aq)} + 2H^+_{(aq)} + 2e^-$

$Cr_2O_7^{2-}{}_{(aq)} + 14H^+_{(aq)} + 6e^- \rightarrow 2Cr^{3+}_{(aq)} + 7H_2O_{(l)}$

Step 4
Multiply the half-reactions through to make equal numbers of electrons in each.

$3UO^{2+'}_{(aq)} + 3H_2O_{(l)} \rightarrow 3UO_2^{2+}{}_{(aq)} + 6H^+_{/(aq)} + 6e^-$

$Cr_2O_7^{2-}{}_{(aq)} + 14H^+_{(aq)} + 6e^- \rightarrow 2Cr^{3+}_{(aq)} + 7H_2O_{(l)}$

Step 5
Combine the half-reactions.

$3UO^{2+}_{(aq)} + 3H_2O_{(l)} + Cr_2O_7^{2-}{}_{(aq)} + 14H^+_{(aq)} + 6e^-$

$\rightarrow 3UO_2^{2+}{}_{(aq)} + 6H^+_{(aq)} + 6e^- + 2Cr^{3+}_{(aq)} + 7H_2O_{(l)}$

Step 6
Simplify by cancelling entities that appear on both sides.

$$3UO^{2+}_{(aq)} + 3H_2O_{(l)} + Cr_2O_7^{2-}{}_{(aq)} + \overset{8}{\cancel{14}}\ H^+{}_{(aq)} + \cancel{6e^-}$$
$$\rightarrow 3UO_2^{2+}{}_{(aq)} + \cancel{6H^+}{}_{(aq)} + \cancel{6e^-} + 2Cr^{3+}{}_{(aq)} + \overset{4}{\cancel{7}}\ H_2O_{(l)}$$

The final balanced equation is as follows:
$$3UO^{2+}_{(aq)} + Cr_2O_7^{2-}{}_{(aq)} + 8H^+{}_{(aq)}$$
$$\rightarrow 3UO_2^{2+}{}_{(aq)} + 2Cr^{3+}{}_{(aq)} + 4H_2O_{(l)}$$

Lesson 3—Redox Titrations

PRACTICE EXERCISES
ANSWERS AND SOLUTIONS

1. A sample of $K_2Cr_2O_{7(aq)}$ of known volume can be titrated with $FeCl_{2(aq)}$. $Cr_2O_7^{2-}{}_{(aq)}$ is a strong oxidizing agent and would oxidize the Fe^{2+} to Fe^{3+}. The balanced redox equation given indicates that for every mole of $Cr_2O_7^{2-}$ present, 6 mol of Fe^{2+} are needed to reduce it to Cr^{3+} (a 1:6 molar ratio). From the titration, the volume of Fe^{2+} can be determined. The value can be multiplied by the known concentration of the Fe^{2+} solution to calculate the number of moles of Fe^{2+}. The number of moles of Fe^{2+} would be divided by 6 to get the number of moles of $Cr_2O_7^{2-}$ in the original solution, which could then be used to calculate the concentration of the $K_2Cr_2O_{7(aq)}$ solution.

3. $n_{Cr_2O_7^{2-}}$ $n_{Sn^{2+}}$
    0.015 0 L   0.020 0 L
    0.0300 mol/L   ?

    $$n_{Cr_2O_7^{2-}} = (0.0300\ \text{mol/L}) \times 0.0150\ \text{L}$$
    $$= 0.000\ 450\ \text{mol}$$
    $$n_{Sn^{2+}} = 0.000\ 450\ \text{mol} \times \frac{3}{1}$$
    $$= 0.001\ 35\ \text{mol}$$
    $$[Sn^{2+}] = \frac{0.001\ 35\ \text{mol}}{0.0200\ \text{L}}$$
    $$= 0.0675\ \text{mol/L}$$

5. **a)** $Fe^{2+} \rightarrow Fe^{3+}$
            $MnO_4^- \rightarrow Mn^{2+}$

    b) Balance the half-reactions.
    $$Fe^{2+} \rightarrow Fe^{3+} + e^-$$
    $$MnO_4^- + 8H^+ + 5e^- \rightarrow Mn^{2+} + 4H_2O$$

Multiply to balance electrons.
$$5Fe^{2+} \rightarrow 5Fe^{3+} + 5e^-$$
$$MnO_4^- + 8H^+ + 5e^- \rightarrow Mn^{2+} + 4H_2O$$

Combine, and simplify.
$$Fe^{2+} + MnO_4^- + 8H^+ \rightarrow 5Fe^{3+} + Mn^{2+} + 4H_2O$$

c) $n_{Fe^{2+}}$ $n_{MnO_4^-}$
      1.635 g   0.02487 L
      55.85 g/mol   ?

$$n_{Fe^{2+}} = \frac{1.635\ \text{g}}{55.85\ \text{g/mol}}$$
$$= 0.029\ 27\ \text{mol}$$
$$n_{MnO_4^-} = 0.029\ 27\ \text{mol} \times \frac{1}{5}$$
$$= 0.005\ 855\ \text{mol}$$
$$[KMnO_4] = [MnO_4^-]$$
$$= \frac{0.005\ 855\ \text{mol}}{0.024\ 87\ \text{L}}$$
$$= 0.235\ 4\ \text{mol/L}$$

Lesson 4—Voltaic Cells

PRACTICE EXERCISES
ANSWERS AND SOLUTIONS

1.

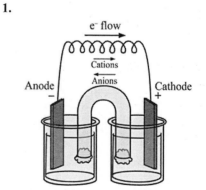

3. The external circuit connects the two half-reactions occurring in each cell. It is by this connection that the electrons can transfer from the anode to the cathode. Without a means to transfer electrons, the cell would generate no current.

5. In cell notation, the left side always describes the anode, and the right side always describes the cathode. Also, this is a voltaic cell because the two solutions are separated by a physical barrier represented by the symbol ‖. The reaction at the cathode is the reduction of dichromate onto a platinum electrode.

The reaction at the anode is the oxidation of silver. The half-reactions are as follows:

$$Ag_{(s)} \rightarrow Ag^+_{(aq)} + e^-$$
$$Cr_2O_7^{2-}_{(aq)} + 14H^+_{(aq)} + 6e^- \rightarrow 2Cr^{3+}_{(aq)} + 7H_2O_{(l)}$$

7. All standard reduction potentials are measured in comparison with the standard hydrogen half-cell, which is represented by the following half-reaction:

$$2H^+_{(aq)} + 2e^- \square \ H_{2(g)} \quad E^\circ_r = 0.00 \text{ V}$$

A voltaic cell is constructed with the hydrogen half-cell and a half-cell of the reaction of interest. Then, a voltmeter is placed between the cells. The positive terminal on the voltmeter should always be attached to the cathode in order to get a positive cell potential.

When the reaction between hydrogen and another half-cell gives a positive reading, it means the half-cell that happens to be hooked up to the positive terminal is the cathode. If hydrogen is the cathode, then the other cell has a reduction potential equal to zero minus the voltmeter reading. If hydrogen is the anode, the voltmeter reading is exactly the standard reduction potential of the other half-cell. Therefore, when an entity is a better oxidizing agent than hydrogen, it will act as the cathode, and it will have a positive reduction potential. When an entity is a better reducing agent than hydrogen, it will act as the anode, and it will have a negative standard reduction potential. The following equations illustrate this:

$$E^\circ_{r(anode)} = E^\circ_{r(cathode)} - E^\circ_{cell}$$
$$\text{since } E^\circ_{cell} = E^\circ_{r(cathode)} - E^\circ_{r(anode)}$$

E°_{cell} is always positive, and either the cathode or the anode is zero. If the cathode is zero, a negative standard reduction potential results. If the anode is zero, a positive one results.

9. Either oxidation or reduction could occur. A metal ion may collide with the electrode, gain electrons from it, and be converted to a metal atom (M). The ion is reduced. Alternatively, the metal atom (M) on the surface of the electrode may lose electrons to the electrode and enter the solution as a metal ion.

11. $E^\circ_{cell} = E^\circ_{\frac{Cl_2}{Cl^-}} - E^\circ_{\frac{Fe^{2+}}{Fe^{3+}}}$

$\quad = +1.36 \text{ V} - (+0.77 \text{ V})$

$\quad = 0.59 \text{ V}$

Lesson 5—Electrolytic Cells

PRACTICE EXERCISES
ANSWERS AND SOLUTIONS

1. The reaction that occurs in a voltaic cell is spontaneous, so the cell potential is always greater than zero, and energy (voltage) is produced. An electrolytic cell does not have a spontaneous reaction. It is used to perform electrolysis, which is the forcing of a non-spontaneous reaction. Voltaic cells are primarily used for batteries in flashlights, watches, cars, and other electrical equipment. Electrolytic cells are commonly used electroplating, refining metals, and recharging car batteries.

3. $2H_2O_{(l)} + 2Cl^-_{(aq)} \rightarrow H_{2(g)} + 2OH^-_{(aq)} + Cl_{2(g)}$

$E^\circ_{cell} = E^\circ_{r(cathode)} - E^\circ_{r(anode)}$
$E^\circ_{cell} = -0.83 \text{ V} - (1.36 \text{ V})$
$E^\circ_{cell} = -2.19 \text{ V}$

The difference between a voltaic and an electrolytic cell is that the reaction is spontaneous in the voltaic cell but non-spontaneous in the electrolytic cell. In the given cell, the E°_{cell} is negative; therefore, the reaction is non-spontaneous, and it is an electrolytic cell.

5. The batteries provide electricity/voltage for these portable devices. In order for a reaction to produce electricity/voltage, it must undergo a spontaneous reaction, which makes them voltaic cells. During the process of recharging, a voltage source is provided to force the reverse, non-spontaneous reaction. During recharging, the batteries act as electrolytic cells.

7. a) $E^\circ_{cell} = E^\circ_{r(cathode)} - E^\circ_{r(anode)}$
$\quad = +1.69 \text{ V} - (-0.36 \text{ V})$
$\quad = 2.05 \text{ V}$

b) The reaction is spontaneous because the E°_{cell} value is positive. When the battery is running (discharging), the spontaneous reaction produces electricity. In order for the battery not to die, an external energy is applied to the battery while the car is running, which recharges the battery. At times, the lead-acid storage acts as both a voltaic and an electrolytic cell.

Lesson 6—Faraday's Law and Electrical Energy

PRACTICE EXERCISES
ANSWERS AND SOLUTIONS

1. Faraday's constant gives the amount of charge for every mole of electrons. It allows you to calculate the number of electrons given amount of charge (current) and the amount of time. Each redox half-reaction has the number of electrons needed for each atom produced embedded in it. Therefore, the amount of pure substance produced from a redox reaction can be calculated.

3.
$$n_{e^-} = \frac{It}{F}$$
$$= \frac{(0.175 \text{ C/s})(1.5 \text{ h})(3\ 600 \text{ s/h})}{9.65 \times 10^4 \text{ C/mol e}^-}$$
$$= 9.79 \times 10^{-3} \text{ mol e}^-$$

5.
$$n_{Ag_{(s)}} = \frac{m}{M}$$
$$= \frac{0.150 \text{ g}}{107.87 \text{ g/mol}}$$
$$= 1.39 \times 10^{-3} \text{ mol/spoon}$$
$$= 1.39 \times 10^{-1} \text{ mol for 100 spoons}$$
$$n_{Ag_{(s)}} = n_{e^-}$$
$$n_{e^-} = \frac{It}{F}$$
$$1.39 \times 10^{-1} \text{ mol e}^- = \frac{(0.247 \text{ C/s})t}{9.65 \times 10^4 \text{ C/mol e}^-}$$
$$t = 54\ 327 \text{ s}$$
$$t = 54\ 327 \text{ s} \times \frac{1 \text{ h}}{3\ 600 \text{ s}} = 15.1 \text{ h}$$

Practice Test

ANSWERS AND SOLUTIONS

1. Reduction is defined as a chemical process in which the oxidation number of the element decreases.

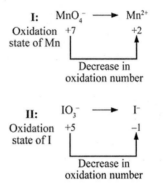

Therefore, half-reactions I and II represent the process of reduction.

Oxidation is defined as a chemical process in which the oxidation number of the element increases.

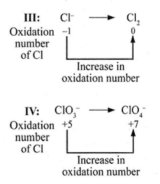

Therefore, half-reactions III and IV represent the process of oxidation.

3. • Species that undergo a loss of electrons during reactions are called reducing agents.
   • Reducing agents are readily oxidized by the loss of electrons.
   • One of the elements in a reducing agent has an increase in its oxidation number.
   • According to the table of the standard reduction potentials of half-cells, strong reducing agents have negative reduction potentials.

5. The oxidation numbers for the atoms in the reaction are as follows:

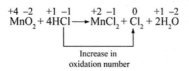

The oxidation number of chlorine changes from –1 to 0.

The oxidation number of manganese changes from +4 to +2.

7. In redox reactions, oxidation and reduction occur simultaneously by the transfer of electrons from the reducing agent to the oxidizing agent.

Oxidation and reduction occur in the reactions represented by equations **A**, **B**, and **C**. Therefore, these reactions are redox reactions.

A.

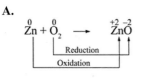

B.

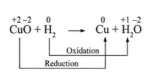

C.

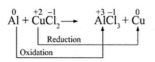

D. The oxidation numbers for equation IV are as follows:

$$\overset{+3}{Fe_2}\overset{-2}{O_3} + \overset{+1}{H}\overset{-1}{Cl} \rightarrow \overset{+3}{Fe}\overset{-1}{Cl_3} + \overset{+1}{H_2}\overset{-2}{O}$$

It can be observed from the reaction that the oxidation numbers of all the atoms are unchanged. Therefore, this reaction does not represent a redox reaction.

9. A substance that involves a decrease in the oxidation number of one or more of its elements is said to be reduced, and a substance that involves an increase in the oxidation number of one or more of its elements is said to be oxidized.

The oxidation numbers for the reaction are as follows:

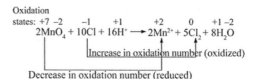

Therefore, in the given reaction, chlorine is oxidized, and manganese is reduced.

11. The solution of Fe^{3+} is capable of oxidizing copper metal to Cu^{2+}. Therefore, Fe^{3+} is a stronger oxidizing agent than Cu^{2+}. The solution of Fe^{2+} is not capable of reacting with Cu. Therefore, Fe^{2+} is a weaker oxidizing agent then Cu^{2+}.

Ordered from weakest to strongest, the oxidizing agents are: Fe^{2+}, Cu^{2+}, and Fe^{3+}.

13. Mg^{2+} (an oxidizing agent) is below Ni (a reducing agent) in the table. Therefore, according to the rule of spontaneity, these reactants will not react spontaneously.
Cu^{2+} is an oxidizing agent, and iron (Fe) is a reducing agent. Cu^{2+} is above iron on the table of standard electrode potentials. Therefore, according to the rule of spontaneity, iron will react spontaneously to reduce Cu^{2+} to Cu and will get oxidized to Fe^{2+}.

Mg^{2+} (an oxidizing agent) is below Zn (a reducing agent) in the table. These reactants will not react spontaneously.

Ca^{2+} (an oxidizing agent) is placed below Al (a reducing agent) in the table. These reactants will not react spontaneously.

15. The oxidation numbers for the reaction are as follows:

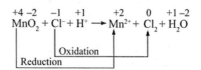

MnO_2 gets reduced to Mn^{2+} in the given reaction. Therefore, the reduction half-reaction is represented as follows:
$MnO_2 \rightarrow Mn^{2+}$.

The balanced reduction half-reaction is represented as follows:
$$MnO_2 + 4H^+ + 2e^- \rightarrow Mn^{2+} + 2H_2O$$

17. The chemical species involved in the given cell are Zn, Zn^{2+}, Cu, Cu^{2+}, SO_4^{2-}, and H_2O.

Zn is the strongest reducing agent, and Cu^{2+} is the strongest oxidizing agent.

Therefore, the Zn electrode acts as the anode, and the Cu electrode acts as the cathode.

In a voltaic cell, the electrons flow from the anode to the cathode in the external circuit.

In the given cell, electrons flow from the zinc electrode to the copper electrode through the external circuit.

19. Aluminum is a stronger reducing agent than iron. It will get oxidized during the process.

Reaction at cathode (reduction):
$$Fe^{2+}_{(aq)} + 2e^- \rightarrow Fe_{(s)}$$

Reaction at anode (oxidation):
$$Al_{(s)} \rightarrow Al^{+3} + 3e^-$$

Therefore, iron is formed at the cathode, and aluminum is consumed at the anode. The mass of the cathode increases, and the mass of the anode decreases.

21. When voltage is applied across molten NaCl, the cations (Na^+), which are positively charged, move toward the cathode, which is the negatively charged electrode. The anions (Cl^-), which are negatively charged, move toward the anode, which is the positively charged electrode.

Therefore, Na^+ ions move toward the cathode, and the following reaction occurs at the cathode:
$$Na^+_{(l)} + e^- \rightarrow Na_{(s)}$$

23. Zn is the strongest reducing agent, and Ni^{2+} is the strongest oxidizing agent. The Ni electrode acts as the cathode, and the Zn electrode acts as the anode.

The cathode half-reaction is as follows:
$$Ni^{2+}_{(aq)} + 2e^- \rightarrow Ni_{(s)}; \ E^°_r = -0.26 \text{ V}$$

The anode half-reaction is as follows:
$$Zn_{(s)} \rightarrow Zn^{2+}_{(aq)} + 2e^-; \ E^°_r = -0.76 \text{ V}$$

The net equation is as follows:
$$Ni^{2+}_{(aq)} + Zn_{(s)} \rightarrow Ni_{(s)} + Zn^{2+}_{(aq)}$$

Therefore, the value of $E^°_{cell}$ can be calculated as follows:
$$E^°_{cell} = E^°_{r(cathode)} - E^°_{r(anode)}$$
$$= -0.26 - (-0.76)$$
$$= +0.50 \text{ V}$$

The net voltage produced by the electrochemical cell is +0.50 V.

25. $Cu^{2+} + 2e^- \rightarrow Cu_{(s)}$

$$n_{e^-} = \frac{It}{F}$$
$$= \frac{(5.0 \text{ C/s} \times 10.0 \text{ min} \times 60.0 \text{ s/min})}{9.65 \times 10^4 \text{ C/mol e}^-}$$
$$= 0.0311 \text{ mol e}^-$$

$$n_{Cu_{(s)}} = 0.0311 \text{ mol e}^- \times \frac{1 \text{ mol Cu}_{(s)}}{2 \text{ mol e}^-}$$

$$\text{mass Cu}_{(s)} = 0.01555 \text{ mol Cu} \times 63.55 \text{ g/mol}$$

Therefore, the mass of copper that was electroplated was 0.99 g.

ORGANIC CHEMISTRY

Lesson 1—Organic Chemistry and Alkanes

PRACTICE EXERCISES ANSWERS AND SOLUTIONS

1. The carbon compounds that are not organic include oxides, carbides, carbonates, bicarbonates, and cyanides. Organic compounds must be covalently bonded.

a) Hydrogen cyanide is not organic because it contains an ionic bond.

b) Sodium carbonate is not organic because it is a salt that dissociates in water.

c) $C_3H_6O_2$ is an organic ester called methyl ethanoate. The structure of $C_3H_6O_2$ is shown in the following diagram:

$$\begin{array}{c} \quad \quad O \\ \quad \quad \| \\ CH_3-C-O-CH_3 \end{array}$$

d) Sodium bicarbonate is an inorganic salt.

e) Acetic acid is an organic compound containing carbon, hydrogen, and oxygen.

f) $C_6H_{12}O_6$ is an organic compound known as glucose.

g) Carbon monoxide is an inorganic carbon compound.

h) Hypochlorous acid is an inorganic substance that is formed using ionic bonds.

3. a) Methane and propane gas have different boiling points, so they can be separated by a process of fractional distillation because they will change from a gas to a liquid at a different temperature. The mixture of the gases can be heated and then cooled in a distillation tower, where they will condense to a liquid at different temperatures.

b) Water is a polar substance, and oil is not. The two liquids are immiscible, which means that they neither dissolve nor react chemically with one another. In order to separate a mixture of the two, the water could be frozen or boiled. It would also be possible to let the two liquids separate from one another, since crude oil has a lower density and will float atop water.

5. The products of hydrocarbon combustion are energy, carbon dioxide, and water.

The combustion of propane gas is represented by the following equation:
$$C_3H_{8(g)} + 5O_{2(g)} \rightarrow 3CO_{2(g)} + 4H_2O_{(g)}$$

7. a) The branches must be numbered so they are attached to the lowest numbered carbon in the parent chain, and the parent chain must be the longest continuous chain of carbons. This alkane is 3-methylhexane.

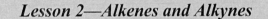

b) The parent chain must be the longest continuous chain of carbons. This alkane is 2,4-dimethylhexane.

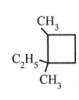

c) The branches must be numbered so they are attached to the lowest numbered carbon in the parent chain. This alkane is 2,3-dimethylpentane.

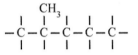

d) The branches must be numbered so they are attached to the lowest numbered carbon in the parent chain. This alkane is 2-methylpentane.

9.

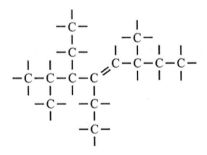

Lesson 2—Alkenes and Alkynes

PRACTICE EXERCISES
ANSWERS AND SOLUTIONS

1. The structural diagram for 3,4-diethyl-2,6-dimethyloct-4-ene is drawn as follows:

3. The three alkene isomers of C_4H_8 are listed and sketched as follows:

But-1-ene

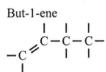

But-2-ene

2-methylprop-1-ene

5. a) Always begin numbering a cyclic alkene from the double bond, and number the carbons so that the branches are attached to the lowest-numbered carbons. According to IUPAC conventions, the molecule is named 4-ethyl-3,3-dimethylcyclobutene.

b) The IUPAC name for the given molecule is 1-methylcyclopenta-1,3-diene.

d) This is the structural formula for 4,5-dimethylhex-2-ene.

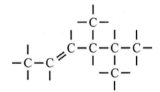

e) The structural diagram for ethyne is as follows:

$$H-C\equiv C-H$$

f) This is the structural diagram for 2-ethyl-4-methylpent-1-ene.

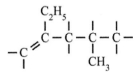

g) There are three isomers that can represent the molecule C_3H_4.

Prop-1-yne

Prop-1,2-diene

H\,C=C=C\,/H (H on each end)

Cyclopropene

(triangle symbol)

h) 4-methylpent-2-yne can be represented by the following structural diagram.

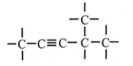

Lesson 3—Isomers

PRACTICE EXERCISES
ANSWERS AND SOLUTIONS

1. a) The molar mass of ethanol is found by multiplying the molar mass of carbon by 2, adding 6 times the molar mass of hydrogen, and adding the molar mass of oxygen.

$$2\times(12.01)+6\times(1.01)+16.00$$
$$=46.08 \text{ g/mol}$$

b) Dimethyl ether has a different structural formula but the same number and types of elements as ethanol. Therefore, its molar mass is the same as that of ethanol: 46.08 g/mol.

c) Ethanol and dimethyl ether have the same composite elements but different structures. They are therefore isomers of one another.

Lesson 4—Aromatics

PRACTICE EXERCISES
ANSWERS AND SOLUTIONS

1. **a)** 1,2-dimethylbenzene

   b) 1-ethyl-2-methylbenzene

   c) 1-ethyl-2,3-dimethylbenzene

   d) 2-methyl-2-phenylheptane

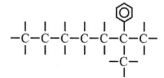

   e) 2-phenylpropane

   This compound is also referred to as isopropylbenzene.

   f) 1-methyl-3-propylbenzene or 3-propyltoluene

   An older IUPAC standard names this meta-methylpropylbenzene.

Lesson 5—Functional Groups

PRACTICE EXERCISES
ANSWERS AND SOLUTIONS

1. Aryl halides contain an aromatic ring, and alkyl halides do not.

   a) This compound is an alkyl halide.

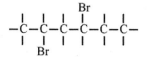

   b) This compound is an alkyl halide.

   c) This compound is an aryl halide.

3. **a)** Ethyl ethanoate is formed from ethanoic acid and ethanol. The component acid and alcohol that form ethyl ethanoate are ethanoic acid and ethanol, respectively. The following illustration shows the formation of ethyl ethanoate.

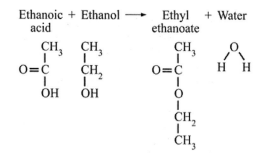

---

b) Propanol and butanoic acid react to form an ester named propyl butanoate and water, as shown in the following illustration.

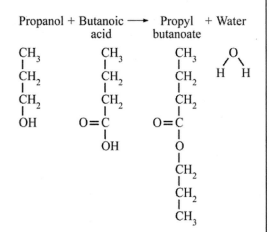

Propanol + Butanoic ⟶ Propyl + Water
acid butanoate

c) The ester shown is ethyl propanoate, which is formed during a reaction between ethanol and propanoic acid. The other product of this esterification reaction is water.

5. a) This molecule has two halide groups attached to an aromatic ring. The halides are the functional groups, and the name of the compound is 1,4-dichlorobenzene.

b) The illustration depicts an alcohol, identifiable by the two functional hydroxyl groups. The name of the compound is butan-2,3-diol.

```
         OH
     |   |   |   |
   - C - C - C - C -
     |   |   |   |
             OH
```

c) The molecule depicted is a carboxylic acid because it has a carbonyl functional group, a hydroxyl functional group, and a carboxyl functional group attached to the same carbon. The name of the molecule is propanoic acid.

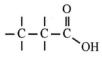

d) The following diagram shows methyl ethanoate. It is an ester because of its carbonyl group and oxygen bond to another carbon chain.

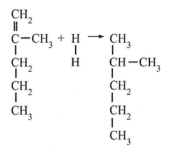

Lesson 6—Organic Reactions

PRACTICE EXERCISES
ANSWERS AND SOLUTIONS

1. a) Hydrogen and 2-methylpent-1-ene form 2-methylpentane in an addition reaction, as shown in the following diagram:

```
CH,
‖
C—CH,  + H  ⟶  CH,
|          |         |
CH,        H         CH—CH,
|                    |
CH,                  CH,
|                    |
CH,                  CH,
                     |
                     CH,
```

b) Butane forms but-1-ene and hydrogen in an elimination reaction, as shown in the following diagram:

```
CH,  ⟶  CH,  + H
|        ‖       |
CH,      CH      H
|        |
CH,      CH,
|        |
CH,      CH,
```

c) Cyclohexane and ethane require a reforming reaction in order to produce ethylcyclohexane and hydrogen, as shown in the following diagram:

```
⬡  +  CH,   ⟶   ⬡   + H
      |              |
      CH,     C,H,   H
```

d) Chloroethane and chlorine undergo a substitution reaction and produce 1,2-dichloroethane, as shown in the following diagram:

$$
\begin{array}{ccc}
\overset{\displaystyle Cl}{\underset{\displaystyle |}{}} & & \overset{\displaystyle Cl}{\underset{\displaystyle |}{}} \\
CH_2 + Cl-Cl \longrightarrow H-Cl + CH_2 \\
\underset{\displaystyle |}{} & & \underset{\displaystyle |}{} \\
CH_3 & & CH_2 \\
& & \underset{\displaystyle |}{} \\
& & Cl
\end{array}
$$

e) Ethanol and ethanoic acid undergo an esterification (also called condensation) reaction to produce ethyl ethanoate and water as products. The reaction entities are shown in the following diagram:

$$
\begin{array}{ccccc}
CH_3 & CH_3 & & CH_3 \\
| & | & & | \\
CH_2 + & C=O & \longrightarrow & C=O & + \quad {\Large\diagdown}O{\diagup} \\
| & | & & | & \;\;H\quad\;H \\
O & O & & O \\
| & | & & | \\
H & H & & CH_2 \\
& & & | \\
& & & CH_3
\end{array}
$$

f) Cyclohexanol reacts in the presence of H_2SO_4 and heat to produce cyclohexene through an elimination reaction, as shown in the following diagram:

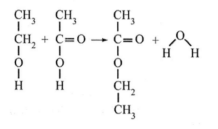

3. a) Butane undergoes a substitution reaction with chlorine to yield 1-chlorobutane and hydrogen chloride.

b) The combustion of ethanol in an oxygenated environment yields carbon dioxide and water vapour.

c) Hydroxide ions reacts with 1-chlorobutane in an elimination reaction to produce but-1-ene, water, and aqueous chloride ions.

d) The reaction of bromine and ethene is an addition reaction (halide addition). The product of this reaction is 1,2-dibromoethane.

e) But-2-ene and water participate in an addition reaction (hydration addition) to create butan-2-ol.

f) But-2-ene and hydrogen undergo an addition reaction (hydrogenation addition) to form butane.

g) Cyclopentene and hydrogen fluoride undergo an addition reaction (halide addition) in order to form fluorocyclopentane.

h) Water and ethene undergo an addition reaction (hydration addition) and produce ethanol.

i) Alcohols and carboxylic acids form esters in esterification reactions (also called condensation reactions). Ethanol and propanoic acid undergo an esterification reaction to form ethyl propanoate and water.

Practice Test

ANSWERS AND SOLUTIONS

1. Organic compounds must contain carbon atoms. Plants, petroleum, and coal all contain carbon, and can therefore be classified as organic compounds.

3. An alkyne is a hydrocarbon that contains a triple carbon-carbon bond. Alkynes are unsaturated.

Pent-1-yne is an example of an alkyne.

$$
-C\equiv C-\overset{|}{\underset{|}{C}}-\overset{|}{\underset{|}{C}}-\overset{|}{\underset{|}{C}}-
$$

5. There is an ethyl group attached to a six-carbon chain at the third carbon from the nearest end of the chain. The IUPAC name for the compound is therefore 3-ethylhexane. This compound is an alkane.

7. This compound is ethyne. Ethyne contains a triple carbon-carbon bond and is therefore highly reactive. Ethyne is classified as an alkyne, which can be described as unsaturated hydrocarbons.

9. The structure in the given diagram shows a five-carbon ring compound containing one double C-C bond and four single C-C bonds. The name for this compound is cyclopentene.

11. The diagram depicts an eight-carbon linear chain that has two methyl groups and two bromine atoms bonded to it. One methyl group and one bromine atom are bonded to the second and fourth carbons from the nearest termination of the chain. The IUPAC name for this compound is 2,4-dibromo-2,4-dimethyloctane.

13. The given diagram shows a double-bonded, two-carbon molecule with two fluorine atoms bonded on opposite ends of the chain. If the fluorines were on the same side, this would be a *cis*-isomer. Instead, this is a *trans*-difluoro ethene compound. The compound is named *trans*-1,2-difluoroethene.

15. The compound shown in the given diagram is a six-carbon ring with one double bond and two chlorine atoms bonded to each carbon in the double bond. The compound is named 1,2-dichlorocyclohexene.

17. The given structure shows a three-carbon chain attached to a –COO group. This is an ester. The name for the compound is propylmethanoate.

19. The nine isomers of heptane are shown and named as follows:

Heptane

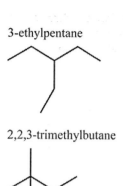

2-methylhexane

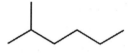

3-methylhexane

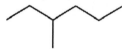

2,2-dimethylpentane

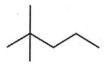

2,3-dimethylpentane

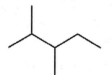

2,4-dimethylpentane

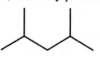

3,3-dimethylpentane

3-ethylpentane

2,2,3-trimethylbutane

21. A polypropylene molecule consists of a repeating chain of hydrocarbon structures like the one shown.

$$\left[\begin{array}{cc} H & H \\ | & | \\ -C & -C- \\ | & | \\ H & CH_3 \end{array} \right]$$

Therefore, a three-monomer chain of polypropylene would look like the following illustration:

$$\begin{array}{ccccccc}
H & CH_3 & H & CH_3 & H & CH_3 \\
| & | & | & | & | & | \\
H-C & -C & -C & -C & -C & -C-H \\
| & | & | & | & | & | \\
H & H & H & H & H & H
\end{array}$$

23. Distillation would separate the two liquids because they have different boiling points. This means they have different temperatures at which they will condense into liquids. As vaporized water and methanol climb from the heated distillation container, the water will condense as soon as the temperature drops below 100°C. The methanol will continue as a gas until it reaches a point at which the temperature drops below 65°C, where it can be collected in a different vessel than water.

25. Four structural isomers of an eight-carbon structure with two attached methyl groups are shown in the following diagrams:

2,2-dimethylhexane

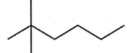

2,3-dimethylhexane

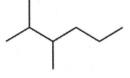

2,4-dimethylhexane

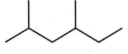

3,3-dimethylhexane

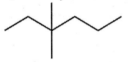

EQUILIBRIUMS OF ACID-BASE SYSTEMS

Lesson 1—Equilibrium

PRACTICE EXERCISES
ANSWERS AND SOLUTIONS

1. A static system is one that exists without motion. Static equilibrium occurs because all the forces associated with the system act in equal opposition. Therefore, the system remains unchanged with time. A boulder sitting on top of a hill is an example of static equilibrium; the force of the boulder's weight is equally opposed by the upward push of the mountain. The boulder will not roll down the mountain until another force pushes it to destroy the equilibrium. A dynamic system is one that is associated with moving parts. Dynamic equilibrium means that the motion of each part is compensated for by the motion of another part. Therefore, the overall appearance of the system is preserved. For example, thousands of people enter and leave a big city every day, but the overall population of the city stays the same. Water evaporates and rain falls every day, but the overall sea level on the planet does not noticeably change.

3. A closed system is a state where no matter can enter or leave; for example, a sealed soft drink bottle. A closed system is necessary because equilibrium is a state that is achieved based on the amounts of products and reactants. If the amount of products and reactants are changing with time as a result of matter either entering or leaving the system, equilibrium cannot be achieved.

5. a) An equilibrium constant that is greater than 1 and less than 10 indicates that the products of the reaction are favoured.

   b) Any equilibrium constant that is smaller than 1 indicates that the reactants are favoured.

   c) An equilibrium constant that is greater than 10 indicates a tremendous tendency toward the products of the reaction. More than 99% of the component entities in the reaction will form products. The products are favoured.

   d) An equilibrium value of 1.0 indicates that the concentrations of the reactants and the products will be approximately equal. Neither the products nor the reactants are favoured.

e) From left to right, the order is as follows:

b)   **d)**   **a)**   **c)**

7. The equation describing the equilibrium is as shown:

$$AgNO_{3(s)} \;\rightleftharpoons\; Ag^+_{(aq)} + NO_3^-{}_{(aq)}$$

The equilibrium law expression K_c does not include the solid silver nitrate; it includes only the species in the solution. K_c is the ratio of products over reactants to the power of their respective coefficients.

Therefore, for this reaction, K_c can be expressed as follows:

$$K_c = \left[Ag^+_{(aq)} \right]\left[NO_3^-{}_{(aq)} \right]$$

Lesson 2—Le Châtelier's Princple

PRACTICE EXERCISES
ANSWERS AND SOLUTIONS

1. **a)** An increase in volume creates a corresponding decrease in pressure. Since there are equal numbers of moles of gases on both sides of the equation, there will be no change in equilibrium.

b) As the volume of the reaction is reduced, pressure and temperature both increase. Since there are more moles of product in this reaction than reactant, an increase in pressure would tend toward the production of reactants; therefore, the equilibrium would shift to the left.

c) Adding an inert gas to the reaction would increase the pressure in the container because of the greater number of gaseous molecules in the fixed-volume container. However, the concentration (in mol/L) of each gas that participates in the reaction is unchanged, so there will be no change in equilibrium concentrations.

d) The introduction of a catalyst into a reaction between gaseous carbon monoxide and water would increase the rate at which hydrogen and carbon dioxide are formed. In addition, the reverse reaction will be increased by the same amount. The equilibrium would therefore remain unchanged.

e) As an exothermic reaction is heated, it tends to favour heat absorption and will proceed toward the reverse endothermic reaction. The equilibrium in this case would shift to the left.

f) As the conditions of an exothermic reaction are cooled, the reaction tends to shift to produce more heat in order to achieve a new equilibrium. In this case, the production of aqueous ions produces more heat, and so the equilibrium shift would be to the right, toward the forward exothermic reaction.

g) The addition of a strong ionic base to an aqueous solution containing hydronium ions would cause a neutralization reaction. As sodium hydroxide is added to the solution, the hydroxide ion neutralizes the hydronium ion and decreases the concentration of $H_3O^+_{(aq)}$. Therefore, the equilibrium shift is to the right and the production of more $H_3O^+_{(aq)}$ ions.

h) As aqueous hydrochloric acid is added to the solution, its ions dissociate in the water, forming hydronium ions and chloride ions. The $H_3O^+_{(aq)}$ ions neutralize the $OH^-_{(aq)}$ ions, resulting in a decrease in the concentration of $OH^-_{(aq)}$. The equilibrium will shift to the right to produce more $OH^-_{(aq)}$.

i) Adding sodium thiocyanate to this reaction leads to an increased concentration of thiocyanate ions. In order to maintain equilibrium, the equation would need to increase the formation of products, causing the equilibrium to shift to the right.

j) Removing sulfur dioxide from this equation would cause a shift to the left in the equilibrium as the sodium trioxide would decompose to compensate for the loss of reactants.

3. Le Châtelier's principle identifies those factors that can change the amount of reactants or products from one side of an equilibrium equation to another. Chemists who wish to maximize the products of a reaction can then manipulate the variables identified by Le Châtelier that will shift the reaction to produce more products. For example, the Haber process is a typical example of manipulating temperature and pressure to produce ammonia.

5. When an equilibrium reaction is cooled, the tendency is for the exothermic reaction to occur is favoured, as this compensates for the loss of heat energy. The formation of gas bubbles in this aqueous solution indicates the generation of chlorine gas, a product found to the right-hand side of the equilibrium system. Because of this tendency, it may be concluded that this reaction (the forward reaction) is exothermic.

Lesson 3—Acids, Bases, and Conjugate Pairs

PRACTICE EXERCISES ANSWERS AND SOLUTIONS

1. According to the Brønsted–Lowry theory, a proton donor is an acid, and a proton acceptor is a base. Substances are not categorized as acids or bases in a general definition sense. They can only be acids or bases in a particular reaction and are only defined as such for that reaction. Therefore, is not possible to classify a species as an acid or a base without knowing the specific reaction that occurs.

    For example, a substance can be a proton donor in one reaction and an acceptor in another. Therefore, it could be either an acid or a base, depending on the situation.

3. The reaction is drawn as proceeding in one direction because nitric acid is a strong acid and therefore fully dissociates. Nitric acid acts as the proton donor (Brønsted–Lowry acid), and water acts as the proton acceptor (Brønsted–Lowry base).

$$\overset{\frown}{\underset{\text{Acid}}{HNO_{3(aq)}} + \underset{\text{Base}}{H_2O_{(l)}}} \overset{H^+}{\longrightarrow} H_3O^+_{(aq)} + NO_3^-_{(aq)}$$

5. The first equation is written as follows:

$$\overset{H^+}{\overset{\frown}{\underset{\text{Acid}}{HCN_{(aq)}} + \underset{\text{Base}}{CO_3^{2-}_{(aq)}}}} \rightleftharpoons CN^-_{(aq)} + HCO_3^-_{(aq)}$$

    In this equation, $HCN_{(aq)}$ is the acid, and $CO_3^{2-}_{(aq)}$ is the base in the forward reaction.

The second equation is written as follows:

$$\overset{H^+}{\overset{\frown}{\underset{\text{Acid}}{HCN_{(aq)}} + \underset{\text{Base}}{HCO_3^-_{(aq)}}}} \rightleftharpoons CN^-_{(aq)} + H_2CO_{3(aq)}$$

In this equation, $HCN_{(aq)}$ is the acid, and $HCO_3^-_{(aq)}$ is the base in the forward reaction.

Hydrogen carbonate and carbonate are a conjugate pair.

7. a) The reaction of an ammonium ion with a sulfite ion can be represented as shown:

$$\underset{\text{Acid}}{NH_4^+} + \underset{\text{Base}}{SO_3^{2-}} \rightleftharpoons \underset{\text{Acid}}{HSO_3^-} + \underset{\text{Base}}{NH_3}$$

        In the forward reaction, the NH_4^+ ion acts as a Brønsted–Lowry acid as it donates a proton to the SO_3^{2-} ion. The SO_3^{2-} ion acts as a Brønsted–Lowry base.

        Similarly, HSO_3^- acts as an acid and NH_3 acts as a base in the reverse reaction.

        Since by definition, conjugate acid–bases differ from each other by the loss or gain of a proton, NH_4^+ and NH_3 form a conjugate acid–base pair, as do SO_3^{2-} and HSO_3^-.

    b) An amphiprotic species is one that can either act as an acid or as a base; that is, it can lose or gain a proton, depending on the other reactant.

        HSO_3^- can act as an acid by donating its proton to form an SO_3^{2-} ion, or it can act as a base by accepting a proton to form H_2SO_3.

        Similarly, NH_3 can act as an amphiprotic species. It can act as a base to form NH_4^+, and it can act as an acid to form NH_2^-.

Lesson 4—Special Equilibrium Constants (K_w, K_a, K_b)

PRACTICE EXERCISES ANSWERS AND SOLUTIONS

1. In a Brønsted–Lowry reaction, the side of the equilibrium that has the weaker acid is favoured.

    Remember that in a net acid-base equation, the significant components are those that donate or accept protons. Any other ions that may form salts or act as catalysts are ignored, since they do not affect the pH of the net solution.

    a) The reactants are favoured in this equilibrium reaction, which is shown in the following balanced chemical equation:
    $$HCO_3^-{}_{(aq)} + NH_4^+{}_{(aq)} \overset{<50\%}{\rightleftharpoons} H_2CO_3{}_{(aq)} + NH_3{}_{(aq)}$$

    b) The equilibrium in this reaction favours the products, as shown in the following equation:
    $$HSO_4^-{}_{(aq)} + CH_3COO^-{}_{(aq)}$$
    $$\overset{<50\%}{\rightleftharpoons} SO_4^{2-}{}_{(aq)} + CH_3COOH_{(aq)}$$

    c) The acid can be completely neutralized. The products can be rewritten as shown in the following equation:
    $$HCO_3^-{}_{(aq)} + HOCl_{(aq)}$$
    $$\rightleftharpoons H_2O_{(l)} + CO_{2(g)} + OCl^-{}_{(aq)}$$

    If sufficient $NaHCO_{3(s)}$ is added, and the $CO_{2(g)}$ is allowed to escape, the quantity of $HOCl_{(aq)}$ that is neutralized will approach 100%.

    d) This reaction is quantitative. This means the reaction so heavily favours the products that all of the reactants will be consumed. The net acid-base reaction is as follows:
    $$H_3O^+{}_{(aq)} + OH^-{}_{(aq)} \rightarrow 2H_2O_{(l)}$$

    e) Sulfuric acid and calcium carbonate will react in a quantitative manner. The reaction will favour the products completely because $H_2SO_{4(aq)}$ is a strong acid. The balanced chemical equation is as follows:
    $$CO_3^{2-}{}_{(aq)} + H_3O^+{}_{(aq)} \rightarrow HCO_3^-{}_{(aq)} + H_2O_{(l)}$$

    f) Using the following equation, baking soda is capable of completely neutralizing vinegar (acetic acid).

$$HCO_3^-{}_{(aq)} + CH_3COOH_{(aq)}$$
$$\rightarrow CO_{2(g)} + H_2O_{(l)} + CH_3COO^-{}_{(aq)}$$

If sufficient sodium bicarbonate is added and the carbon dioxide is allowed to escape, the quantity of acetic acid that is neutralized will approach 100%.

3. The equilibrium expression is as follows:
$$K_c = \frac{\left[OH^-{}_{(aq)}\right]\left[HClO_{(aq)}\right]}{\left[ClO^-{}_{(aq)}\right]}$$

Note that water is not included because its concentration does not change. This is a special case of equilibrium involving the weak base ClO^-. Therefore, it is a K_b expression.

5. a) The appropriate equation to describe the ionization of 2,4,6-trichlorophenol is as follows:
    $$HOC_6H_2Cl_{3(aq)} + H_2O_{(l)}$$
    $$\rightleftharpoons OC_6H_2Cl_3^-{}_{(aq)} + H_3O^+{}_{(aq)}$$

    b) The following steps illustrate the calculation of the value of the acid ionization constant of 2,4,6-trichlorophenol.
    $$\left[H_3O^+\right] = 10^{-pH} = 10^{-3.55}$$
    $$= 2.8 \times 10^{-4} \text{ mol/L}$$
    $$\left[H_3O^+\right] = \left[OC_6H_2Cl_3^-\right]$$

    $$K_a = \frac{\left[OC_6H_2Cl_3^-\right]\left[H_3O^+\right]}{\left[HOC_6H_2Cl_3\right]}$$

    $$K_a = \frac{\left(2.8 \times 10^{-4} \text{ mol/L}\right)\left(2.8 \times 10^{-4} \text{ mol/L}\right)}{\left(0.10 \text{ mol/L}\right)}$$
    $$= 7.8 \times 10^{-7}$$

    c) The base ionization constant for the conjugate base of 2,4,6-trichlorophenol can be found using the following method.
    $$K_{b\left(OC_6H_2Cl_3^-\right)} = \frac{K_w}{K_{a\left(HOC_6H_2Cl_3\right)}}$$
    $$= \frac{1.00 \times 10^{-14}}{7.8 \times 10^{-7}}$$
    $$= 1.3 \times 10^{-8}$$

d) The ionization equation for the conjugate base of 2,4,6-trichlorophenol is written as follows:

$$OC_6H_2Cl_3{}^-{}_{(aq)} + H_2O_{(l)}$$
$$\rightleftharpoons HOC_6H_2Cl_{3(aq)} + OH^-{}_{(aq)}$$

The equilibrium constant for the conjugate base is calculated as follows:

$$K_b = \frac{[HOC_6H_2Cl_3][OH^-]}{[OC_6H_2Cl_3{}^-]}$$

Lesson 5—Titration

PRACTICE EXERCISES
ANSWERS AND SOLUTIONS

1. a) $HBb_{(aq)} + H_2O_{(l)} \rightleftharpoons Bb^-{}_{(aq)} + H_3O^+{}_{(aq)}$
　　yellow　　　　　　　blue

b) The colour transition for bromothymol blue occurs between pH 6.0 and 7.6.

　　i) If the pH is equal to 4, the solution will appear yellow because the indicator is mostly in its acid form, $HBb_{(aq)}$.

　　ii) If the pH is equal to 7, the solution will appear green because the indicator contains a relatively equal mix of $HBb_{(aq)}$ and $Bb^-{}_{(aq)}$.

　　iii) If the pH is equal to 10, the solution will appear blue because the indicator is mostly in its basic form, $Bb^-{}_{(aq)}$.

Lesson 6—Buffers

PRACTICE EXERCISES
ANSWERS AND SOLUTIONS

1. Titration curves plot the amount of acid or base added to a solution versus the resulting pH. Buffering regions are areas of the curve where the pH undergoes a minimal amount of change relative to the amount of titrant added. These regions occur when a buffer solution is formed during the titration of a weak acid or weak base. They are the slightly flattened regions before the equivalence point.

Buffering solutions are a combination of a weak acid or base and its respective conjugate. These solutions resist changes in pH until the amount of titrant added is more than the amount of buffer in the solution.

3. The concentration of HA increases slightly, and [A⁻] decreases slightly as the buffer equilibrium shifts left. This produces a small increase in the [HA]/[A⁻] ratio, a small increase in $[H_3O^+]$ and therefore a small decrease in pH.

5. a) The equilibrium reaction for the buffer system is as follows:

$$CH_3COOH_{(aq)} + H_2O_{(l)}$$
$$\rightleftharpoons CH_3COO^-{}_{(aq)} + H_3O^+{}_{(aq)}$$

b) The equilibrium constant expression for the buffer system is as follows:

$$K_a = \frac{[CH_3COO^-][H_3O^+]}{[CH_3COOH]}$$

c) The calculations involved in determining the $[H_3O^+]$ of the buffer are as follows:

$$K_a = \frac{[CH_3COO^-][H_3O^+]}{[CH_3COOH]}$$
$$[H_3O^+] = K_a \times \frac{[CH_3COOH]}{[CH_3COO^-]}$$
$$= (1.8 \times 10^{-5})\frac{(0.15 \text{ mol/L})}{(0.10 \text{ mol/L})}$$
$$= 2.7 \times 10^{-5}$$

Since the concentration of hydronium ions is known, the pH is found by taking the negative logarithm of that value.

$$pH = -\log[H_3O^+]$$
$$= -\log(2.7 \times 10^{-5} \text{ mol/L})$$
$$= 4.57$$

d) The net acid-base reaction equation that describes the neutralization is as follows:

$$CH_3COOH_{(aq)} + OH^-{}_{(aq)}$$
$$\rightleftharpoons CH_3COO^-{}_{(aq)} + H_2O_{(aq)}$$

e) The solution pH will increase by a small amount. Added $NaOH_{(s)}$ will result in a small decrease in $[CH_3COOH]$, a small increase in $[CH_3COO^-]$, and a small drop in $[H_3O^+]$. In this way, the solution pH will increase by a small amount.

Practice Test

ANSWERS AND SOLUTIONS

1. The greater the value of K_c, the greater is the concentration of products at equilibrium.

   A. Products are favoured $(K > 1)$

   B. Reactants are favoured $(K < 1)$

   C. Reactants are favoured $(K < 1)$

   D. Reactants are favoured $(K < 1)$

3. In a saturated solution of an ionic compound, the ions are always in equilibrium with the undissolved solute.

   • The rate of the forward rate is equal to the reverse rate; in this case, the rate of precipitation is equal to the rate of dissolution.

   • At equilibrium, the following equation is true:

   $$\left[Ca^{2+} \right] = \frac{3}{2} \left[PO_4^{3-} \right]$$

   • The concentration of Ca^{2+} and PO_4^{3-} remain constant. However, the following equivalency is not true: $\left[Ca^{2+} \right] = \left[PO_4^{3-} \right]$

5. **a)** An increase in [HI] will shift the equilibrium in the reverse direction (to the left).

   b) A decrease in the concentration of I_2 will cause the equilibrium to shift left.

   c) In the given reaction, 2 mol of reactants combine to form 2 mol of products; that is, there is no change in the number of moles. According to Le Châtelier's principle, a change in pressure will not affect the equilibrium of the system.

   d) An increase in temperature will favour the forward reaction (shift the equilibrium to the right), which proceeds by absorbing heat.

7. When H_2 is removed from the reaction mixture (its concentration is reduced), the reaction will move in the reverse direction, and more HI will dissociate into H_2 and I_2.

   $$H_{2(g)} + I_{2(g)} \ \square \ 2HI_{(g)}$$

The value of K_c is dependent only on the temperature of the system; any change in the concentration does not alter the value of K_c. Therefore, its value remains constant.

9. When NaOH, a base, is added to the phenolphthalein indicator, hydroxide (OH^-) will react quantitatively with H_3O^+ ions, thereby reducing the concentration of H_3O^+. According to Le Châtelier's principle, the equilibrium will shift toward the right. Therefore, the addition of sodium hydroxide favours the formation of $In^-_{(aq)}$. As a result, the colour of the solution becomes pinker.

11. **a)** For the given equilibrium, the equilibrium constant is calculated as follows:

$$K_c = \frac{\left[NH_3 \right]^2}{\left[N_2 \right]\left[H_2 \right]^3}$$

$$= \frac{\left(\dfrac{0.500}{50.0} \right)^2}{\left(\dfrac{1.00}{50.0} \right)\left(\dfrac{3.00}{50.0} \right)^3}$$

$$= \frac{\left(0.0100 \right)^2}{\left(0.0200 \right)\left(0.0600 \right)^3}$$

$$= 23.1$$

b) Since the value of K_c, which was found in part **a**, is greater than 1.6×10^{-4}, the reaction will move toward the left as the equilibrium is re-established. Therefore, more ammonia will dissociate into the reactants.

$$K_c = \frac{\left[CO \right]\left[H_2O \right]}{\left[CO_2 \right]\left[H_2 \right]}$$

$$\left[CO_2 \right] = \frac{0.1908 \text{ mol}}{2.0 \text{ L}} = 0.0954 \text{ mol/L}$$

$$\left[H_2 \right] = \frac{0.0908 \text{ mol}}{2.0 \text{ L}} = 0.0454 \text{ mol/L}$$

$$\left[CO \right] = \frac{0.0092 \text{ mol}}{2.0 \text{ L}} = 0.0046 \text{ mol/L}$$

$$\left[H_2O \right] = \frac{0.0092 \text{ mol}}{2.0 \text{ L}} = 0.0046 \text{ mol/L}$$

Substitute these values in the expression for K_c.

$$K_c = \frac{\left[0.0046 \right]\left[0.0046 \right]}{\left[0.0954 \right]\left[0.0454 \right]}$$

$$= \frac{0.000 \ 021 \ 2}{0.004 \ 331 \ 2}$$

$$= 4.9 \times 10^{-3}$$

13. The equilibrium expression for the given reaction is as follows:

$$K_c = \frac{[C_2H_6]}{[C_2H_4][H_2]}$$

Let x be the amount of change.

	C_2H_4	H_2	C_2H_6
I	0.335	0.526	0.00
C	$-x$	$-x$	$+x$
E	0.235	$0.526-x$	x

Determine the change in concentration x as follows:

$$x = \Delta[C_2H_4]$$
$$= (0.335 - 0.235)\ \text{mol/L}$$
$$= 0.100\ \text{mol/L}$$

The concentration of each species at equilibrium is calculated as follows:
$[C_2H_4] = 0.235$ mol/L
$[C_2H_6] = x = 0.100$ mol/L
$[H_2] = 0.526 - x = 0.426$ mol/L

15. Salts that are formed by the reaction of a strong acid with a weak base are acidic in nature.

   a) NaCl dissociates in water to produce $Na^+_{(aq)}$ (a neutral cation) and $Cl^{-(aq)}$ (a neutral anion). Since neither ion undergoes any hydrolysis, this solution will be neutral.

   b) K_2SO_4 dissociates in water to produce $K^+_{(aq)}$ (a neutral cation) and $SO_4^{2-}_{(aq)}$ (a very weakly basic anion, $K_b = 1 \times 10^{-12}$), so this solution is weakly basic. The net ionic equation for the hydrolysis of SO_4^{2-} is:
   $$SO_4^{2-}_{(aq)} + H_2O_{(l)} \rightleftharpoons HSO^{4-}_{(aq)} + OH^-_{(aq)}$$

   c) $NH_4Cl_{(s)}$ dissociates in water to produce $NH_4^+_{(aq)}$ (an acidic cation) and $Cl^-_{(aq)}$ (a neutral anion), so the solution is acidic. The net ionic equation for the hydrolysis of NH_4^+ is:
   $$NH_4^+_{(aq)} + H_2O_{(l)} \rightleftharpoons H_3O^+_{(aq)} + NH_{3(aq)}$$

   d) CH_3COONa dissociates in water to produce $Na^+_{(aq)}$ (a neutral cation) and $CH_3COO^-_{(aq)}$ (a basic anion). The net ionic equation for the hydrolysis of CH_3COO^- is:
   $$CH_3COO^-_{(aq)} + H_2O_{(l)}$$
   $$\rightleftharpoons CH_3COOH_{(aq)} + OH^-_{(aq)}$$

17. Potassium chloride (KCl) is a neutral salt. It becomes completely ionized in its solution. KCl dissociates completely in water to form potassium (K^+) and chloride (Cl^-) ions. The equation for the dissociation of KCl is represented as follows:
$$KCl_{(s)} \xrightarrow{H_2O} K^+_{(aq)} + Cl^-_{(aq)}$$

19. The given equilibrium reaction favours the formation of products. This means that the strongest base must be one of the reactants. According to the Brønsted–Lowry concept of acids and bases, a base accepts a proton during a neutralization reaction. $HCO_3^-_{(aq)}$ accepts a proton to form H_2CO_3. Therefore, HCO_3^- is the strongest base in the given equilibrium reaction.

21. A base formed by the loss of a proton from an acid is called a conjugate base. Therefore, the conjugate base of $H_2SO_{4(aq)}$ is $HSO_4^-_{(aq)}$.

23. A good buffer solution has comparable concentrations of weak acid and its conjugate base or weak base and its conjugate acid. The concentration of CH_3COO^- is 1.0×10^{-4} mol/L, which is very small. Therefore, the given 2.0 mol/L CH_3COOH solution is not considered a good buffer solution.

25. A hydrogen ion (H^+), or proton, reacts with water to form a hydronium ion (H_3O^+). The interaction of water with a proton can be represented as follows:
$$H_2O_{(l)} + H^+_{(aq)} \rightarrow H_3O^+_{(aq)}.$$

27. The self-ionization of water can be represented as follows:
$$2H_2O_{(l)} \rightleftharpoons H_3O^+_{(aq)} + OH^-_{(aq)}$$
The ionization constant of water (K_w) can be represented as follows:
$$K_w = [H_3O^+][OH^-]$$
$$\Rightarrow \log K_w = \log[H_3O^+] + \log[OH^-]$$
$$-\log K_w = -\log[H_3O^+] - \log[OH^-]$$
$$pK_w = pH + pOH$$
At 25°C, $pK_w = 14 = pH + pOH$

29. Acetic acid is a weak acid with $K_a = 1.8 \times 10^{-5}$. A solution of $CH_3COOH_{(aq)}$ can be represented by the following equation:
$$CH_3COOH_{(aq)} + H_2O_{(l)} \rightleftharpoons CH_3COO^-_{(aq)} + H_3O^+_{(aq)}$$

$$K_a = \frac{\left[H_3O^+_{(aq)}\right]\left[CH_3COO^-_{(aq)}\right]}{\left[CH_3COOH_{(aq)}\right]}$$

Let $x = \left[H_3O^+_{(aq)}\right] = \left[CH_3COO^-_{(aq)}\right]$

The values of x and the pH can be calculated as follows:

$$K_a \approx \frac{x^2}{[HA]}$$
$$x = \sqrt{K_a \times [HA]}$$
$$x = \sqrt{1.8 \times 10^{-5} \times 1.00 \text{ mol/L}}$$
$$x = 0.0042 \text{ mol/L}$$
$$pH = -\log(0.0042 \text{ mol/L})$$
$$pH = 2.38$$

Therefore, the pH of the solution is 2.38.

31. $CH_3COO^-_{(aq)}$ is the conjugate base of $CH_3COOH_{(aq)}$. The relation between the ionization constant of an acid and its conjugate base is represented as follows:

$$K_a \times K_b = K_w$$
$$K_b = \frac{K_w}{K_a}$$
$$= \frac{1 \times 10^{-14}}{1.8 \times 10^{-5}}$$
$$= 5.56 \times 10^{-10}$$

Therefore, the value of K_b for CH_3COO^- is 5.6×10^{-10}.

33. Calculate K_b.

$$K_b = \frac{K_w}{K_a}$$
$$= \frac{1.0 \times 10^{-14}}{6.3 \times 10^{-4}}$$
$$= 1.6 \times 10^{-11}$$

Set up an ICE table.

	F^-	HF	OH^-
I	1.00	0.00	0.00
C	$-x$	$+x$	$+x$
E	$1.00 - x$	x	x

$$\therefore K_b = \frac{\left[HF_{(aq)}\right]\left[OH^-_{(aq)}\right]}{\left[F^-_{(aq)}\right]} = \frac{x^2}{1.00 - x}$$

where $x = \left[HF_{(aq)}\right] = \left[OH^-_{(aq)}\right]$

The amount x that dissociates from $F^-_{(aq)}$ is not significant; therefore, the approximation method can be used.

$$K_b \approx \frac{x^2}{1.00}$$
$$1.6 \times 10^{-11} = \frac{x^2}{1.00}$$
$$x = \sqrt{(1.6 \times 10^{-11})(1.00)}$$
$$\left[OH^-_{(aq)}\right] = x = 4.0 \times 10^{-6} \text{ mol/L}$$

Therefore, the $\left[OH^-_{(aq)}\right]$ is 4.0×10^{-6} mol/L.

35. a) The sample being titrated is an acid since its pH is lower than 7 at the start of the titration. The acid is also diprotic, since two equivalence points are observed in the titration curve.

b)

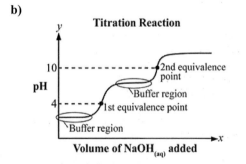

There are two buffer regions (the flat portions of the graph before the equivalence points). These represent the point of the reaction where a buffer is present in the solution.

NOTES

Student Notes and Problems

APPENDICES

CASTLE ROCK
RESEARCH CORP

1	2	3	4	5	6	7	8	9

1   1.01
1+,1−
2.2
H
hydrogen

Table of Common Polyatomic Ions

acetate (ethanoate)	CH_3COO^-	chromate	CrO_4^{2-}	phosphate	PO_4^{3-}
ammonium	NH_4^+	dichromate	$Cr_2O_7^{2-}$	hydrogen phosphate	HPO_4^{2-}
benzoate	$C_6H_5COO^-$	cyanide	CN^-	dihydrogen phosphate	$H_2PO_4^-$
borate	BO_3^{3-}	hydroxide	OH^-	silicate	SiO_3^{2-}
carbide	C_2^{2-}	iodate	IO_3^-	sulfate	SO_4^{2-}
carbonate	CO_3^{2-}	nitrate	NO_3^-	hydrogen sulfate	HSO_4^-
hydrogen carbonate	HCO_3^-	nitrite	NO_2^-	sulfite	SO_3^{2-}
perchlorate	ClO_4^-	oxalate	$OOCCOO^{2-}$	hydrogen sulfite	HSO_3^-
chlorate	ClO_3^-	hydrogen oxalate	$HOOCCOO^-$	hydrogen sulfide	HS^-
chlorite	ClO_2^-	permanganate	MnO_4^-	thiocyanate	SCN^-
hypochlorite	OCl^- or ClO^-	peroxide	O_2^{2-}	thiosulfate	$S_2O_3^{2-}$
		persulfide	S_2^{2-}		

3   6.94   1+   1.0   **Li** lithium

4   9.01   2+   1.6   **Be** beryllium

11   22.99   1+   0.9   **Na** sodium

12   24.31   2+   1.3   **Mg** magnesium

19   39.10   1+   0.8   **K** potassium

20   40.08   2+   1.0   **Ca** calcium

21   44.96   3+   1.4   **Sc** scandium

22   47.87   4+, 3+   1.5   **Ti** titanium

23   50.94   5+, 4+   1.6   **V** vanadium

24   52.00   3+, 2+   1.7   **Cr** chromium

25   54.94   2+, 4+   1.6   **Mn** manganese

26   55.85   3+, 2+   1.8   **Fe** iron

27   58.93   2+, 3+   1.9   **Co** cobalt

37   85.47   1+   0.8   **Rb** rubidium

38   87.62   2+   1.0   **Sr** strontium

39   88.91   3+   1.2   **Y** yttrium

40   91.22   4+   1.3   **Zr** zirconium

41   92.91   5+, 3+   1.6   **Nb** niobium

42   95.94   6+   2.2   **Mo** molybdenum

43   (98)   7+   2.1   **Tc** technetium

44   101.07   3+   2.2   **Ru** ruthenium

45   102.91   3+   2.3   **Rh** rhodium

55   132.91   1+   0.8   **Cs** cesium

56   137.33   2+   0.9   **Ba** barium

57   138.91   3+   1.1   **La** lanthanum

72   178.49   4+   1.3   **Hf** hafnium

73   180.95   5+   1.5   **Ta** tantalum

74   183.84   6+   1.7   **W** tungsten

75   186.21   7+   1.9   **Re** rhenium

76   190.23   4+   2.2   **Os** osmium

77   192.22   4+   2.2   **Ir** iridium

87   (223)   1+   0.7   **Fr** francium

88   (226)   2+   0.9   **Ra** radium

89   (227)   3+   1.1   **Ac** actinium

104   (261)   4+   **Rf** rutherfordium

105   (262)   **Db** dubnium

106   (266)   **Sg** seaborgium

107   (264)   **Bh** bohrium

108   (277)   **Hs** hassium

109   (268)   **Mt** meitnerium

lanthanide and actinide series begin

58   140.12   3+   1.1   **Ce** cerium

59   140.91   3+   1.1   **Pr** praseodymium

60   144.24   3+   1.1   **Nd** neodymium

61   (145)   3+   —   **Pm** promethium

62   150.36   3+, 2+   1.2   **Sm** samarium

90   232.04   4+   1.3   **Th** thorium

91   231.04   5+, 4+   1.5   **Pa** protactinium

92   238.03   6+, 4+   1.7   **U** uranium

93   (237)   5+   1.3   **Np** neptunium

94   (244)   4+, 6+   1.3   **Pu** plutonium

References

Lide, D.R. 2005. *CRC Handbook of Chemistry and Physics*. 86th ed. Boca Raton: CRC Press.

Speight, James G. 2005. *Lange's Handbook of Chemistry*. 16th ed. New York: McGraw-Hill, Inc.

IUPAC *commission on atomic weights and isotopic abundances*. 2002. http://www.chem.qmw.ac.uk/iupac/AtWt/index.html.

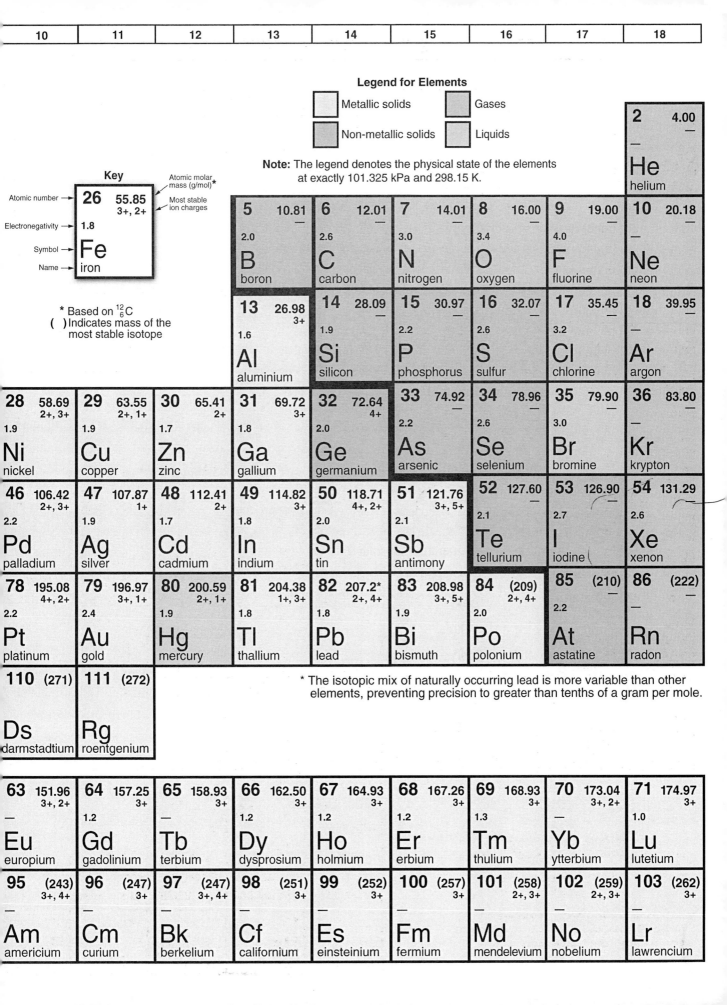

Chemistry Notation

Symbol	Term	Unit(s)
c	specific heat capacity	$J/(g \cdot {}^\circ C)$ or $J/(g \cdot K)$
E°	standard electrical potential	V or J/C
E_k	kinetic energy	kJ
E_p	potential energy	kJ
ΔH	enthalpy (heat)	kJ
$\Delta_f H^\circ$	standard molar enthalpy of formation	kJ/mol
I	current	A or C/s
K_c	equilibrium constant	—
K_a	acid ionization (dissociation) constant	—
K_b	base ionization (dissociation) constant	—
M	molar mass	g/mol
m	mass	g
n	amount of substance	mol
P	pressure	kPa
Q	charge	C
T	temperature (absolute)	K
t	temperature (Celsius)	$^\circ C$
t	time	s
V	volume	L
c	amount concentration	mol/L

Symbol	Term
Δ	delta (change in)
$^\circ$	standard
[ ]	amount concentration

Miscellaneous

25.00 °C is equivalent to 298.15 K

Specific Heat Capacities at 298.15 K and 100.000 kPa

$$c_{air} = 1.01 \text{ J/(g·°C)}$$

$$c_{polystyrene\ foam\ cup} = 1.01 \text{ J/(g·°C)}$$

$$c_{copper} = 0.385 \text{ J/(g·°C)}$$

$$c_{aluminium} = 0.897 \text{ J/(g·°C)}$$

$$c_{iron} = 0.449 \text{ J/(g·°C)}$$

$$c_{tin} = 0.227 \text{ J/(g·°C)}$$

$$c_{water} = 4.19 \text{ J/(g·°C)}$$

Water Autoionization Constant (Dissociation Constant)

$K_w = 1.0 \times 10^{-14}$ at 298.15 K (for ion concentrations in mol/L)

Faraday Constant

$$F = 9.65 \times 10^4 \text{ C/mol e}^-$$

Quadratic Formula

$$x = \frac{-b \pm \sqrt{b^2 - 4ac}}{2a}$$

Selected SI Prefixes

Prefix	Exponential Symbol	Value
tera	T	10^{12}
giga	G	10^{9}
mega	M	10^{6}
kilo	k	10^{3}
milli	m	10^{-3}
micro	μ	10^{-6}
nano	n	10^{-9}
pico	p	10^{-12}

Standard Molar Enthalpies of Formation at 298.15 K

Name	Formula	$\Delta_f H°$ (kJ/mol)
aluminium oxide	$Al_2O_3(s)$	−1 675.7
ammonia	$NH_3(g)$	−45.9
ammonium chloride	$NH_4Cl(s)$	−314.4
ammonium nitrate	$NH_4NO_3(s)$	−365.6
barium carbonate	$BaCO_3(s)$	−1 213.0
barium chloride	$BaCl_2(s)$	−855.0
barium hydroxide	$Ba(OH)_2(s)$	−944.7
barium oxide	$BaO(s)$	−548.0
barium sulfate	$BaSO_4(s)$	−1 473.2
benzene	$C_6H_6(l)$	+49.1
butane	$C_4H_{10}(g)$	−125.7
calcium carbonate	$CaCO_3(s)$	−1 207.6
calcium chloride	$CaCl_2(s)$	−795.4
calcium hydroxide	$Ca(OH)_2(s)$	−985.2
calcium oxide	$CaO(s)$	−634.9
calcium sulfate	$CaSO_4(s)$	−1 434.5
carbon dioxide	$CO_2(g)$	−393.5
carbon monoxide	$CO(g)$	−110.5
chromium(III) oxide	$Cr_2O_3(s)$	−1 139.7
copper(I) oxide	$Cu_2O(s)$	−168.6
copper(II) oxide	$CuO(s)$	−157.3
copper(II) sulfate	$CuSO_4(s)$	−771.4
copper(I) sulfide	$Cu_2S(s)$	−79.5
copper(II) sulfide	$CuS(s)$	−53.1
dinitrogen tetroxide	$N_2O_4(g)$	+11.1
ethane	$C_2H_6(g)$	−84.0
ethanoic acid (acetic acid)	$CH_3COOH(l)$	−484.3
ethanol	$C_2H_5OH(l)$	−277.6
ethene (ethylene)	$C_2H_4(g)$	+52.4
ethyne (acetylene)	$C_2H_2(g)$	+227.4
glucose	$C_6H_{12}O_6(s)$	−1 273.3
hydrogen bromide	$HBr(g)$	−36.3
hydrogen chloride	$HCl(g)$	−92.3
hydrogen fluoride	$HF(g)$	−273.3
hydrogen iodide	$HI(g)$	+26.5
hydrogen perchlorate	$HClO_4(l)$	−40.6
hydrogen peroxide	$H_2O_2(l)$	−187.8
hydrogen sulfide	$H_2S(g)$	−20.6
iron(II) oxide	$FeO(s)$	−272.0
iron(III) oxide	$Fe_2O_3(s)$	−824.2
iron(II,III) oxide (magnetite)	$Fe_3O_4(s)$	−1 118.4
lead(II) bromide	$PbBr_2(s)$	−278.7
lead(II) chloride	$PbCl_2(s)$	−359.4
lead(II) oxide (red)	$PbO(s)$	−219.0
lead(IV) oxide	$PbO_2(s)$	−277.4
magnesium carbonate	$MgCO_3(s)$	−1 095.8
magnesium chloride	$MgCl_2(s)$	−641.3

Standard Molar Enthalpies of Formation at 298.15 K cont'd

Name	Formula	$\Delta_f H°$ (kJ/mol)
magnesium hydroxide	$Mg(OH)_2(s)$	-924.5
magnesium oxide	$MgO(s)$	-601.6
magnesium sulfate	$MgSO_4(s)$	$-1\,284.9$
manganese(II) oxide	$MnO(s)$	-385.2
manganese(IV) oxide	$MnO_2(s)$	-520.0
mercury(II) oxide (red)	$HgO(s)$	-90.8
mercury(II) sulfide (red)	$HgS(s)$	-58.2
methanal (formaldehyde)	$CH_2O(g)$	-108.6
methane	$CH_4(g)$	-74.6
methanoic acid (formic acid)	$HCOOH(l)$	-425.0
methanol	$CH_3OH(l)$	-239.2
nickel(II) oxide	$NiO(s)$	-240.6
nitric acid	$HNO_3(l)$	-174.1
nitrogen dioxide	$NO_2(g)$	$+33.2$
nitrogen monoxide	$NO(g)$	$+91.3$
octane	$C_8H_{18}(l)$	-250.1
pentane	$C_5H_{12}(l)$	-173.5
phosphorus pentachloride	$PCl_5(s)$	-443.5
phosphorus trichloride (liquid)	$PCl_3(l)$	-319.7
phosphorus trichloride (vapour)	$PCl_3(g)$	-287.0
potassium bromide	$KBr(s)$	-393.8
potassium chlorate	$KClO_3(s)$	-397.7
potassium chloride	$KCl(s)$	-436.5
potassium hydroxide	$KOH(s)$	-424.6
propane	$C_3H_8(g)$	-103.8
silicon dioxide (α-quartz)	$SiO_2(s)$	-910.7
silver bromide	$AgBr(s)$	-100.4
silver chloride	$AgCl(s)$	-127.0
silver iodide	$AgI(s)$	-61.8
sodium bromide	$NaBr(s)$	-361.1
sodium chloride	$NaCl(s)$	-411.2
sodium hydroxide	$NaOH(s)$	-425.8
sodium iodide	$NaI(s)$	-287.8
sucrose	$C_{12}H_{22}O_{11}(s)$	$-2\,226.1$
sulfur dioxide	$SO_2(g)$	-296.8
sulfuric acid	$H_2SO_4(l)$	-814.0
sulfur trioxide (liquid)	$SO_3(l)$	-441.0
sulfur trioxide (vapour)	$SO_3(g)$	-395.7
tin(II) chloride	$SnCl_2(s)$	-325.1
tin(IV) chloride	$SnCl_4(l)$	-511.3
tin(II) oxide	$SnO(s)$	-280.7
tin(IV) oxide	$SnO_2(s)$	-577.6
water (liquid)	$H_2O(l)$	-285.8
water (vapour)	$H_2O(g)$	-241.8
zinc oxide	$ZnO(s)$	-350.5
zinc sulfide (sphalerite)	$ZnS(s)$	-206.0

Solubility of Some Common Ionic Compounds in Water at 298.15 K

Ion	Group 1 ions NH_4^+ NO_3^- ClO_3^- ClO_4^- CH_3COO^-	F^-	Cl^- Br^- I^-	SO_4^{2-}	CO_3^{2-} PO_4^{3-} SO_3^{2-}	IO_3^- $OOCCOO^{2-}$	OH^-
Solubility greater than or equal to 0.1 mol/L (very soluble)	most	most	most	most	Group 1 ions NH_4^+	Group 1 ions NH_4^+ $Co(IO_3)_2$ $Fe_2(OOCCOO)_3$	Group 1 ions NH_4^+
Solubility less than 0.1 mol/L (slightly soluble)	$RbClO_4$ $CsClO_4$ $AgCH_3COO$ $Hg_2(CH_3COO)_2$	Li^+ Mg^{2+} Ca^{2+} Sr^{2+} Ba^{2+} Fe^{2+} Hg_2^{2+} Pb^{2+}	Cu^+ Ag^+ Hg_2^{2+} Pb^{2+} Tl^+	Ca^{2+} Sr^{2+} Ba^{2+} Ag^+ Hg_2^{2+} Pb^{2+} Ra^{2+}	most	most	most

Note: This solubility table is only a guideline that is established using the K_{sp} values. A concentration of 0.1 mol/L corresponds to approximately 10 g/L to 30 g/L depending on molar mass. Hg_2^{2+} is a polyatomic ion of mercury.

Flame Colour of Elements

Element	Symbol	Colour
lithium	Li	red
sodium	Na	yellow
potassium	K	violet
rubidium	Rb	violet
cesium	Cs	violet
calcium	Ca	yellowish red
strontium	Sr	scarlet red
barium	Ba	yellowish green
copper	Cu	blue to green
boron	B	yellowish green
lead	Pb	blue-white

Note: The flame test can be used to determine the identity of a metal or a metal ion. Blue to green indicates a range of colours that might appear.

Table of Selected Standard Electrode Potentials*

Reduction Half-Reaction	Electrical Potential $E°$ (V)
$F_2(g) + 2\,e^- \rightleftharpoons 2\,F^-(aq)$	+2.87
$PbO_2(s) + SO_4^{2-}(aq) + 4\,H^+(aq) + 2\,e^- \rightleftharpoons PbSO_4(s) + 2\,H_2O(l)$	+1.69
$MnO_4^-(aq) + 8\,H^+(aq) + 5\,e^- \rightleftharpoons Mn^{2+}(aq) + 4\,H_2O(l)$	+1.51
$Au^{3+}(aq) + 3\,e^- \rightleftharpoons Au(s)$	+1.50
$ClO_4^-(aq) + 8\,H^+(aq) + 8\,e^- \rightleftharpoons Cl^-(aq) + 4\,H_2O(l)$	+1.39
$Cl_2(g) + 2\,e^- \rightleftharpoons 2\,Cl^-(aq)$	+1.36
$2\,HNO_2(aq) + 4\,H^+(aq) + 4\,e^- \rightleftharpoons N_2O(g) + 3\,H_2O(l)$	+1.30
$Cr_2O_7^{2-}(aq) + 14\,H^+(aq) + 6\,e^- \rightleftharpoons 2\,Cr^{3+}(aq) + 7\,H_2O(l)$	+1.23
$O_2(g) + 4\,H^+(aq) + 4\,e^- \rightleftharpoons 2\,H_2O(l)$	+1.23
$MnO_2(s) + 4\,H^+(aq) + 2\,e^- \rightleftharpoons Mn^{2+}(aq) + 2\,H_2O(l)$	+1.22
$Br_2(l) + 2\,e^- \rightleftharpoons 2\,Br^-(aq)$	+1.07
$Hg^{2+}(aq) + 2\,e^- \rightleftharpoons Hg(l)$	+0.85
$OCl^-(aq) + H_2O(l) + 2\,e^- \rightleftharpoons Cl^-(aq) + 2\,OH^-(aq)$	+0.84
$2\,NO_3^-(aq) + 4\,H^+(aq) + 2\,e^- \rightleftharpoons N_2O_4(g) + 2\,H_2O(l)$	+0.80
$Ag^+(aq) + e^- \rightleftharpoons Ag(s)$	+0.80
$Fe^{3+}(aq) + e^- \rightleftharpoons Fe^{2+}(aq)$	+0.77
$O_2(g) + 2\,H^+(aq) + 2\,e^- \rightleftharpoons H_2O_2(l)$	+0.70
$I_2(s) + 2\,e^- \rightleftharpoons 2\,I^-(aq)$	+0.54
$O_2(g) + 2\,H_2O(l) + 4\,e^- \rightleftharpoons 4\,OH^-(aq)$	+0.40
$Cu^{2+}(aq) + 2\,e^- \rightleftharpoons Cu(s)$	+0.34
$SO_4^{2-}(aq) + 4\,H^+(aq) + 2\,e^- \rightleftharpoons H_2SO_3(aq) + H_2O(l)$	+0.17
$Sn^{4+}(aq) + 2\,e^- \rightleftharpoons Sn^{2+}(aq)$	+0.15
$S(s) + 2\,H^+(aq) + 2\,e^- \rightleftharpoons H_2S(aq)$	+0.14
$AgBr(s) + e^- \rightleftharpoons Ag(s) + Br^-(aq)$	+0.07
$2\,H^+(aq) + 2\,e^- \rightleftharpoons H_2(g)$	0.00
$Pb^{2+}(aq) + 2\,e^- \rightleftharpoons Pb(s)$	−0.13
$Sn^{2+}(aq) + 2\,e^- \rightleftharpoons Sn(s)$	−0.14
$AgI(s) + e^- \rightleftharpoons Ag(s) + I^-(aq)$	−0.15
$Ni^{2+}(aq) + 2\,e^- \rightleftharpoons Ni(s)$	−0.26
$Co^{2+}(aq) + 2\,e^- \rightleftharpoons Co(s)$	−0.28
$PbSO_4(s) + 2\,e^- \rightleftharpoons Pb(s) + SO_4^{2-}(aq)$	−0.36
$Se(s) + 2\,H^+(aq) + 2\,e^- \rightleftharpoons H_2Se(aq)$	−0.40
$Cd^{2+}(aq) + 2\,e^- \rightleftharpoons Cd(s)$	−0.40
$Cr^{3+}(aq) + e^- \rightleftharpoons Cr^{2+}(aq)$	−0.41
$Fe^{2+}(aq) + 2\,e^- \rightleftharpoons Fe(s)$	−0.45
$NO_2^-(aq) + H_2O(l) + e^- \rightleftharpoons NO(g) + 2\,OH^-(aq)$	−0.46
$Ag_2S(s) + 2\,e^- \rightleftharpoons 2\,Ag(s) + S^{2-}(aq)$	−0.69
$Zn^{2+}(aq) + 2\,e^- \rightleftharpoons Zn(s)$	−0.76
$2\,H_2O(l) + 2\,e^- \rightleftharpoons H_2(g) + 2\,OH^-(aq)$	−0.83
$Cr^{2+}(aq) + 2\,e^- \rightleftharpoons Cr(s)$	−0.91
$Se(s) + 2\,e^- \rightleftharpoons Se^{2-}(aq)$	−0.92
$SO_4^{2-}(aq) + H_2O(l) + 2\,e^- \rightleftharpoons SO_3^{2-}(aq) + 2\,OH^-(aq)$	−0.93
$Al^{3+}(aq) + 3\,e^- \rightleftharpoons Al(s)$	−1.66
$Mg^{2+}(aq) + 2\,e^- \rightleftharpoons Mg(s)$	−2.37
$Na^+(aq) + e^- \rightleftharpoons Na(s)$	−2.71
$Ca^{2+}(aq) + 2\,e^- \rightleftharpoons Ca(s)$	−2.87
$Ba^{2+}(aq) + 2\,e^- \rightleftharpoons Ba(s)$	−2.91
$K^+(aq) + e^- \rightleftharpoons K(s)$	−2.93
$Li^+(aq) + e^- \rightleftharpoons Li(s)$	−3.04

*For 1.0 mol/L solutions at 298.15 K (25.00 °C) and a pressure of 101.325 kPa

Relative Strengths of Acids and Bases at 298.15 K

Common Name IUPAC / Systematic Name	Acid Formula	Conjugate Base Formula	K_a
perchloric acid aqueous hydrogen perchlorate	$HClO_4(aq)$	$ClO_4^-(aq)$	very large
hydroiodic acid aqueous hydrogen iodide	$HI(aq)$	$I^-(aq)$	very large
hydrobromic acid aqueous hydrogen bromide	$HBr(aq)$	$Br^-(aq)$	very large
hydrochloric acid aqueous hydrogen chloride	$HCl(aq)$	$Cl^-(aq)$	very large
sulfuric acid aqueous hydrogen sulfate	$H_2SO_4(aq)$	$HSO_4^-(aq)$	very large
nitric acid aqueous hydrogen nitrate	$HNO_3(aq)$	$NO_3^-(aq)$	very large
hydronium ion	$H_3O^+(aq)$	$H_2O(l)$	1
oxalic acid	$HOOCCOOH(aq)$	$HOOCCOO^-(aq)$	5.6×10^{-2}
sulfurous acid aqueous hydrogen sulfite	$H_2SO_3(aq)$	$HSO_3^-(aq)$	1.4×10^{-2}
hydrogen sulfate ion	$HSO_4^-(aq)$	$SO_4^{2-}(aq)$	1.0×10^{-2}
phosphoric acid aqueous hydrogen phosphate	$H_3PO_4(aq)$	$H_2PO_4^-(aq)$	6.9×10^{-3}
citric acid 2-hydroxy-1,2,3-propanetricarboxylic acid	$C_3H_5O(COOH)_3(aq)$	$C_3H_5O(COOH)_2COO^-(aq)$	7.4×10^{-4}
hydrofluoric acid aqueous hydrogen fluoride	$HF(aq)$	$F^-(aq)$	6.3×10^{-4}
nitrous acid aqueous hydrogen nitrite	$HNO_2(aq)$	$NO_2^-(aq)$	5.6×10^{-4}
formic acid methanoic acid	$HCOOH(aq)$	$HCOO^-(aq)$	1.8×10^{-4}
hydrogen oxalate ion	$HOOCCOO^-(aq)$	$OOCCOO^{2-}(aq)$	1.5×10^{-4}
lactic acid 2-hydroxypropanoic acid	$C_2H_5OCOOH(aq)$	$C_2H_5OCOO^-(aq)$	1.4×10^{-4}
ascorbic acid 2(1,2-dihydroxyethyl)-4,5-dihydroxy-furan-3-one	$H_2C_6H_6O_6(aq)$	$HC_6H_6O_6^-(aq)$	9.1×10^{-5}

benzoic acid benzenecarboxylic acid	$C_6H_5COOH(aq)$	$C_6H_5COO^-(aq)$	6.3×10^{-5}
acetic acid ethanoic acid	$CH_3COOH(aq)$	$CH_3COO^-(aq)$	1.8×10^{-5}
dihydrogen citrate ion	$C_3H_5O(COOH)_2COO^-(aq)$	$C_3H_5OCOOH(COO)_2^{2-}(aq)$	1.7×10^{-5}
butanoic acid	$C_3H_7COOH(aq)$	$C_3H_7COO^-(aq)$	1.5×10^{-5}
propanoic acid	$C_2H_5COOH(aq)$	$C_2H_5COO^-(aq)$	1.3×10^{-5}
carbonic acid $(CO_2 + H_2O)$ aqueous hydrogen carbonate	$H_2CO_3(aq)$	$HCO_3^-(aq)$	4.5×10^{-7}
hydrogen citrate ion	$C_3H_5OCOOH(COO)_2^{2-}(aq)$	$C_3H_5O(COO)_3^{3-}(aq)$	4.0×10^{-7}
hydrosulfuric acid aqueous hydrogen sulfide	$H_2S(aq)$	$HS^-(aq)$	8.9×10^{-8}
hydrogen sulfite ion	$HSO_3^-(aq)$	$SO_3^{2-}(aq)$	6.3×10^{-8}
dihydrogen phosphate ion	$H_2PO_4^-(aq)$	$HPO_4^{2-}(aq)$	6.2×10^{-8}
hypochlorous acid aqueous hydrogen hypochlorite	$HOCl(aq)$	$OCl^-(aq)$	4.0×10^{-8}
hydrocyanic acid aqueous hydrogen cyanide	$HCN(aq)$	$CN^-(aq)$	6.2×10^{-10}
ammonium ion	$NH_4^+(aq)$	$NH_3(aq)$	5.6×10^{-10}
hydrogen carbonate ion	$HCO_3^-(aq)$	$CO_3^{2-}(aq)$	4.7×10^{-11}
hydrogen ascorbate ion	$HC_6H_6O_6^-(aq)$	$C_6H_6O_6^{2-}(aq)$	2.0×10^{-12}
hydrogen phosphate ion	$HPO_4^{2-}(aq)$	$PO_4^{3-}(aq)$	4.8×10^{-13}
water	$H_2O(l)$	$OH^-(aq)$	1.0×10^{-14}

Note: An approximation may be used instead of the quadratic formula when the concentration of H_3O^+ produced is less than 5% of the original acid concentration (or the concentration of the acid is 1 000 times greater than the K_a). An approximation can also be used for weak bases. The formulas of the carboxylic acids have been written so that the COOH group can be easily recognized. Either the common or IUPAC name is acceptable.

9

Acid–Base Indicators at 298.15 K

Indicator	Suggested Abbreviations	pH Range	Colour Change as pH Increases	K_a
methyl violet	$HMv(aq)$ / $Mv^-(aq)$	0.0 – 1.6	yellow to blue	$\sim 2 \times 10^{-1}$
cresol red	$H_2Cr(aq)$ / $HCr^-(aq)$ $HCr^-(aq)$ / $Cr^{2-}(aq)$	0.0 – 1.0 7.0 – 8.8	red to yellow yellow to red	$\sim 3 \times 10^{-1}$ 3.5×10^{-9}
thymol blue	$H_2Tb(aq)$ / $HTb^-(aq)$ $HTb^-(aq)$ / $Tb^{2-}(aq)$	1.2 – 2.8 8.0 – 9.6	red to yellow yellow to blue	2.2×10^{-2} 6.3×10^{-10}
orange IV	$HOr(aq)$ / $Or^-(aq)$	1.4 – 2.8	red to yellow	$\sim 1 \times 10^{-2}$
methyl orange	$HMo(aq)$ / $Mo^-(aq)$	3.2 – 4.4	red to yellow	3.5×10^{-4}
bromocresol green	$HBg(aq)$ / $Bg^-(aq)$	3.8 – 5.4	yellow to blue	1.3×10^{-5}
methyl red	$HMr(aq)$ / $Mr^-(aq)$	4.8 – 6.0	red to yellow	1.0×10^{-5}
chlorophenol red	$HCh(aq)$ / $Ch^-(aq)$	5.2 – 6.8	yellow to red	5.6×10^{-7}
bromothymol blue	$HBb(aq)$ / $Bb^-(aq)$	6.0 – 7.6	yellow to blue	5.0×10^{-8}
phenol red	$HPr(aq)$ / $Pr^-(aq)$	6.6 – 8.0	yellow to red	1.0×10^{-8}
phenolphthalein	$HPh(aq)$ / $Ph^-(aq)$	8.2 – 10.0	colourless to pink	3.2×10^{-10}
thymolphthalein	$HTh(aq)$ / $Th^-(aq)$	9.4 – 10.6	colourless to blue	1.0×10^{-10}
alizarin yellow R	$HAy(aq)$ / $Ay^-(aq)$	10.1 – 12.0	yellow to red	6.9×10^{-12}
indigo carmine	$HIc(aq)$ / $Ic^-(aq)$	11.4 – 13.0	blue to yellow	$\sim 6 \times 10^{-12}$
1,3,5–trinitrobenzene	$HNb(aq)$ / $Nb^-(aq)$	12.0 – 14.0	colourless to orange	$\sim 1 \times 10^{-13}$

Colours of Common Aqueous Ions

Ionic Species	Solution Concentration	
	1.0 mol/L	0.010 mol/L
chromate	yellow	pale yellow
chromium(III)	blue-green	green
chromium(II)	dark blue	pale blue
cobalt(II)	red	pink
copper(I)	blue-green	pale blue-green
copper(II)	blue	pale blue
dichromate	orange	pale orange
iron(II)	lime green	colourless
iron(III)	orange-yellow	pale yellow
manganese(II)	pale pink	colourless
nickel(II)	blue-green	pale blue-green
permanganate	deep purple	purple-pink

Credits

NOTES

NOTES

BOOK ORDERING INFORMATION

SENIOR HIGH SCHOOL TITLES

Castle Rock Research offers the following resources to support Alberta students. You can order any of these materials online at:

www.castlerockresearch.com/store

SOLARO.com - Study Online		The KEY		SNAP	Prob Solved	Class Notes
$29.95 ea.*		$29.95 ea.*		$29.95 ea.*	$19.95 ea.*	$19.95 ea.*
Biology 30	Mathematics 30-1	Biology 30	Mathematics 30-1	Biology 20	Biology 20	Biology 20
Biology 20	Mathematics 30-2	Biology 20	Mathematics 30-2	Chemistry 30	Chemistry 30	Chemistry 30
Chemistry 30	Mathematics 30-3	Chemistry 30	Mathematics 20-1	Chemistry 20	Chemistry 20	Chemistry 20
Chemistry 20	Mathematics 20-1	Chemistry 20	Mathematics 10 C	Mathematics 30-1	Mathematics 30-1	Mathematics 30-1
Physics 30	Mathematics 20-2	English 30-1	Social Studies 30-1	Mathematics 30-2	Mathematics 30-2	Mathematics 30-2
Physics 20	Mathematics 20-3	English 30-2	Social Studies 30-2	Mathematics 31	Mathematics 31	Mathematics 31
Science 30	Mathematics 20-4	English 20-1	Social Studies 20-1	Mathematics 20-1	Mathematics 20-1	Mathematics 20-1
Science 20	Mathematics 10 C	English 10-1	Social Studies 10-1	Mathematics 10 C	Mathematics 10 C	Mathematics 10 C
Science 10	Mathematics 10-3	Physics 30		Physics 30	Physics 30	Physics 30
English 30-1	Mathematics 10-4	Physics 20		Physics 20	Physics 20	Physics 20
English 30-2	Social Studies 30-1	Science 10		Science 10	Science 10	Science 10
English 20-1	Social Studies 30-2					
English 20-2	Social Studies 20-1					
English 10-1	Social Studies 10-1					
English 10-2						

Prices do not include taxes or shipping.

Study online using **SOLARO,** with access to multiple courses available by either a monthly or an annual subscription.

The KEY Study Guide is specifically designed to assist students in preparing for unit tests, final exams, and provincial examinations.

The **Student Notes and Problems (SNAP) Workbook** contains complete explanations of curriculum concepts, examples, and exercise questions.

The **Problem Solved** contains exercise questions and complete solutions.

The **Class Notes** contains complete explanations of curriculum concepts.

If you would like to order Castle Rock resources for your school, please visit our school ordering page:

www.castlerockresearch.com/school-orders/